MATHS
IN ACTION

Mathematics in Action Group

Members of the Mathematics in Action Group associated with this book:
D. Brown, J. L. Hodge, R. D. Howat, J. Hunter, E. C. K. Mullan, K. Nisbet, A.G. Robertson

STUDENTS'
BOOK

First published in 1988 by Blackie & Son Ltd :
New edition published in 1996 by:
Thomas Nelson and Sons Ltd

Reprinted in 2001 by:
Nelson Thornes Ltd
Delta Place
27 Bath Road
CHELTENHAM
GL53 7TH
United Kingdom

01 02 03 04 05 / 15 14 13 12 11 10 9 8 7

A catalogue record for this book is available from the British Library

ISBN 0-17-431436-1

Cover photograph courtesy of Rutherford Appleton Laboratory
Typeset Tech-Set, Gateshead, Tyne & Wear

Printed and bound in China

CONTENTS

INTRODUCTION

Maths in Action—New Edition provides a course in mathematics that covers the Mathematics 5-14 National Guidelines, Standard Grade and Higher Grade in Scotland, the Northern Ireland Curriculum and the National Curriculum (1995 Order) in England and Wales.

The new edition builds on experience gained in the classroom with the original series, and particular attention has been paid to providing a differentiated course at every stage. Book 4A provides a course for Standard Grade at General level and for NIC/NC at levels 5–8, while Book 4B aims mainly at Credit and levels 7 upwards. Each chapter starts with a Looking Back exercise, which can be used for revision and to assess readiness for the topic, and ends with a Check-up exercise giving a further element of revision and assessment. Investigative work features prominently in each chapter in the many puzzles, projects, challenges, brainstormers and investigations. Answers to every question (except puzzles, challenges, brainstormers, investigations and 'Topics to Explore') are to be found at the end of this book. The Review sections provide a systematic and thorough revision of earlier work.

Each *Students' Book* is supported by a *Teacher's Resource Book* and, in the case of Books 1 and 2, by revised books of *Extra Questions* and *Further Questions*.

The *Teacher's Resource Book* contains Standard Grade, Northern Ireland Curriculum and National Curriculum references for every chapter, photocopiable worksheets, notes and suggestions for further activities, and the answers to the puzzles, challenges, brainstormers, investigations and 'Topics to Explore' in the *Students' Book*. In addition, there are grids which may be photocopied and used to record and assess students' progress.

1 On which parts of this short journey does the car travel:
a fastest **b** slowest?
Explain how you can tell.

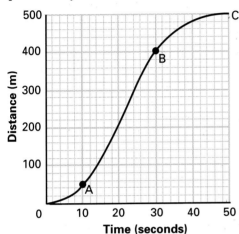

2 Calculate the value of $\dfrac{BC}{AB}$ in its simplest form.

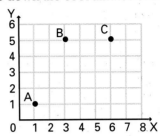

3 Write in their simplest form:
a $\dfrac{6}{2}$ **b** $\dfrac{4}{8}$ **c** $\dfrac{-2}{2}$ **d** $\dfrac{3}{-6}$ **e** $\dfrac{0}{3}$

4 Calculate:
a $9-5$ **b** $5-9$ **c** $8-0$ **d** $0-8$ **e** $1-7$

5 This map of a river estuary has a grid of 1 km squares. The Southern Star sails from A to B.
a How far is B: (i) east of A (ii) north of A?
b How far is D: (i) east of C (ii) south of C?

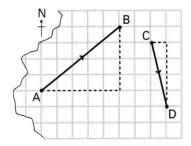

6 a Copy this diagram on squared paper, then complete the parallelogram ABCD.
b Write down the coordinates of D.

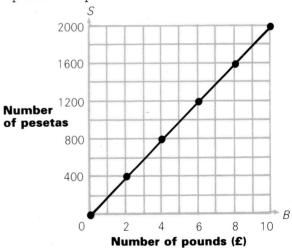

7 Copy and complete these tables:

a $y = 4x$

x	0	1	2	3	4	5
y						

b $y = x-2$

x	0	1	2	3	4	5
y						

c $y = 7x$

x	−2	−1	0	1	2	3
y						

8 The graph shows the rate of exchange between pounds and pesetas.

a Copy and complete this table, using the information in the graph:

Number of £s (B)	0	2	4	6	8	10
Number of pesetas (S)	0					

b How many pesetas would you get in exchange for: (i) £1 (ii) £7 (iii) £20?

1

THE GRADIENT OF A LINE

EXERCISE 1/CLASS DISCUSSION

(i) (ii) (iii)

1 All skiers know that ski-slopes are colour-coded. Blue for gentle slopes, red for medium, black for steeper slopes.
  a How would you colour-code the slopes in the pictures above?
  b Which of the three slopes above would suit a beginner?

2 a Which section of this mountain road would you prefer to cycle? Why?

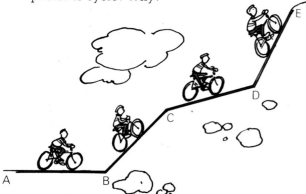

  b List the slopes in order—steepest first.

3 Tom, Dick and Harry are cleaning windows.

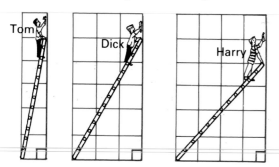

  a Whose ladder is dangerous? Why?
  b Can you think of ways of comparing the slopes of the ladders?
  c Arrange the slopes in order, steepest last.

4 How could you measure the gradient of the flight-path of this climbing aircraft?

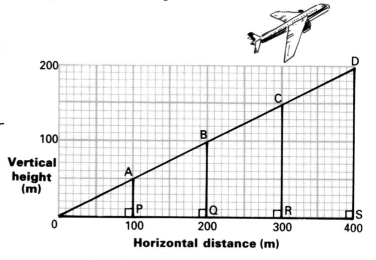

For OA, in $\triangle$OAP, $\dfrac{PA}{OP} = \dfrac{50}{100} = \dfrac{1}{2}$.

Calculate these, in their simplest form:

a for OB, $\dfrac{QB}{OQ}$ **b** for OC, $\dfrac{RC}{OR}$ **c** for OD, $\dfrac{SD}{OS}$.

What do you find?

For every point on the flight-path,

$$\frac{\text{vertical height above O}}{\text{horizontal distance from O}} = \frac{1}{2} = \text{gradient of the flight-path.}$$

The gradient of a line =

$$\frac{\textbf{vertical height between each end}}{\textbf{horizontal distance between each end}}$$

EXERCISE 2

1 Calculate the gradient of each ladder, $\dfrac{\text{vertical height}}{\text{horizontal distance}}$, as a fraction or whole number.

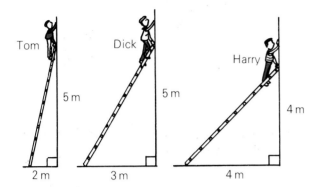

Tom   Dick   Harry
5 m   5 m   4 m
2 m   3 m   4 m

2 For each *pair* of pictures below:
(i) estimate, by looking at them, which ladder is steeper
(ii) calculate the gradient of each ladder.

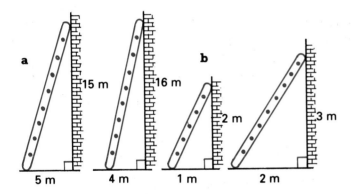

a   15 m   16 m
b   2 m   3 m
5 m   4 m   1 m   2 m

3 Calculate the gradient of each sloping line below.

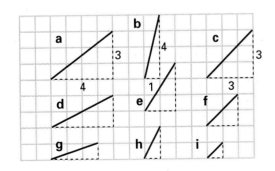

4 Calculate the gradient of each of these two staircase lines.

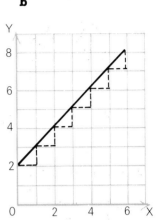

a   **b**

5 Calculate the gradient of each straight line.

a

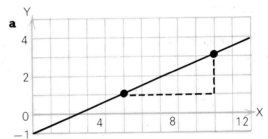

b   **c**

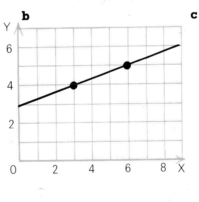
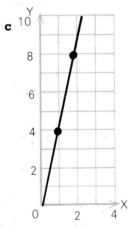

6 What can you say about the gradient of a line which slopes up at an angle:
a of 45° to OX   **b** between 45° and 90° to OX
c of less than 45° to OX?

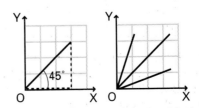

45°

O   X   O   X

3

7 This line starts at (0, 2) and has gradient $\frac{3}{5}$.

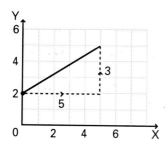

Draw these lines on a sheet of squared paper.

Line	I	II	III	IV
Starting point	(0, 1)	(1, 0)	(0, 0)	(6, 0)
Gradient	$\frac{2}{1}$	$\frac{1}{2}$	1	5

8 a Calculate the gradient of this escalator.

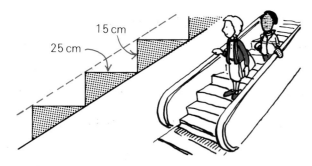

b How could you alter the steps to make the angle of slope 45°?

Katie and Fatima are on the seesaw.

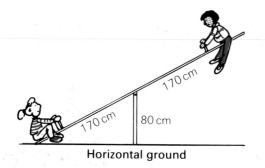

Horizontal ground

a Why can you not calculate the gradient of the seesaw with the lengths shown?
b Use Pythagoras' Theorem to calculate the length you need, then find the gradient.

PRACTICAL PROJECT

Close your textbook and place a rubber on one end of the cover. Tilt the book carefully until the rubber slides slowly down onto the desk. Calculate the gradient of the cover at this point. Repeat this experiment for different books and sliding objects. Make a table of results.

BRAINSTORMER

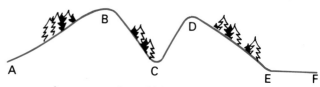

A cross-section of hills and valleys

a *From left to right*, name:
  (i) the uphill slopes   (ii) the downhill slopes
  (iii) the level part.
b Which is the steeper:
  (i) uphill slope   (ii) downhill slope?
c At which points does the gradient change from up to down?
d Estimate, then calculate, the gradients of the straight slopes between A and B, and between C and D.

UPHILL AND DOWNHILL

In mathematics, the gradient of a line $= \dfrac{\textbf{\textit{y}-step}}{\textbf{\textit{x}-step}}$.

A y-step downwards is negative.

A line sloping **up from left to right** has a **positive gradient**.

A line sloping **down from left to right** has a **negative gradient**.

Examples

a

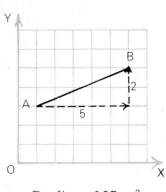

b

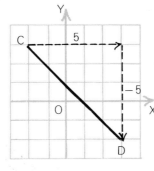

c

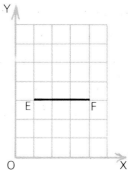

Gradient of AB $= \frac{2}{5}$

Gradient of CD $= \frac{-5}{5} = -1$

Gradient of EF $= \frac{0}{3} = 0$

EXERCISE 3A

1 Calculate the gradient of each line, $\dfrac{y\text{-step}}{x\text{-step}}$.

Watch out for y-steps in the negative direction of the y-axis.

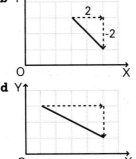

2 Calculate the gradient of each staircase straight line.

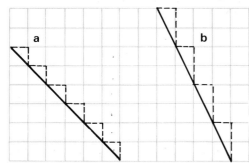

3 Calculate the gradient of each line below.

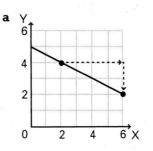

4 a Calculate the gradient of each line below.
  b What do you notice about your answers?

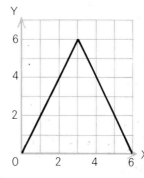

5

5 a Look at the steps and the slide. Which slopes:
  (i) up from left to right
  (ii) down from left to right?
  b Calculate their gradients.

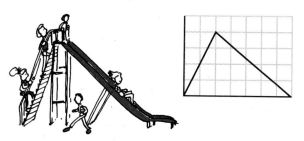

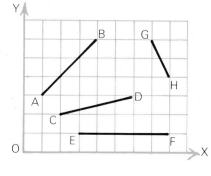

6 Calculate the gradients of these lines.

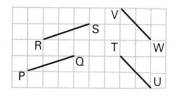

7 Calculate the gradients of these lines.

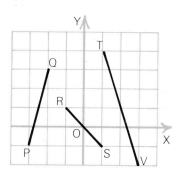

8 On squared paper draw the set of lines through the origin with gradients:
2, 1, $\frac{1}{2}$, 0, $-\frac{1}{2}$, -1 and -2.

EXERCISE 3B

1 a Calculate the gradients of the four lines below.
  b Name the pairs of parallel lines.

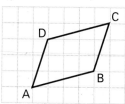

2 a Calculate the gradients of the sides of ABCD.
  b What kind of quadrilateral is ABCD?

3 a Calculate the gradients of the sides of PQRS.
  b What kind of quadrilateral is PQRS?

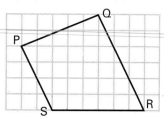

4 a Plot each pair of points on squared paper, and calculate the gradient of the line joining them.
  b Which lines are parallel?
  (i) A(1, 2), B(5, 6) (ii) C(4, 3), D(7, 0)
  (iii) E(7, 3), F(8, 7) (iv) G(0, 8), H(3, 5)

5 a Plot these points on squared paper:
  E(1, 2), F(5, 3), G(6, 1), H(2, 0).
  b Calculate the gradients of EF, FG, GH and EH.
  c What kind of quadrilateral is EFGH?

6 Draw these lines on one sheet of squared paper.

Line	I	II	III	IV
Starting point	(0, 6)	(0, 8)	(0, 4)	(0, 9)
Gradient	-1	$-\frac{1}{2}$	-2	$-\frac{3}{2}$

INVESTIGATION

Find out about the ways in which road and rail engineers, or geographers, measure and display gradients. Check the use of colours and contours in an atlas.

STRAIGHT LINE GRAPHS

EXERCISE 4

1 The graph with equation $y = x$.

a Copy and complete this table: $y = x$.

x	-4	-3	-2	-1	0	1	2	3	4
y	-4	-3							4

b Draw x and y-axes on squared paper, with x-values from -4 to 4, and y-values from -12 to 12.

c Plot the points in the table, and draw the straight line through them.
Compare the graph below.

d How far could you draw the line in each direction?

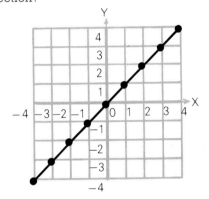

2 The graph with equation $y = 2x$.

a Copy and complete this table: $y = 2x$.

x	-4	-3	-2	-1	0	1	2	3	4
y	-8	-6			0				8

b Plot these points on the same diagram as in question **1**, and draw the straight line through them.

3 The graph with equation $y = 3x$.

a Copy and complete this table: $y = 3x$.

x	-4	-3	-2	-1	0	1	2	3	4
y	-12								12

b Again plot the points on the same diagram, and draw the straight line through them.

4 a Which point do the lines $y = x$, $y = 2x$ and $y = 3x$ pass through?

b Calculate the gradients of the lines.

c What is the connection between the equations of the lines and their gradients?

> The equation of every straight line through the origin (apart from the y-axis) is $y = ax$, where a is the gradient of the line.

5 For each of these lines through the origin, write down its gradient and its equation, $y = \ldots x$.

a 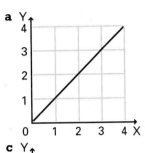 **b**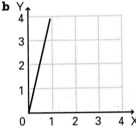

c 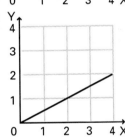 **d**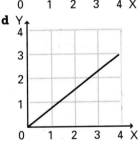

6 a Copy and complete a table like this for:
(i) $y = x + 1$ (ii) $y = x + 3$

x	-4	-3	-2	-1	0	1	2	3	4
y									

b Plot the sets of points, and draw the two straight lines on the same diagram.

c What do you notice about the lines?

d What is their gradient?

7 Try question **6** again for the two straight lines with equations:
(i) $y = 2x + 1$ (ii) $y = 2x - 1$

8 Write down the gradients of the straight lines with equations:

a $y = 2x$ **b** $y = 4x$ **c** $y = 10x$ **d** $y = x$
e $y = x + 5$ **f** $y = 3x + 1$ **g** $y = 7x - 2$

STRAIGHT LINE MODELS

Hiram III had 'done' Europe, and was off home. First he had to change his British pounds to American dollars. An exchange rate table helped him.

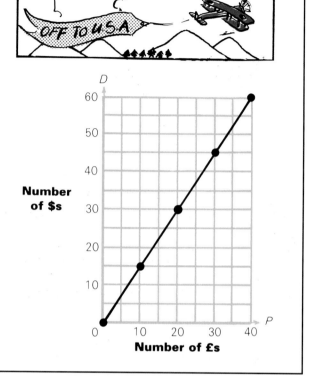

Number of £s (P)	0	10	20	30	40
Number of $s (D)	0	15	30	45	60

Graph D against P, and you'll find a straight line graph through O.

The line is a *mathematical model* of the connection between pounds and dollars.

Its equation is of the form $D = \ldots P$ (compare $y = ax$).

From the graph, the gradient of the line $= \frac{60}{40} = \frac{3}{2}$.

So its equation is $D = \frac{3}{2}P$.

Number of $s

Number of £s

EXERCISE 5A

1 Simon was buying bottles of cola for a party.
   a From the graph, how many litres would he get from:
   (i) one bottle
   (ii) three bottles?

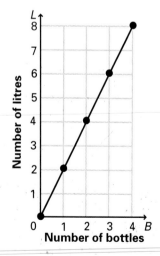

Number of litres

Number of bottles

b The line goes through O, so its equation is like '$y = ax$'; here $L = \ldots B$. Calculate the gradient, and write down the equation of the line.
c How many litres would he get from nine bottles?

2 Sarah drove along the motorway.

   a How far did she travel in
   (i) two hours
   (ii) four hours?

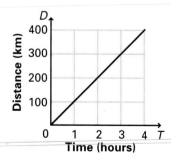

Distance (km)

Time (hours)

b The equation of the line is $D = \ldots T$. Calculate the gradient, and write down the equation of the line.
c At the same average speed, how far would Sarah drive in 7 hours?

3 Did you know? The width of a curtain is often much greater than the length of the rail. The graph shows this.

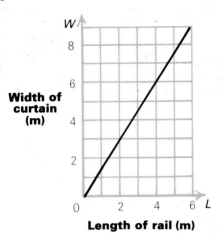

Width of curtain (m)

Length of rail (m)

a What width of fabric is needed for a rail length of: (i) 2 m (ii) 6 m?
b The equation of the line is $W = \ldots L$. Calculate the gradient, and write down the equation of the line.
c Calculate the width of curtain required for a rail 7 m long.

4 Adjoa's favourite subject is biology. Here she is magnifying the sizes of some specimens.

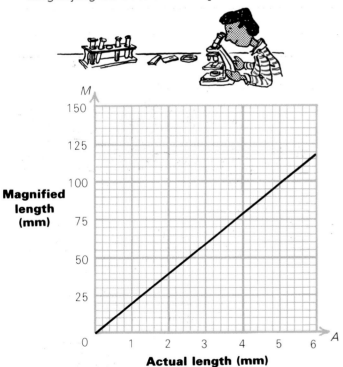

Magnified length (mm)

Actual length (mm)

a Calculate the gradient of the line.
b The equation of the line is $M = \ldots A$. Write down the actual equation.
c Calculate the magnified lengths of lines:
(i) 7 mm long (ii) 8 mm long (iii) 1 cm long

5 Mrs Williams uses her own marking scheme.
a Copy and complete this table:

Number correct (C)	0	1	2	3	4	5	6	7	8
Total marks (M)	0	3	6	9					

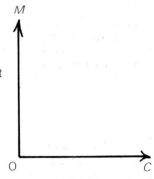

b Draw a graph, using these axes and $\frac{1}{2}$ cm squares.
c Calculate the gradient of the line, and write down its equation.
d How many marks would she give for 15 correct answers?

6 a In a cycle race, Chris keeps up a steady speed. Copy and complete the table.

Time (T h)	0	1	2	3	4	5
Distance (D km)	0	10	20			

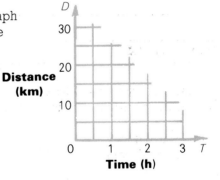

Distance (km)

Time (h)

b Draw a graph using these scales.
c Calculate the gradient of the line, and write down its equation.
d How far would she cycle in:
(i) $2\frac{1}{2}$ hours (ii) $5\frac{1}{2}$ hours?
e What is the connection between the gradient of the line, and the speed at which Chris cycles?

EXERCISE 5B

Every line through O (apart from the y-axis) has an equation like $y = ax$, where a is its gradient.

Every parallel line has an equation like $y = ax + b$, where the line cuts the y-axis b units from O.

Example

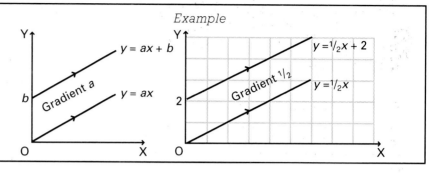

1 Peter the plumber has a call-out charge, plus an hourly charge.

2 Quick Fire Electronics also charge a call-out fee, and then an hourly rate for the job. This graph tells you the charges.

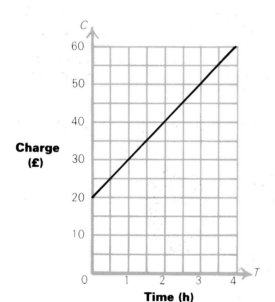

Time (h)

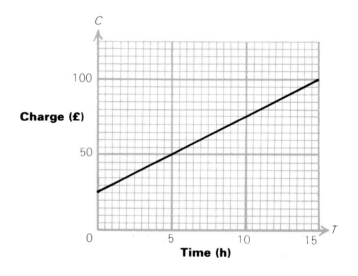

The graph of his charges against time is a straight line, so its equation is of the form $y = ax + b$, here $C = aT + 20$.

a Calculate the gradient, a, of the line.
b Write down the equation of the line.
c Use your equation to calculate the cost of a 12-hour job.

Its equation is of the form $C = aT + b$.
a Calculate the gradient of the line.
b Explain why the equation of the line is $C = 5T + 25$.
c Use your equation to calculate the charge for a 20-hour job.

3

a Copy and complete the table of charges:

Distance (D miles)	0	1	2	3	4	5	6
Charge (£C)	2	3	4				

b Draw the graph on squared paper, as shown below.

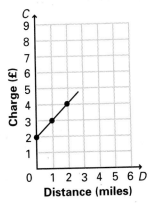

Distance (miles)

c Its equation is of the form $C = aD + b$.
Find: (i) the gradient of the line
        (ii) the equation of the line.
d Calculate the cost of a 30-mile hire.

4

a Copy and complete:

Number of payments (N)	0	1	2	3	4	5	6
Total paid (£T)	20	25	30				

b Use the same scales as in question **1** to draw the graph.
c Its equation is like $T = aN + b$. Find:
   (i) the gradient
   (ii) the actual equation connecting N and T.
d How much has been paid after four payments?

5 Water is flowing from the tank, as the graph shows.
The equation of the graph is like $V = aT + b$.

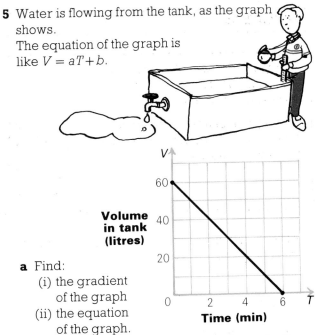

a Find:
   (i) the gradient of the graph
   (ii) the equation of the graph.
b Calculate the volume of water in the tank after five minutes, and check your answer on the graph.

6 Susan slowly and steadily lets the air out of the spare tyre in her car.

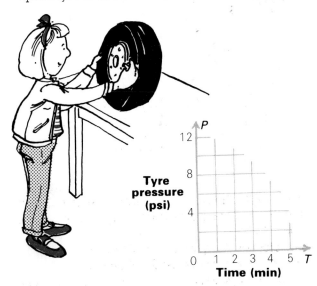

Time (T min)	0	1	2	3	4
Pressure (P psi)	24	18	12	6	0

a Draw a graph of pressure against time, using the scales shown.
b Calculate the gradient of your graph, and write down its equation.
c Calculate the pressure after 3 minutes 10 seconds.

CHECK-UP ON GRADIENTS AND GRAPHS OF STRAIGHT LINES

1 Arrange these lines in three sets, which have:
a positive gradients   **b** negative gradients
c zero gradient.

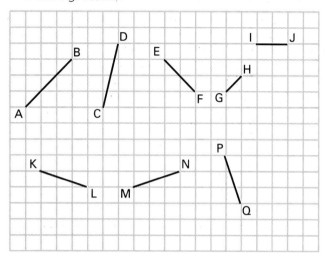

2 Calculate the gradient of each line in the diagram for question **1**.

3 On squared paper draw the line from (0, 0) with gradient: **a** 2   **b** $-\frac{1}{2}$ **c** 0.

4 Plot the points A(4, 7) and B(6, 12). Calculate the gradient of AB.

5 a Join L(0, 3) to M(6, 0) to N(7, 4) to P(1, 7) to L.
b Calculate the gradients of the four lines.
c Why is LMNP a parallelogram?

6 Calculate the gradient of each of the five parts of this fire escape.

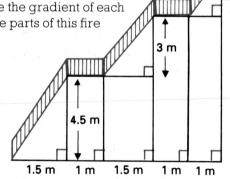

7 a Copy and complete this table for $y = \frac{1}{3}x$.

x	-6	-4	-2	0	2	4	6
y	-2						

b Draw x and y-axes on squared paper, plot the points, and draw the straight line through them. Write down the gradient of the line.

8 Water is flowing into Rachel's bath, as shown by the graph.

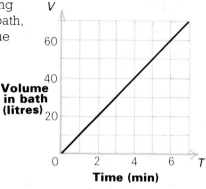

The equation of the graph is of the form $V = aT$, where a is its gradient.
a Calculate the gradient.
b Write down the equation of the graph.
c Calculate the volume after eight minutes.

9

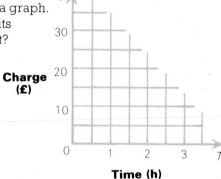

a Copy and complete this table.

Time (Th)	0	1	2	3	4	5
Charge (£C)	0	10				

b Use these scales to draw a graph. What is its gradient?

c Its equation is like $C = aT$. Find the actual equation.
d Calculate the cost for 15 hours.

10 The shop in question **9** changes to a call-out charge of £15, followed by a charge of £10 an hour.
a Draw a new graph, on the same sheet.
b Its equation is of the form $C = aT + 15$. Find the equation, and the charge for 12 hours.

2 TRIGONOMETRY

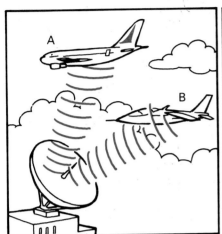

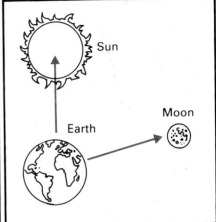

This chapter is about the calculation of distances and angles.

LOOKING BACK

1 Use your calculator to find x, correct to 1 decimal place:

a $x = 14 \times 0.66$ **b** $x = \dfrac{12}{0.34}$ **c** $x = \dfrac{8}{9}$

2 Calculate $y°$ in each triangle.

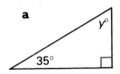 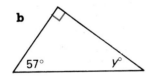

3 In the right-angled $\triangle PQR$ below:
 a name the hypotenuse
 b use Pythagoras' Theorem to calculate PR, correct to 1 decimal place.

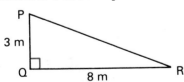

4 Write down, in its simplest form the value of each ratio:

 a $\dfrac{AD}{OA}$ **b** $\dfrac{BE}{OB}$ **c** $\dfrac{CF}{OC}$

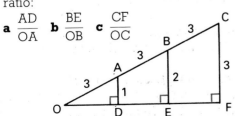

5 Name the three right-angled triangles in the diagram for question **4**.

6 a Name the angle of elevation of C from A.
 b Calculate the angle of elevation if AB = BC.

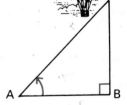

7 Use the 'cover up' method to solve:

 a $\dfrac{x}{2} = 4$ **b** $\dfrac{x}{10} = 3$ **c** $\dfrac{x}{6} = 7$

8 (i) Solve $\dfrac{x}{4} = 5$ by multiplying each side by 4.

 (ii) Use this method to solve the equations in question **7**.

9 The *Silver Spray* sails 5 km north from B to C, then 9 km west to D.
 a Use a scale of 1 cm to 1 km to make a scale drawing of the trip.
 b Measure BD. How far is the boat from B?
 c Calculate BD, correct to 1 decimal place.
 d Measure the angles at B and D, to the nearest degree. Check that $\angle B + \angle C + \angle D = 180°$.

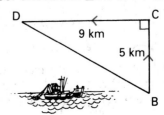

THE SINE OF AN ANGLE

EXERCISE 1/CLASS ACTIVITY

The ramp to the carpark is 25 m long, and slopes up at 30° to the horizontal. What height is the carpark above the ground?

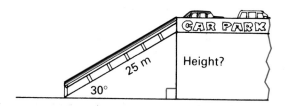

You can find the height approximately from a scale drawing. But there is a way to *calculate* it accurately. Make these measurements and calculations first.

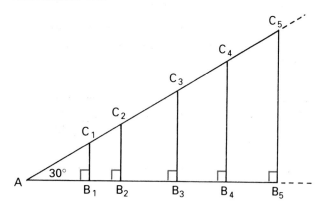

1 Copy and complete:

a In $\triangle AB_1C_1$, $B_1C_1 = \ldots$ mm, $AC_1 = \ldots$ mm,

so $\dfrac{B_1C_1}{AC_1} = \dfrac{\ldots}{\ldots} = 0.\ldots$

b In $\triangle AB_2C_2$, $B_2C_2 = \ldots$ mm, $AC_2 = \ldots$ mm,

so $\dfrac{B_2C_2}{AC_2} = \dfrac{\ldots}{\ldots} = 0.\ldots$

c Continue the measurements and calculations for $\triangle$s AB_3C_3, AB_4C_4 and AB_5C_5.

2 Do you find that for every triangle like this, with angle A = 30°, the value of $\dfrac{BC}{AC}$ is the same?

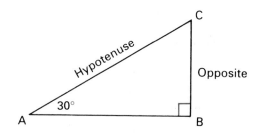

3 On your calculator, key $\boxed{\text{sin}}$ 30, or 30 $\boxed{\text{sin}}$, and compare with $\dfrac{BC}{AC}$.

The ratio $\dfrac{\textbf{Opposite A}}{\textbf{Hypotenuse}}$ is the same for all right-angled triangles with the same angle A.

It is called the sine of angle A, written sin A. Here, sin 30° = 0.5.

So, to calculate the height of the carpark:
The ramp's triangle is just a bigger version of all the right-angled triangles AB_1C_1, AB_2C_2, ... in the diagram on the left.

So $\dfrac{h}{25} = \dfrac{\text{Opposite}}{\text{Hypotenuse}} = \sin 30°,$

and $h = 25 \times \sin 30° = 25 \times 0.5 = 12.5$
The carpark is 12.5 m above the ground.

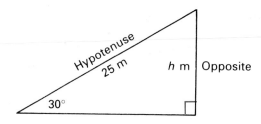

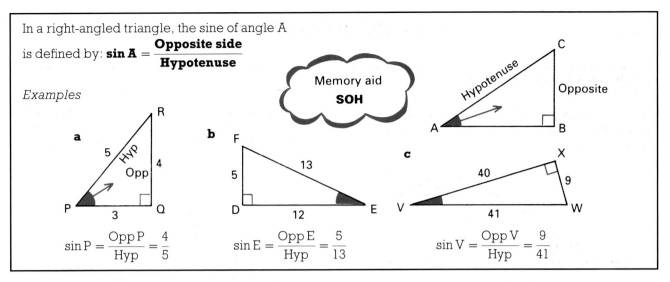

In a right-angled triangle, the sine of angle A is defined by: **sin A = $\dfrac{\textbf{Opposite side}}{\textbf{Hypotenuse}}$**

Examples

Memory aid **SOH**

$$\sin P = \frac{Opp\,P}{Hyp} = \frac{4}{5} \qquad \sin E = \frac{Opp\,E}{Hyp} = \frac{5}{13} \qquad \sin V = \frac{Opp\,V}{Hyp} = \frac{9}{41}$$

Throughout this chapter, give angles to the nearest degree and lengths correct to 1 decimal place, unless there are other instructions.

EXERCISE 2

1 Copy each triangle, and mark the side opposite angle A 'Opp' and the hypotenuse 'Hyp'. Then write down the ratio for sin A in each triangle.

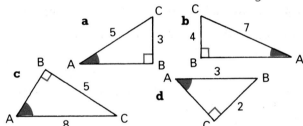

2 Write down the ratio for sin A in each triangle below.

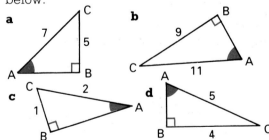

3 Calculate the value of sin A, correct to 2 decimal places, in each triangle below.

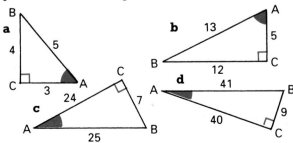

4 For each triangle in question **3**, write down the ratio for sin B, then calculate sin B, correct to 2 decimal places.

Your calculator has a list of sines built into it. Check that sin 30° = 0.5, by keying [sin] 30, or 30 [sin].

5 Use the [sin] key on your calculator to list the sines of these angles, correct to 2 decimal places:

Angle A	10°	20°	30°	40°	50°	60°	70°	80°
Sin A								

6 Find the values of these sines, correct to 2 decimal places:
  a sin 22° **b** sin 65° **c** sin 9° **d** sin 90°
  e sin 38° **f** sin 77° **g** sin 5° **h** sin 0°

7 a Draw △ABC with ∠A = 45°, ∠B = 90°.
  b Measure the lengths of BC and AC.
  c Calculate $\dfrac{BC}{AC}$, and express it as a decimal, correct to 2 places.
  d Compare your answer in **c** with sin 45° on your calculator.

CALCULATING DISTANCES

Charlie runs up the plank, which is four metres long, to the top of the wall. Calculate his height above the ground.

In $\triangle$ ABC, $\angle$ B = 90°

$$\text{Sin A} = \frac{\text{Opp}}{\text{Hyp}},$$

so $\sin 18° = \dfrac{h}{4}$

$h = 4 \times \sin 18° = 1.2$

He is 1.2 m above the ground.

SOH

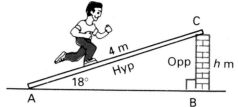

4 $\boxed{\times}$ $\boxed{\sin}$ 18 $\boxed{=}$, or 4 $\boxed{\times}$ 18 $\boxed{\sin}$ $\boxed{=}$

EXERCISE 3

Remember: give lengths correct to 1 decimal place.

1 Copy and complete:

$$\sin 33° = \frac{x}{\dots}$$

So $x = \dots \times \sin 33°$

$ = \dots$

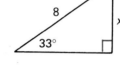

2 Calculate x in each triangle below.

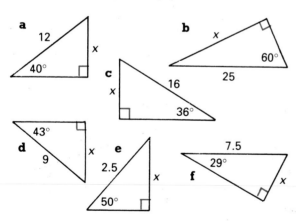

3 Calculate x in each right-angled triangle in these diagrams.

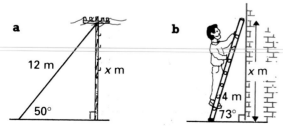

4 Calculate d cm in each diagram below.

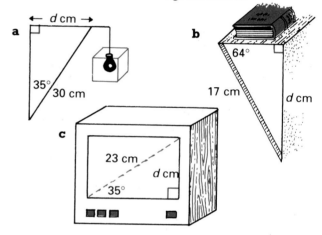

5 Calculate the height, h metres, of the front of the window.

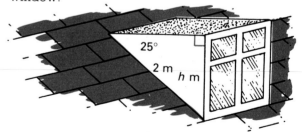

6 The ship sails from C on a course 038°. When it reaches B, how far is it from the oil-rig at A?

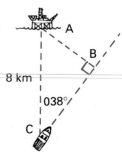

8 km

7 The cable-car climbs at 15° to the horizontal. AB = 60 m and BC = 40 m. Calculate the vertical height:
a BX, in △ABX
b CY, in △ACY.

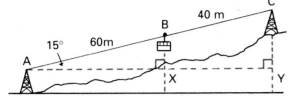

8 Two wires support the television mast. PN is 12 m long, at 52° to the ground. PQ is 18 m long, at 65° to the ground. Calculate:
a MN in △PMN
b MQ in △PMQ
c NQ.

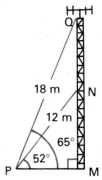

CALCULATING ANGLES

Example
The ladder will slip if the angle it makes with the ground is less than 40°. Will this ladder slip?

$\sin x° = \dfrac{3}{4}$

$x° = 49°$, to the nearest degree.

So the ladder won't slip.

SOH

2nd F ⌈sin⌉ ⌈(⌉ 3 ÷ 4 ⌈)⌉ = , or 3 ÷ 4 = 2nd F ⌈sin⌉ =

EXERCISE 4

Remember: give angles to the nearest degree.

1 For each diagram:
(i) write down the ratio for sin x°
(ii) use the ⌈2nd F⌉⌈sin⌉ keys on your calculator to find x.

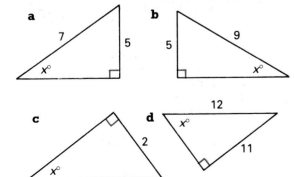

2 Calculate x° in each triangle below.

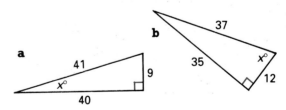

3 a Calculate ∠A and ∠B in △ABC.
b Check that ∠A + ∠B = 90°.

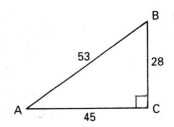

17

4 Calculate $x°$ in each diagram below.

a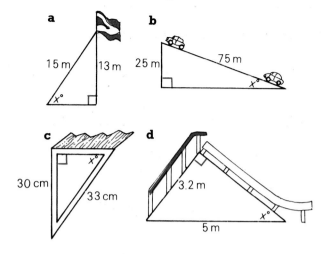

b

c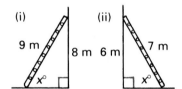

d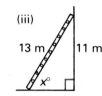

5 a Calculate the size of the angle, $x°$, that each ladder makes with the ground.

b Arrange the ladders in order, steepest first.

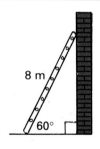

(i)   (ii)   (iii)

6 Calculate $x°$ in each diagram.

a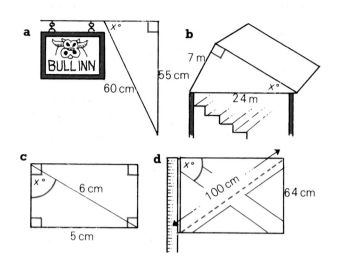

b

c

d

7 a Draw $\triangle ABC$ with $AB = 8\,cm$, $\angle ABC = 90°$ and $BC = 6\,cm$.

b Measure angles A and C.

c Use Pythagoras' Theorem to calculate AC.

d Use the sines of angles A and C to calculate the angles, and compare with your measurements in **b**.

THE COSINE OF AN ANGLE

For safety, Sean aims to set the ladder at 60° to the ground. How far out from the wall should the foot of the ladder be?

This time the hypotenuse must be linked with the other side adjacent to A (next to A).

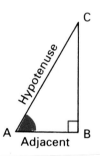

We define another new ratio, $\dfrac{\text{Adjacent side}}{\text{Hypotenuse}}$, called the cosine of the angle.

$$\textbf{Cos A} = \frac{\textbf{Adjacent side}}{\textbf{Hypotenuse}}$$

Memory aid
CAH

For the ladder, $\cos 60° = \dfrac{d}{8}$

So $d = 8 \times \cos 60° = 4$

The foot of the ladder should be 4 m from the wall.

8 $\boxed{\times}$ $\boxed{\cos}$ 60 $\boxed{=}$, or 8 $\boxed{\times}$ 60 $\boxed{\cos}$ $\boxed{=}$

EXERCISE 5

1 Copy each triangle, and mark the hypotenuse 'Hyp', *then* the side adjacent to angle A 'Adj'. Now write down the ratio for cos A in each of these right-angled triangles.

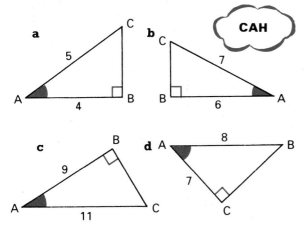

2 Write down the ratio for cos A in each triangle below.

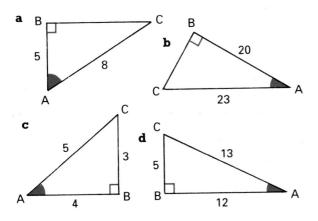

3 Use the [cos] key on your calculator to list the cosines of these angles, correct to 2 decimal places.

Angle A	10°	20°	30°	40°	50°	60°	70°	80°
Cos A								

4 Copy and complete:

$$\cos 32° = \frac{x}{\ldots}$$

So $x = \ldots \times \cos 32°$

$= \ldots$

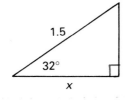

5 Calculate x in each of these triangles.

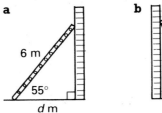

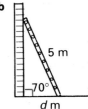

6 Calculate the distance, d m, of the foot of each ladder from the wall.

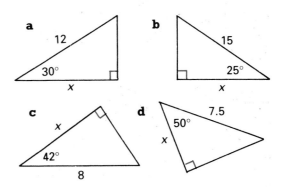

7 Calculate d in each right-angled triangle.

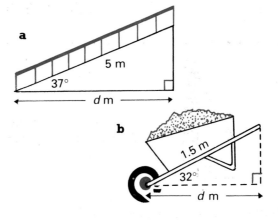

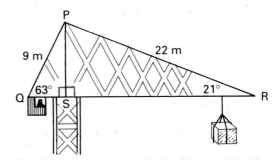

8 On this crane, calculate:
  a QS, in △QPS   **b** RS, in △PRS   **c** QR

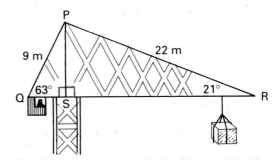

19

EXERCISE 6

Example
Calculate angle B in right-angled △ABC.

$$\cos B = \frac{\text{Adj}}{\text{Hyp}}$$

$$= \frac{5}{8}$$

So B = 51°

 CAH

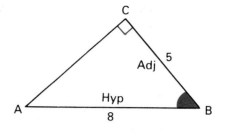

2nd F | cos | (| 5 | ÷ | 8 |) | = , or 5 | ÷ | 8 | = | 2nd F | cos | =

---

1 Use the [2nd F] [cos] keys on your calculator to find angle A, given:
   a $\cos A = 0.25$ **b** $\cos A = 0.09$
   c $\cos A = \frac{3}{4}$ **d** $\cos A = \frac{1}{2}$ **e** $\cos A = \frac{8}{9}$

2 For each diagram:
   (i) write down the ratio for $\cos x°$
   (ii) calculate $x°$.

a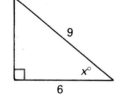

b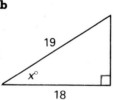

c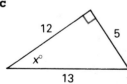

d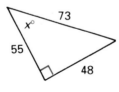

3 Calculate the angle $x°$ that AB makes with the vertical AC.

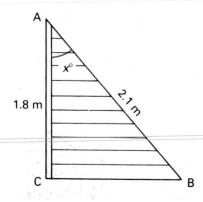

4 Calculate the submarine's angle $x°$.

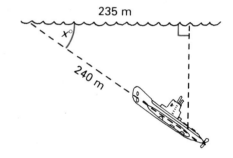

5 Calculate the lorry's tipping angle, $x°$.

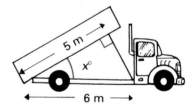

6 Calculate $x°$.

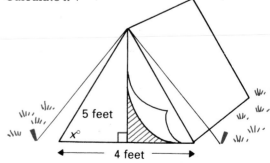

7 B is 200 km north of A. A plane leaves A and flies in a straight line for 300 km to point C, which is east of B. What course did the pilot fly from A?

THE TANGENT OF AN ANGLE

How could you find the height of this school building?
Climb up? Use a scale drawing?
Try using trigonometry—it's quick and accurate.
Here we have to link the sides opposite and adjacent to
the angle.

The ratio $\dfrac{\text{Opposite side}}{\text{Adjacent side}}$ is called the tangent of angle A.

$$\textbf{Tan A} = \dfrac{\textbf{Opposite side}}{\textbf{Adjacent side}}$$

Memory aid
TOA

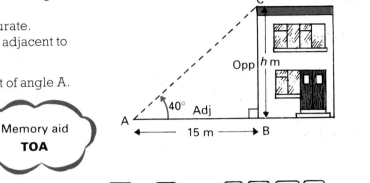

For the school building, $\tan 40° = \dfrac{h}{15}$

So $h = 15 \times \tan 40° = 12.6$

The height of the school is 12.6 m.

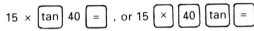

$15 \times \boxed{\tan}\ \boxed{40}\ \boxed{=}$, or $15\ \boxed{\times}\ \boxed{40}\ \boxed{\tan}\ \boxed{=}$

EXERCISE 7A

1 Copy each triangle, and mark the hypotenuse
'Hyp', *then* the sides opposite 'Opp' and
adjacent 'Adj' to angle A. Write down the ratio
for tan A in each triangle below.

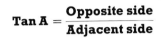

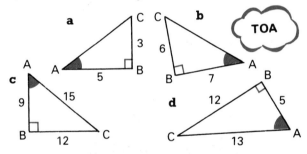

2 Calculate the value of tan $x°$ in each triangle,
correct to 2 decimal places.

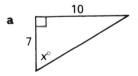
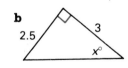

3 Calculate y in each of these triangles.

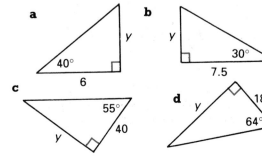

4 Calculate x in each diagram.

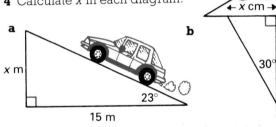

5 Calculate the width, w m, of each river.

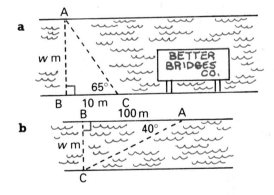

6 Calculate the height of St Paul's Cathedral, to the
nearest metre.

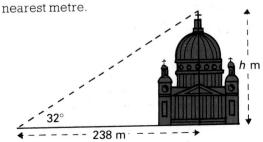

7 Use the $\boxed{\text{2nd F}}$ $\boxed{\text{tan}}$ keys on
your calculator to find the
angle between the guy-rope
and the ground.

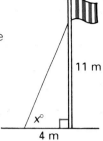

11 m

4 m

8 Calculate $x°$ in each triangle below.

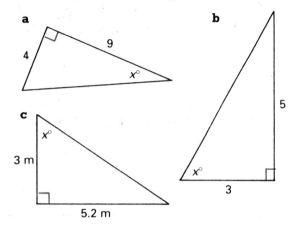

a
4
9
$x°$

b
5
3
$x°$

c
$x°$
3 m
5.2 m

9 Calculate the angles $x°$ in these diagrams.

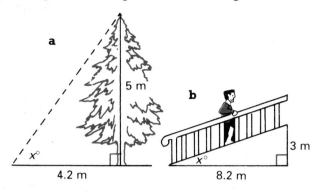

a
5 m
$x°$
4.2 m

b
3 m
$x°$
8.2 m

10 Calculate the angle of slope, $x°$, of each roof.

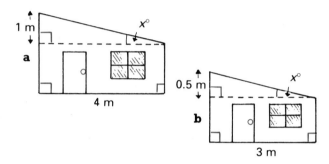

a
1 m
$x°$
4 m

b
0.5 m
$x°$
3 m

EXERCISE 7B

1 Calculate the height, h m, of the tree, to the
nearest metre.

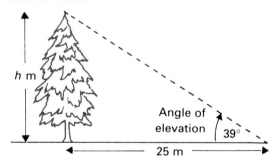

h m

Angle of
elevation 39°

25 m

2 The angles of elevation (shown in the circles) of
these famous buildings were measured from a
point 250 m from their bases. Sketch a right-
angled triangle for each one, and calculate its
height, to the nearest metre.

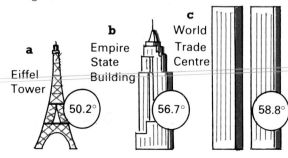

a
Eiffel
Tower
50.2°

b
Empire
State
Building
56.7°

c
World
Trade
Centre
58.8°

3 a What size is $\angle$PBM? Why?
 b Calculate the height of the cliff.

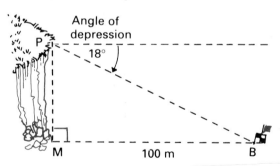

Angle of
depression
P
18°
M
100 m
B

4 A rescue helicopter at a height of 150 m spots a
dinghy at an angle of depression of 26°.
 a Calculate $x°$.
 b How far, to the nearest metre, is the dinghy
from the point on the sea directly below the
helicopter?

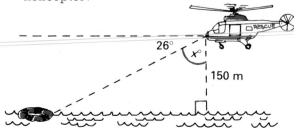

26°
$x°$
150 m

WHICH RATIO?

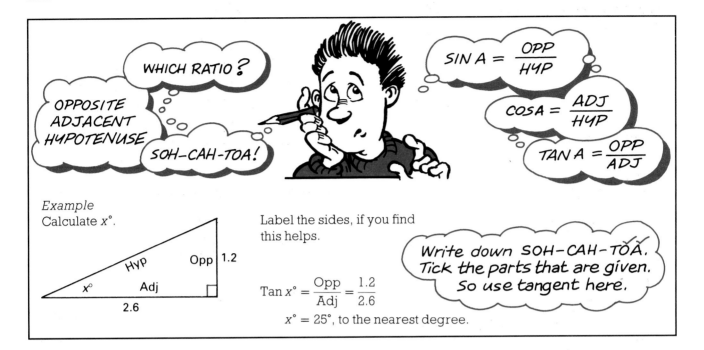

Example
Calculate $x°$.

Label the sides, if you find this helps.

$$\text{Tan } x° = \frac{\text{Opp}}{\text{Adj}} = \frac{1.2}{2.6}$$

$x° = 25°$, to the nearest degree.

EXERCISE 8A

1 Write down ratios for $\sin x°$, $\cos x°$ and $\tan x°$ in each triangle, using the letters on the sides.

a For example,

$$\sin x° = \frac{\text{Opp}}{\text{Hyp}} = \frac{p}{q}$$

$$\cos x° = \ldots$$

$$\tan x° = \ldots$$

b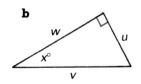

c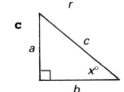

2 Choose your ratio, and calculate x in each triangle.

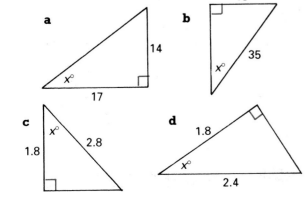

3 Choose your ratio, and calculate d in the triangles below.

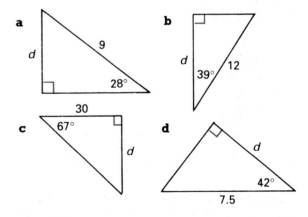

4 Calculate h m, the height of the paraglider.

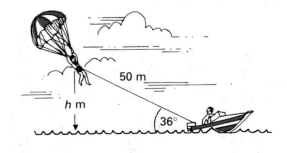

5 Calculate $x°$, the angle of slope of the car ramp

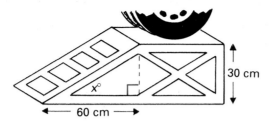

6 Calculate the height of Blackpool Tower, to the nearest foot.

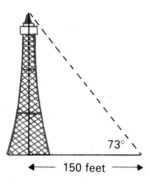

7 Calculate, to the nearest cm:
  a the height of the TV screen
  b the width of the screen.

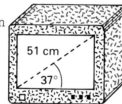

8 Calculate angle $x°$.

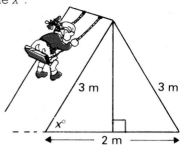

9 Frances measures the angle of elevation of the top of the school building, from 15 m away. Calculate:
  a h
  b the height of the building.

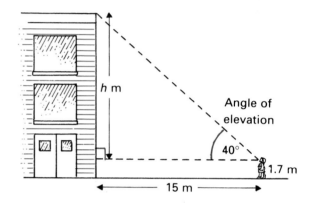

EXERCISE 8B

1 A trawler sails 12 km from A to B on a course 035°. Calculate how far it is then:
  a north of A
  b east of A.

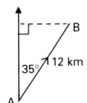

2 Is it easier to score from the penalty spot at football or hockey?
Calculate the angles at A and B to compare the shooting angles. What do you find? Are there other factors to think about?

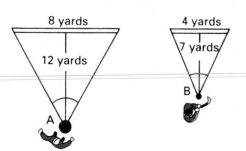

3 Calculate d in each diagram.

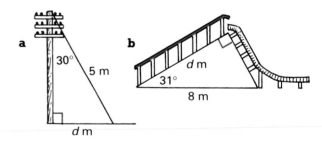

4 a Calculate all the angles in this rectangle.
  b Use Pythagoras' Theorem to calculate the length of the diagonals.

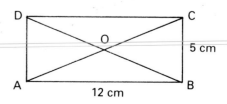

5 A youth group has to calculate the height of the church spire, to find the winner of a 'Guess the height' competition. Their measurements are shown.
Calculate the height of the spire to the nearest 10 cm.

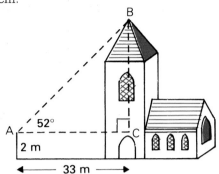

6 a Calculate the length of YZ.
b Use Pythagoras' Theorem to calculate XZ.

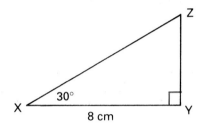

BRAINSTORMER

A surveyor is measuring the height of a mountain. At 3 km horizontally from the summit the angle of elevation is 18°. The surveyor is 45 m above sea-level.
a *Is the mountain above or below 1000 m?*
b *By how much?*

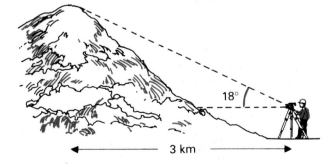

INVESTIGATION

1 *Complete this table, giving values correct to 2 decimal places.*

Angle A	Sin A	Cos A
0°	0	1.00
10°	0.17	0.98
20°	0.34	
⋮	⋮	⋮

a *As angle A increases from 0° to 90°, what happens to sin A and cos A?*
b *(i) When is sin A = cos A?   (ii) Why?*
c *(i) Sin 10° = cos . . .*
(ii) Sin 20° = cos . . .
Copy and complete these. Can you find a rule?

2 *Copy and complete this table, giving values correct to 1 decimal place. What is happening? What happens at 90°?*

tan 75°	3.7
tan 76°	4.0
tan 77° ⋮ tan 90°	

3 a *Why are sin A and cos A never more than 1?*
b *Why can tan A be greater than 1?*

4 *Use your calculator to find A when tan A = cos A, and 0° < A < 90°.*

PRACTICAL PROJECT

Use an anglemeter made from a large protractor and a plumbline, or a clinometer, to measure the angle of elevation of the school or some other landmark.
Make the necessary measurements and calculate the height.
Can you think of any other situations where the tangent method would help to calculate awkward distances or heights?

CHECK-UP ON TRIGONOMETRY

1 Copy these two triangles, and label the sides 'Hyp', 'Opp' and 'Adj' for angle A.

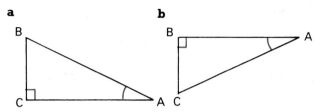

2 For angle A in each triangle below, which ratio connects the sides ticked—sin, cos or tan?

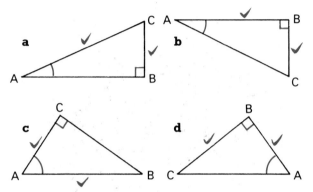

3 Write down ratios for these sines, cosines and tangents:

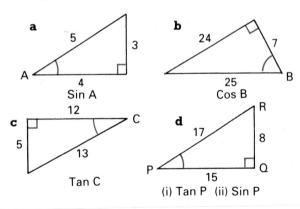

4 Calculate $x°$ in each triangle.

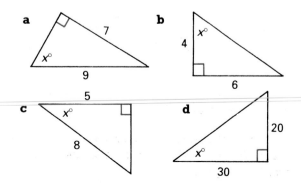

5 Calculate d in each triangle.

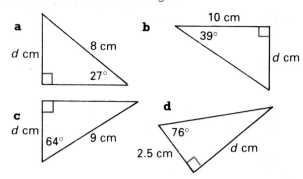

6 Calculate the angle of slope of these stairs.

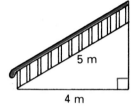

7 An aircraft flies 200 km from A on a course 053°. Calculate how far it then is:
a north of A **b** east of A.

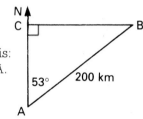

8 Calculate the angle of depression of Q from P.

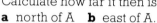
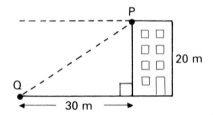

9 A tunnel is dug at 14.5° to the horizontal. One air-vent is needed every 100 m along the shaft. Calculate, to the nearest metre, the depth of each of the three shafts.

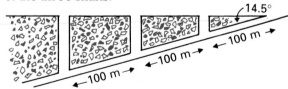

10 Calculate:
a x **b** y **c** h **d** w

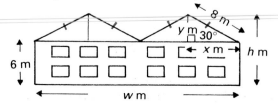

26

REVIEW: NUMBERS

CALCULATIONS 1

Do these calculations mentally, or using pen/pencil and paper—no calculators allowed!

1 a Add 371 and 732.
  b Subtract 371 from 732.

2 a Multiply 234 by 5.
  b Divide 876 by 6.

3 Write each of these correct to:
  (i) 2 decimal places   (ii) 2 significant figures.
  a 3.142 **b** 15.876

4 Write down the value of:
  a 2^3 **b** 10^2 **c** $\sqrt{49}$ **d** $\sqrt{100}$

5 Calculate:
  a $\frac{1}{5}$ of £30 **b** $\frac{1}{4}$ of 10 kg **c** $\frac{2}{3}$ of 12 hours

6 Calculate:
  a 10% of 50 cm **b** 50% of 10 cm

7 Change:
  a 7 cm to mm **b** 2 m to cm **c** 1 km to m

8 *Estimate*, then calculate, the areas of this rectangle and square.

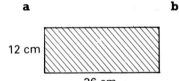

a

12 cm

36 cm

b

52 cm

9 Express 24 minutes as a:
  a fraction of an hour, in its simplest form
  b decimal fraction **c** percentage of an hour.

10 a Multiply by 100: (i) 31 (ii) 0.8
  b Divide by 10: (i) 120 (ii) 1.5

11 Calculate:
  a $4 + 3 \times 5$ **b** $12 \div (4 - 2)$

12 Calculate the average of:
  a 12, 14 and 19 hours **b** $7°, -1°, 3°, 11°$

13 Write down the value of:
  a £36.15 + £8.25 **b** £36.15 − £8.25

14 £1 = $1.6. How many $s for £8?

15 120 km in 5 hours. What is the average speed?

16 Earnings of £950 a month. How much is earned in a year?

17 The interest rate is 5% per annum. How much interest is given on £360 for one year?

18 Calculate:
  a the area of each face on this cube
  b the volume of the cube.

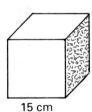

15 cm

19 A journey lasts from 14 30 hours until 16 20 hours. How long is this?

20 The length of a needle is measured—6 cm, to the nearest cm. Write down its greatest and least possible lengths.

CALCULATIONS 2

Use a calculator now, if you wish.

1 This table shows the amounts of money that Annabel, Bethany and Carly pay for their insurance premiums.

	Monthly	Annually	In 20 years
Annabel	£34		
Bethany		£336	
Carly			£11 280

  a Copy and complete the table.
  b Calculate the average of their 20-year payments.

2 North Academy's minibus has seats for 15 students.
  a How many trips would it have to make to take 69 students to a sports meeting?
  b How many spare seats would there be?

3 CDs cost £12.35 each.
  a How many could be bought with £400?
  b How much change would there be?

4 Write down two more terms for each of these sequences, and give the rule you use.
  a 3, 10, 17, 24, . . .   **b** 80, 71, 62, 53, . . .
  c 1, 3, 9, 27, . . .   **d** 2, 5, 10, 17, . . .

5 Calculate:
  a $6 + 7 \times 4$ **b** $3 \times 5 + 8 \times 6$ **c** 2×5^2
  d $12 \div (9 - 3)$ **e** $(4 - 4) \times 1$ **f** $2^3 \times 3^2$

6 Use the memory or brackets facility on your calculator for this question.
  a $C = \frac{5}{9}(F - 32)$. Calculate C when $F = 183.65$.
  b The mean cost of 75 chairs at £17.80 each and 36 stools at £13.40 each is given by
$$£\frac{75 \times 17.80 + 36 \times 13.40}{75 + 36}.$$
  Calculate the mean cost, to the nearest penny.

7 a Calculate the cost per ml of toothpaste in each tube, correct to the nearest penny.
  b List the tubes in order, best buy first.

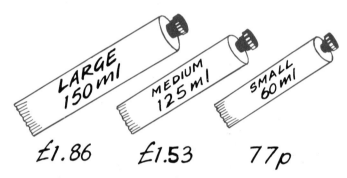

8 Look at **a–d** below. Say whether each machine increases or decreases the input number, and calculate the output from each machine for an input of 600.

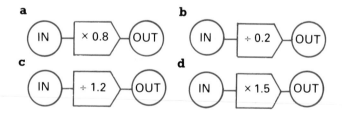

9 The formula $A = P \times \left(1 + \dfrac{r}{100}\right)^n$ calculates the amount of money (£A) in a bank account when £P is invested at $r\%$ per annum for n years. Calculate the amount of money when £2000 is invested at 8% per annum for 10 years.

10 Use a trial and improvement method to calculate, correct to 1, 2 and 3 decimal places:
  a $\sqrt{10}$ **b** $\sqrt{50}$ **c** $\sqrt{200}$

ESTIMATION AND APPROXIMATION

1 Athens

3949	Madrid	
3010	1273	Paris
817	2097	1476	Rome

Road distances, in kilometres

a Copy the table, and fill in the distances to the nearest 1000 km.

b Copy the table again, and fill in the distances to the nearest 100 km.

2 How much farther is it from Athens to Paris than from Madrid to Rome, to the nearest:
a 10 km **b** 100 km **c** 1000 km?

3 Use 1 km = 0.6214 mile to calculate, to the nearest mile, the distance from:
a Athens to Paris **b** Athens to Madrid.

4 Copy the table in question **1** again, and fill in all the distances, correct to 3 significant figures.

5 1 cm ≑ 0.3937 inch, 1 m ≑ 1.0936 yards and 1 km ≑ 0.6214 mile. Round each of these numbers to:
a 1 decimal place **b** 2 decimal places
c 3 decimal places.

6 A history book has about 18 words per line and 43 lines per page.
There are 387 pages.
Estimate the number of:
a words on a page
b words in the book.

7 a Use Pythagoras' Theorem to calculate the length of AB.

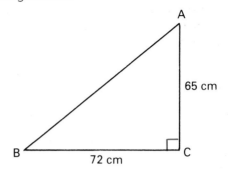

b *Estimate*, then calculate:
   (i) the perimeter of the triangle
   (ii) the area of the triangle
   (iii) the size of ∠ABC, to the nearest degree.

8 Here is the Tomlinsons' gas bill.

Gas Bill				1 April–30 June
Meter readings		Number of units used	Cost per unit	Charges (£)
Previous	Present			
15749	17688	A	5.92p	B
Standing charge				28.86
Sub-total				C
VAT at 17.5%				D
TOTAL				E

a *Estimate* the entries A, B, C, D and E in this gas bill.

b Calculate the entries, and compare them with your estimates.

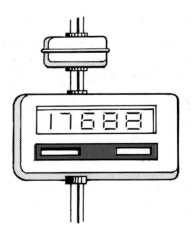

UNITS

1 'mph' measures speed. What do these units measure?
a kilogram **b** °C **c** seconds **d** m²
e ml **f** cm³ **g** km/h **h** mm

2 Copy and complete:
a 1 km = ... m **b** 1 cm = ... mm
c 1 g = ... mg **d** 1 litre = ... ml
e 1 hour = ... seconds **f** 1 tonne = ... kg

3 Change to cm:
a 3 m **b** 45 mm **c** 6.09 m **d** 380 mm

4 Copy and complete the following to give an approximate conversion for each:
a 1 inch = ... cm
b 1 kg = ... lb (pounds)
c 1 gallon = ... litres
d 1 mile = ... km

5 This scale is in milligrams. Write down the weight shown in: **a** mg **b** g

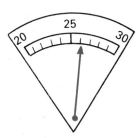

6 The temperature is given in °F.
a What is the reading, to the nearest 10°F?
b Estimate the reading, to the nearest degree.

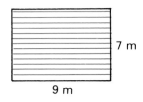

7 Alan's time in the 100 m race is 11.6 seconds, to the nearest tenth of a second.
Between which two times does his time lie?

8 This rectangular floor has been measured to the nearest metre.

7 m

9 m

a Write down the lower and upper limits of its length and breadth.
b Calculate, to the nearest m², the lower and upper limits of its area.

9 Convert:
a 72 km/h to m/s **b** 140 m/s to km/h.

SOME SPECIAL NUMBERS

1 Calculate:
a 6^2 **b** 5^3 **c** 10^4 **d** $\sqrt{81}$ **e** $\sqrt[3]{27}$

2 Mrs Green plants two daffodils. Each year the number of daffodils will double. How many will there be after:
a 2 years **b** 4 years **c** 6 years?

3 Calculate the length of each side of the square and the cube.

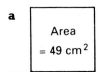

a Area = 49 cm²   **b** Volume = 64 cm³

4 List all the prime numbers between 1 and 20.

5 Which of these are prime numbers?
23, 27, 39, 51, 97

6 Choose a number from this collection which is:
a a square number
b a prime number
c a multiple of 7
d a factor of 18
e an even number
f greater than all the others
g a cubic number.

25 48 45 35 8 6 5

7 a List all the multiples of:
(i) 6, up to 54 (ii) 8, up to 56.
b Write down:
(i) the first two common multiples of 6 and 8
(ii) the least common multiple (lcm) of 6 and 8.

8 a List all the factors of each of these numbers:
2, 3, 4, 5, 6, 7, 8, 9, 10.
b Which special numbers have an odd number of factors?

9 Sheila and Barbara are training by running round the track. They start together. Sheila takes 6 minutes to run a lap while Barbara takes 4 minutes.
  a After how long will both be at the start again together: (i) for the first time
                    (ii) for the second time?
  b Nina joins them, but she runs laps in 9 minutes. Repeat part **a** for all three runners.

10 a List the factors of: (i) 42   (ii) 63.
   b What is the highest common factor of 42 and 63?

11 Write each of these as a product of prime factors:
   a 10 **b** 18 **c** 81 **d** 75 **e** 100 **f** 160

12 Write your answer to **11** in index form.

RATIO AND PROPORTION

1 Write these ratios in their simplest form:
  a 2:6 **b** 10:5 **c** 9:6 **d** 30:36

2 Simplify these ratios:
  a £1:20p **b** 1 cm:1 m **c** 4 hours:1 day

3 Divide:
  a £9 in the ratio 1:2
  b 24 kg in the ratio 5:1
  c 100 m in the ratio 3:2
  d 1 km in the ratio 3:5

4 Winston is very keen on DIY. He needs 12 litres of wallpaper paste to paper his hall. The carton says 'mix 3 parts powder to 1 part water'. How much of each should he use?

5 Jill uses 240 g flour, 60 g margarine, 30 g sugar and 150 ml milk to make eight scones. How much of each will she need for twelve scones?

6 A model train is made to a scale of 1:5.
  a If the model train is 3 m long, how long is the real train?
  b If the real train is 200 cm wide, how wide is the model train?

7 Use a scale of 1 cm to 4 yards to make a drawing of this soccer penalty area. What is the actual direct distance from P to Q, correct to 1 decimal place?

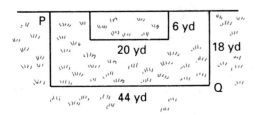

8 Tough Tarmac can resurface a 200 m length of road in 4 hours. What length could they resurface, at the same rate, in:
  a 1 hour **b** 3 hours **c** 10 hours?

9 How much would each person receive if there were only four winners?

10 a Copy and complete this table for changing £s to francs.

£s	10	20	30	40	50	60	70	80
Francs	80	160						

   b Draw a graph of £s against francs.
   c Use the graph to convert:
     (i) £45 to francs   (ii) 600 francs to £s.

11 a Copy and complete this table for a journey of 240 km at various average speeds.

Speed (km/h)	20	30	40	50	60
Time (hours)	12	8			

   b Draw a graph of speed against time.
   c Use the graph to find the time taken at 48 km/h.

STANDARD FORM

1 Write these numbers in full:
  a 3×10^2 **b** 6×10^4 **c** 7.5×10^3
  d 1.23×10^4 **e** 7×10^{-1} **f** 9×10^{-2}
  g 3.8×10^{-2} **h** 6.5×10^{-3}

2 Write these numbers in standard form, $a \times 10^n$:
  a 60 **b** 9000 **c** 48 000 **d** 9 200 000 000
  e 0.8 **f** 0.0001 **g** 0.029 **h** 0.000 000 7

3 Write out the meaning of these calculator displays, in standard form and in full:

a ⟦2 04⟧ **b** ⟦7.3 03⟧ **c** ⟦4.44 05⟧
d ⟦3 -01⟧ **e** ⟦2.5 -03⟧ **f** ⟦8.99 -5⟧

4 Write each number below in standard form.
  a The distance from the Earth to the moon is 384 000 km.
  b The diameter of the Earth's orbit round the sun is 300 000 000 km.
  c The gap in a sparkplug is 0.035 inch.
  d A nucleus diameter is 0.000 000 000 000 001.

5 The *Daily Cheer* sells 950 000 copies, six days a week. Find the total number sold in 52 weeks, in standard form.

6 The edge of a computer chip is 9 mm long. It is divided into 1500 equal parts. Express the length of each part in standard form.

7 Calculate, in standard form:
  a $(2.6 \times 10^9) \times (7.5 \times 10^8)$
  b $(2.6 \times 10^9) + (7.5 \times 10^8)$

8 a Light travels at 3×10^5 km/s. In one year it travels $3 \times 10^5 \times 60 \times 60 \times 24 \times 365$ km. How many km is this, in standard form?
  b A galaxy is ten million light years away. How many km is this, in standard form?

DISTANCE–SPEED–TIME

1 Write down formulae for distance (D km), speed (S km/h) and time (T hours):
  a $D = \ldots$ **b** $S = \ldots$ **c** $T = \ldots$

(Triangle diagram: D over S | T)

2 a Rashid cycles 240 km in 15 hours. Calculate his average speed.
  b Kerry drives 200 km at 80 km/h. How long does this take?
  c Neil travels for three hours at an average speed of 85 km/h. How far does he go?

3 Yvonne sets off at 9.30 am to visit her friend 24 km away. She cycles at an average speed of 16 km/h. When does she arrive?

4 a Steve walks from Newlands to Oldport in six hours at an average speed of 6 km/h. How far is it from Newlands to Oldport?
  b He cycles back at 18 km/h. How long does he take?
  c Calculate:
    (i) the total distance there and back
    (ii) his total time
    (iii) his average speed for the trip to Oldport and back.

5

Timetable		
Ashdale		18 45
Bushton	arr. 19 57	
	dep. 20 07	
Corkside		

Bushton   Corkside

Ashdale

Ashdale   *Distances in km*

78	Bushton	
158	80	Corkside

  a Calculate the average speed of the train from Ashdale to Bushton.
  b The train averages 60 km/h from Bushton to Corkside. When does it reach Corkside?

6 Rachel and John drive separately from their home to visit friends 150 miles away.
Describe each journey in as much detail as you can—times, distances, average speeds, etc.

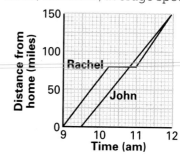

3 FRACTIONS, DECIMALS AND PERCENTAGES

LOOKING BACK

1 What fraction of each shape, in simplest form, is shaded?

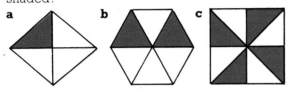

a   **b**   **c**

2 Between midnight on Sunday and midnight on Monday, Harry sleeps for six hours and works for eight hours. For what fraction, in its simplest form, of the time is he:
  a asleep **b** working **c** doing other things?

3 Calculate:
  a $\frac{1}{2}$ of £5 **b** $\frac{1}{3}$ of £18 **c** $\frac{3}{4}$ of £16 **d** $\frac{7}{10}$ of £30

4 Calculate:
  a 10% of £3 **b** 25% of £12 **c** 5% of £500

5 Correct to 2 decimal places, $\pi = 3.14$.
The 3 stands for 3 units. What does:
  a 1 stand for **b** 4 stand for?

6 List in order, smallest first:
10.8, 9.06, 11, 8.99, 10

7 The Big Wheel turns anti-clockwise. What fraction of a complete turn, in simplest form, takes P to:
  a A **b** B **c** C
  d D **e** E **f** F
  g G **h** H **i** I
  j J **k** K?

8 A report recommends that students should use their time in school like this:

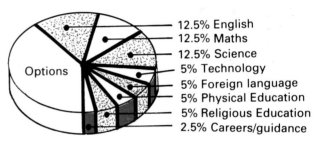

Options

12.5% English
12.5% Maths
12.5% Science
5% Technology
5% Foreign language
5% Physical Education
5% Religious Education
2.5% Careers/guidance

Calculate:
  a the total marked percentages
  b the percentage of time left for other options.

9 A new office block is to be 16 storeys high. Nine storeys have been built. What fraction of the building: **a** has been built **b** is still to be built?

10 a Add 12, 7.5 and 3.81.
  b Subtract 13.8 from 18.3.
  c Multiply 2.34 by: (i) 10 (ii) 100 (iii) 1000.

11 Copy and complete:

Fraction	$\frac{1}{4}$	$\frac{1}{5}$				
Decimal	0.25		0.5	0.75		
Percentage	25%				12%	5%

12 The new bottle contains 10% extra shampoo.

  a How many extra ml does the new bottle have?
  b What is the volume of its contents?

USING FRACTIONS, DECIMALS AND PERCENTAGES

Examples

a Calculate 72% of £120.

72% of £120 = £$\frac{72}{100} \times \frac{120}{1}$ = £86.40

or 72% of 120 = 72 $\boxed{\%}$ $\boxed{\times}$ 120 $\boxed{=}$ 86.4

so 72% of £120 = £86.40

b Calculate $\frac{3}{4}$ of 96 km.

$\frac{3}{4}$ of 96 km = $\frac{3}{4} \times \frac{96}{1}$ km = 72 km

or 3 $\boxed{\times}$ 96 $\boxed{\div}$ 4 = 72

so $\frac{3}{4}$ of 96 km = 72 km

EXERCISE 1A

1 Calculate:
   a 1% of £300   **b** 10% of £75
   c 30% of £6.50   **d** 6% of 50p

2 Calculate:
   a $\frac{1}{5}$ of £7   **b** $\frac{2}{3}$ of £6.90
   c $\frac{3}{8}$ of £48   **d** $\frac{5}{6}$ of 30p

3 The lengths and breadths of stamps in a catalogue are shown as $\frac{2}{3}$ of the real size. Calculate the catalogue dimensions of this stamp.

4 There are 1340 students at Westfield High School. One Monday, 90% were present. How many were:
   a present   **b** absent?

5 In the first week of June, Crown Crafts' sales totalled £4620. Profits were estimated to be $\frac{1}{6}$ of sales. Calculate the profits.

6 Calculate:
   (i) the perimeter   (ii) the area of each shape.

a   Square   3.5 cm

b   2.3 cm   Rectangle   6.8 cm

7 18-carat gold contains $\frac{18}{24}$ pure gold, the rest is alloy. How much pure gold is there in:
   a 144 g of 18-carat gold
   b 312 g of 10-carat gold?

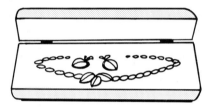

8 There were 23 000 births in Midborough in 1994. 52% of them were boys.
   a How many: (i) boys   (ii) girls were born?
   b How many more boys than girls were born?

9 Which of these is the better buy? By how much?

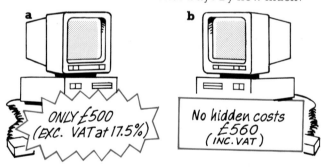

ONLY £500 (EXC. VAT at 17.5%)

No hidden costs £560 (INC. VAT)

10 The weights of a rowing crew are 72.4 kg, 83.6 kg, 76.4 kg and 69.2 kg. Estimate, then calculate, the average weight of a rower.

EXERCISE 1B

1 There are 120 students in Jamal's year group. 45 of them chose German, and the rest chose French. What fraction, in its simplest form, of all the students chose:
a German   **b** French?

2 80 learner drivers took lessons at the Demon Driving School. 28 passed their test first time. Calculate the percentage who:
a passed   **b** failed first time.

3 Calculate the number of:
a German marks for £850
b £s for 4800 marks.

£1 = 2.4 marks

4 Hanif has £380 in Safe Savings, and Lisa has £340 in Top Interest. Who gets more interest after one year? How much more?

SAFE SAVINGS 6% pa

TOP INTEREST 7% pa

5 The Jones family travel 544 km while on holiday. Their car averages 8.5 km per litre of petrol. Calculate:
a the number of litres they used
b the total cost of the petrol, correct to the nearest penny
c the cost per km of petrol, correct to 0.1p.

58.9 PER LITRE
☆☆☆☆☆
SUPER POWER

6 Sarah is confused by her test marks in English for October and February.

Calculate her percentage mark for each test. Had she improved?

7 Mrs Wilson teaches biology. She found that in one of her classes, 12 out of the 20 students refused to hold a frog in their hands.
a What percentage was this?
b After a demonstration by the Countryside ranger, 9 out of 18 were still not keen (two were absent). Was the demonstration effective?

8 Max sowed five different kinds of flower seeds. This table shows the results. Copy and complete it.

Type	A	B	C	D	E
Number of plants	40	35	23	42	13
Number of seeds	50	40	25	60	20
Percentage success	80%				

FRACTIONAL AND PERCENTAGE CHANGES

Karl puts £200 into the Moneymaker Building Society.
a How much interest will he receive after one year?
b How much will be in his account then?

a Interest = 6% of £200 = £$\frac{6}{100}$ × 200 = £12

(**or** 6% of 200 = 6 %× 200 = 12).

b He now has £200 + £12 = £212.

EXERCISE 2A

1 Ann Marshall earns £360 a week. She receives a pay rise of 5%. Calculate:
  a how much more she will receive each week
  b her new weekly earnings.

2 Calculate:
  a the discount offered on this mountain bike
  b the sale price of the bike.

3 The population of Alderton was 17 500 at the last census. Since then it has fallen by $\frac{1}{10}$th. Calculate:
  a the fall in population
  b the population now.

4 The Jetstream fighter can fly 40% faster than the speed of sound (1200 km/h at sea-level). Calculate its top speed.

5 Wonder weighing machines are guaranteed to give readings to within 2% of the actual weights. Calculate the greatest and least readings the machine might show for actual weights of a:
  a 2000 g bag of sugar
  b 350 g bunch of grapes
  c 60 g bar of chocolate.

6 Calculate the interest on £400 for one year at 7% per annum.

7 Christina inherits £20 000, and invests it in the Moneymaker Building Society at 6% per annum interest.
  a Calculate:
    (i) the interest after one year
    (ii) the amount in her account then.
  b She leaves this amount in for one more year. Calculate:
    (i) the interest paid in the second year
    (ii) the amount in her account then.

EXERCISE 2B

Reminder

Percentage increase or decrease
$$= \frac{\text{increase or decrease}}{\text{original value}} \times 100\%$$

Example

Over a period, the price of CDs rose from £12 to £14. Calculate:
a the increase in price
b the percentage increase.

BUY NOW BEFORE PRICE INCREASE

a Increase = £14 − £12 = £2
b Percentage increase = $\frac{2}{12} \times 100\% = 16.7\%$, correct to 1 decimal place.

---

1 The price of the *Daily Moan* newspaper rose from 40p to 45p. Calculate:
a the increase in price
b the percentage increase.

2 The price of the *Daily Cheer* newspaper was reduced from 36p to 33p. Calculate:
a the reduction in price
b the percentage reduction, correct to 1 decimal place, based on the original price.

3 Kevin bought a new car for £15 000. A year later it was worth £12 000. Calculate:
a its fall in value
b its percentage fall, based on its value when new.

4 Sue thinks that her weight is about 51 kg. But the weighing machine says 48 kg. Calculate:
a the error in her estimate
b the error, as a percentage of her actual weight.

5 When heated, the length and breadth of this metal plate increase by 2%.

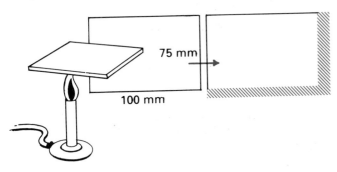

75 mm

100 mm

Calculate:
a the length and breadth of the plate after heating
b the area before and after heating
c the increase in area
d the percentage increase in area, based on the area before heating.

6 The table shows the number of votes cast for two candidates in Central constituency.

Candidate	Now	Last election
C. Morris	46 230	38 672
R. Field	35 302	29 402

Which candidate had:
a the greater increase in votes
b the greater percentage increase, based on the earlier election?

7 The height of a sunflower is measured at the beginning of each week, and its increase during the week is recorded.

Week	1	2	3	4	5	6
Height (mm)	100	105	115	125	140	150
Increase (mm)	4	5	10	10	15	10
% increase	4%					

Calculate the percentage increase each week, correct to 1 decimal place.

8 Mike puts £620 in a bank account. After one year, he has £647.90.
a Calculate:
   (i) the increase in his money
   (ii) the percentage increase (the rate of interest).
b If the interest rate stays the same, how much would he have after another year?

9 The Jones family went to France on holiday this year. For £300 cash they received 2418 francs, compared to 2955 francs last year. Calculate:
a the exchange rate (£1 = ... francs) each year
b the percentage change in the rate from last year to this year, correct to 1 decimal place, based on last year's rate.

LINKING FRACTIONS, DECIMALS AND PERCENTAGES

Reminders

Per cent means **per hundred**	0.3 means 3 tenths	$\frac{2}{5}$ means 2 divided by 5	$\frac{1}{4} = \frac{1}{4} \times 100\%$
$10\% = \frac{10}{100} = \frac{1}{10} = 0.1$	$0.3 = \frac{3}{10}$	$\frac{2}{5} = 2 \div 5 = 0.4$	$= 25\%$

EXERCISE 3A

1 Change these percentages to decimal fractions.
For example, $35\% = \frac{35}{100} = 0.35$
a 45% **b** 80% **c** 8% **d** 12% **e** 120%

2 Change these percentages to fractions in their simplest form.

For example, $40\% = \dfrac{\overset{2}{\cancel{40}}}{\underset{5}{\cancel{100}}} = \dfrac{2}{5}$

a 30% **b** 80% **c** 2% **d** 120% **e** 18%

3 Change these decimal fractions to percentages.
For example, $0.19 = 0.19 \times 100\% = 19\%$
a 0.45 **b** 0.33 **c** 0.8 **d** 1.5 **e** 0.07

4 Change these fractions to percentages.
For example, $\frac{2}{5} = \frac{2}{5} \times 100\% = 40\%$
a $\frac{3}{10}$ **b** $\frac{13}{100}$ **c** $\frac{7}{100}$ **d** $\frac{4}{5}$ **e** $\frac{1}{8}$

5 Change these decimal fractions to fractions in their simplest form.
For example, $0.6 = \frac{6}{10} = \frac{3}{5}$
a 0.7 **b** 0.8 **c** 0.03 **d** 0.06 **e** 0.35

6 Change these fractions to decimal fractions, correct to 2 decimal places where necessary.
For example, $\frac{1}{6} = 1 \div 6 = 0.17$
a $\frac{3}{4}$ **b** $\frac{3}{10}$ **c** $\frac{2}{5}$ **d** $\frac{1}{3}$ **e** $\frac{4}{7}$

CHALLENGE

Find pairs of equal numbers below.

> 5% $\frac{1}{20}$ 25% $\frac{1}{25}$ $\frac{3}{25}$ 20%
> $\frac{1}{4}$
> $\frac{1}{5}$ 12% 2.5 250% 4%

EXERCISE 3B

1 Which is greater in each pair?
a $\frac{1}{2}$ or 0.6 **b** $\frac{2}{3}$ or 60% **c** 10% or 0.09
d 20% or $\frac{1}{4}$ **e** $\frac{5}{6}$ or 83% **f** 0.85 or $\frac{7}{8}$

2 Change each of these to a decimal fraction, *and to* a fraction in its simplest form.
a 25% **b** 40% **c** 5%

3 Change each of these to a fraction in its simplest form, *and* to a percentage.
a 0.16 **b** 0.1 **c** 0.09

4 a Use the π key on your calculator to write down the value of π to as many decimal places as it gives.
b $3\frac{1}{7}$ is sometimes used as an approximation for π. Is this the same as in **a** for:
(i) 1 (ii) 2 (iii) 3 (iv) more than 3 decimal places?

5 List each set of numbers in order, smallest first:
a $\frac{1}{3}$, 30%, 0.33 **b** 65%, $\frac{5}{8}$, 0.62 **c** 1.6, $1\frac{4}{7}$, 150%

6 Ann sees a table priced £350 on sale at Lowprice at 30% off, and at Hivalue at a $\frac{2}{5}$ reduction. Which shop has the better offer, and by how much?

7 Copy and complete this table, giving fractions in their simplest form.

Fraction	$\frac{4}{5}$			$\frac{3}{8}$
Decimal		0.36		
Percentage			68%	

		$1\frac{7}{20}$		
0.26			2.45	
	4%			305%

CHALLENGE

a Using pairs of numbers from 1 to 9, make a list of all the fractions, in their simplest form, you can find which are less than 1; for example $\frac{3}{7}$, $\frac{1}{8}$, and so on. Try to be methodical.

b By changing the fractions to decimal form if necessary, arrange them in order, smallest first.

MIXED NUMBERS (WHOLE NUMBERS AND FRACTIONS)

Examples

a Change the 'top heavy' fraction $\frac{5}{3}$ to a mixed number.

$$\frac{5}{3} = \frac{3}{3} + \frac{2}{3} = 1\frac{2}{3}$$

b Change $5\frac{3}{4}$ to a proper fraction.

$$5\frac{3}{4} = \frac{20}{4} + \frac{3}{4} = \frac{23}{4}$$

EXERCISE 4

1 Write as mixed numbers:
a $\frac{3}{2}$ **b** $\frac{9}{4}$ **c** $\frac{11}{8}$ **d** $\frac{7}{2}$ **e** $\frac{12}{5}$

2 Write as proper fractions:
a $3\frac{1}{2}$ **b** $1\frac{3}{4}$ **c** $2\frac{1}{5}$ **d** $5\frac{1}{3}$ **e** $1\frac{1}{10}$

3 Write as mixed numbers:
a $\frac{11}{8}$ **b** $\frac{16}{3}$ **c** $\frac{14}{5}$ **d** $\frac{23}{10}$ **e** $\frac{20}{9}$

4 Write as proper fractions:
a $4\frac{2}{3}$ **b** $3\frac{3}{8}$ **c** $2\frac{7}{10}$ **d** $1\frac{1}{8}$ **e** $5\frac{7}{8}$

5 Write each number below as a proper fraction.

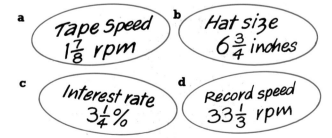

a Tape Speed $1\frac{7}{8}$ rpm
b Hat size $6\frac{3}{4}$ inches
c Interest rate $3\frac{1}{4}$%
d Record speed $33\frac{1}{3}$ rpm

6 Copy and complete this table. The lengths are in inches.

Length of bolt	$1\frac{3}{8}$ $=\frac{11}{8}$	$4\frac{1}{4}$ $=\frac{}{4}$	$2\frac{3}{10}$ $=\frac{}{10}$	$3\frac{7}{8}$ $=\frac{}{8}$	$5\frac{3}{4}$ $=\frac{}{4}$
Width of 1 turn	$\frac{1}{8}$	$\frac{1}{4}$	$\frac{1}{10}$	$\frac{1}{8}$	$\frac{1}{4}$
Number of turns	11				

7 In each pair below, find which number is greater by changing them to mixed numbers.
a $\frac{3}{2}$ or $\frac{5}{4}$ **b** $\frac{4}{3}$ or $\frac{6}{5}$ **c** $\frac{10}{3}$ or $\frac{7}{2}$ **d** $\frac{19}{4}$ or $\frac{22}{5}$

8 Check your answers to question **7** by changing all the fractions to decimal form.

9 Check your answers to question **7** by writing each pair of fractions with a common denominator.
For example $\frac{5}{6}$, $\frac{3}{4}$; lowest common denominator is 12.
$\frac{5}{6} = \frac{10}{12}$, $\frac{3}{4} = \frac{9}{12}$. So $\frac{5}{6} > \frac{3}{4}$.

ADDING AND SUBTRACTING FRACTIONS

Examples

a $\frac{3}{8} - \frac{1}{8} = \frac{2}{8} = \frac{1}{4}$

b $\frac{3}{4} + \frac{3}{4} = \frac{6}{4} = \frac{4}{4} + \frac{2}{4} = 1\frac{1}{2}$

c $\quad 4\frac{3}{8} - 2\frac{1}{8}$
$= 4 + \frac{3}{8} - 2 - \frac{1}{8}$
$= 4 - 2 + \frac{3}{8} - \frac{1}{8}$
$= 2\frac{2}{8}$
$= 2\frac{1}{4}$

EXERCISE 5A

Simplify the sums or differences in questions **1–8**.

1 a $\frac{3}{5} + \frac{1}{5}$ **b** $\frac{3}{8} + \frac{1}{8}$ **c** $\frac{1}{2} + \frac{1}{2}$ **d** $\frac{3}{7} + \frac{2}{7}$

2 a $\frac{4}{5} - \frac{1}{5}$ **b** $\frac{5}{6} - \frac{1}{6}$ **c** $\frac{1}{3} - \frac{1}{3}$ **d** $\frac{9}{10} - \frac{7}{10}$

3 a $\frac{3}{5} + \frac{2}{5}$ **b** $\frac{3}{5} - \frac{2}{5}$ **c** $\frac{3}{10} + \frac{1}{10}$ **d** $\frac{3}{10} - \frac{1}{10}$

4 a $\frac{3}{5} + \frac{3}{5}$ **b** $\frac{7}{8} + \frac{4}{8}$ **c** $\frac{7}{8} + \frac{5}{8}$ **d** $\frac{7}{10} + \frac{9}{10}$

5 a $\frac{4}{3} - \frac{1}{3}$ **b** $\frac{7}{5} - \frac{4}{5}$ **c** $\frac{5}{2} - \frac{1}{2}$ **d** $\frac{11}{10} - \frac{1}{10}$

6 a $2\frac{1}{3} + 1\frac{1}{3}$ **b** $3\frac{1}{4} + 2\frac{1}{4}$ **c** $1\frac{3}{5} + 1\frac{2}{5}$ **d** $3 + \frac{1}{2}$

7 a $3\frac{3}{4} - 1\frac{1}{4}$ **b** $2\frac{3}{8} - 1\frac{1}{8}$ **c** $3 - \frac{1}{2}$ **d** $5 - 1\frac{1}{2}$

8 a $1\frac{2}{3} + 1\frac{1}{3}$ **b** $1\frac{2}{3} - 1\frac{1}{3}$ **c** $2\frac{1}{2} + 1\frac{1}{2}$ **d** $4\frac{7}{10} - 3\frac{1}{10}$

9 Calculate:
(i) the difference between the length and breadth of each rectangle
(ii) the perimeters of both rectangles.

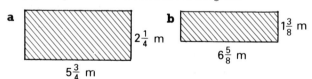

a $2\frac{1}{4}$ m, $5\frac{3}{4}$ m

b $1\frac{3}{8}$ m, $6\frac{5}{8}$ m

10 How far is it from:
a the village to the coast
b the village to the lighthouse
c the coast to the lighthouse, along the same road?

VILLAGE $3\frac{1}{4}$ miles COAST $2\frac{1}{4}$ miles LIGHTHOUSE 4 miles

11 Samir's new car holds nine gallons of petrol when the tank is full. How much is left after:
a $3\frac{1}{2}$ gallons are used
b another $3\frac{1}{2}$ gallons are used?

12 A video cassette lasts three hours. How much time is left after Joe records programmes which last for:
a $\frac{3}{4}$ hour **b** another $\frac{1}{4}$ hour
c a further hour and a half?

CHALLENGE

Copy and complete this magic square. (Each row, column and diagonal has the same total.)

1		3
	$2\frac{1}{2}$	
2		

INVESTIGATION

Using the fraction key $\boxed{a^b\!/_c}$ **on a calculator**

1 a *For* $\frac{2}{3}$, *key* 2 $\boxed{a^b\!/_c}$ 3, *giving* $\boxed{2\,r\,3}$
b *Key in the fractions* $\frac{1}{2}, \frac{3}{4}, \frac{9}{10}$ *and watch the display.*

2 a *For* $5\frac{1}{4}$, *key* 5 $\boxed{a^b\!/_c}$ 1 $\boxed{a^b\!/_c}$ 4, *giving* $\boxed{5\,r\,1\,r\,4}$
b *Key in* $2\frac{1}{2}, 3\frac{4}{5}, 1\frac{7}{8}$ *and watch the display.*

3 a *For* $\frac{2}{4}$, *key* 2 $\boxed{a^b\!/_c}$ 4. *Now watch the display as you key* $\boxed{=}$, *then* $\boxed{a^b\!/_c}$. *Explain what you see.*
b *Repeat* **a** *for the fractions* $\frac{4}{8}, \frac{6}{8}, \frac{2}{10}, \frac{2}{6}, \frac{4}{14}$.

4 a *For* $\frac{6}{3}$, *key* 6 $\boxed{a^b\!/_c}$ 3 $\boxed{=}$.
b *Key* 5 $\boxed{a^b\!/_c}$ 2 $\boxed{=}$ $\boxed{a^b\!/_c}$, *and explain what you see.*
c *Repeat* **b** *for the fractions* $\frac{7}{4}, \frac{6}{5}, \frac{9}{8}, \frac{10}{3}$.

5 *A set of spanners comes in* $\frac{1}{16}, \frac{2}{16}, \frac{3}{16}, \ldots, \frac{16}{16}$ *inch sizes. Write each of these sizes in simplest fractional form and in decimal form.*

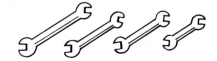

EXERCISE 5B

Examples (without, and with, a calculator)

a $\frac{1}{4}+\frac{2}{3}$

$=\frac{3}{12}+\frac{8}{12}$ (the lowest common multiple, lcm, of 4 and 3 is 12)

$=\frac{11}{12}$

or 1 $\boxed{a^{b}/_{c}}$ 4 + 2 $\boxed{a^{b}/_{c}}$ 3 $\boxed{=}$ $\boxed{\boxed{1\,1\,r\,12}}$

b $5\frac{3}{5}-2\frac{1}{2}$

$=5+\frac{3}{5}-2-\frac{1}{2}$

$=3+\frac{6}{10}-\frac{5}{10}$ (lcm of 5 and 2 is 10)

$=3\frac{1}{10}$

or 5 $\boxed{a^{b}/_{c}}$ 3 $\boxed{a^{b}/_{c}}$ 5 $\boxed{-}$ 2 $\boxed{a^{b}/_{c}}$ 1 $\boxed{a^{b}/_{c}}$ 2 $\boxed{=}$ $\boxed{3\,r\,1\,r\,10}$

Simplify the sums or differences in questions **1–6**.

1 a $\frac{1}{2}+\frac{1}{4}$ **b** $\frac{1}{2}+\frac{1}{3}$ **c** $\frac{1}{2}+\frac{1}{8}$ **d** $\frac{1}{2}+\frac{1}{5}$

2 a $\frac{2}{3}+\frac{1}{6}$ **b** $\frac{1}{3}+\frac{2}{5}$ **c** $\frac{3}{4}+\frac{1}{8}$ **d** $\frac{3}{4}+\frac{1}{2}$

3 a $\frac{1}{2}-\frac{1}{4}$ **b** $\frac{5}{8}-\frac{1}{2}$ **c** $\frac{4}{5}-\frac{1}{4}$ **d** $\frac{5}{6}-\frac{1}{3}$

4 a $\frac{7}{10}-\frac{1}{5}$ **b** $\frac{7}{8}-\frac{1}{4}$ **c** $\frac{1}{5}-\frac{1}{10}$ **d** $\frac{9}{10}-\frac{4}{5}$

5 a $1\frac{1}{2}+\frac{1}{4}$ **b** $1\frac{1}{2}+\frac{3}{4}$ **c** $2\frac{2}{3}+\frac{1}{6}$ **d** $3\frac{1}{5}+\frac{3}{10}$

6 a $2\frac{1}{2}-1\frac{1}{5}$ **b** $3\frac{1}{4}-1\frac{1}{8}$ **c** $4\frac{5}{6}-1\frac{2}{3}$ **d** $1\frac{7}{8}-\frac{1}{2}$

7 A bottle of wine holds $\frac{7}{10}$ litre. $\frac{1}{2}$ litre is poured out. How much is left?

8 A lorry weighs $4\frac{1}{2}$ tonnes. It picks up a load of sand weighing $2\frac{3}{4}$ tonnes. Calculate the total weight.

9 a Barbara catches these two fish in a competition. Calculate their total weight.
b Paul catches two fish weighing $4\frac{1}{4}$ lb and $2\frac{1}{2}$ lb. Calculate the weight of his catch.
c Who had the heavier catch? By how much?

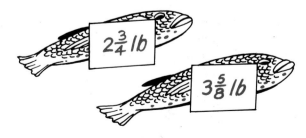

10 Geoff uses $\frac{1}{3}$ of the area of his garden for vegetables and $\frac{2}{5}$ for flowers. The rest is grass. What fraction of the garden is grass?

11 $\frac{1}{4}$ of the seats in a theatre are in the front stalls, $\frac{5}{12}$ in the back stalls and the rest in the balcony. The theatre has 720 seats. How many are in the balcony?

12 One morning, half the students at Jane's school arrived before 8.55, and another three eighths of them arrived before 9. What fraction of the students arrived:
a before 9 **b** at 9 o'clock or later?

13 In a year group election, $\frac{1}{2}$ the students voted for Janice, $\frac{1}{4}$ for Lana and $\frac{1}{8}$ for Sean. The rest voted for Andrew.
a What fraction of the votes did Andrew get?
b 100 students voted. How many votes did each candidate get?

/ **CHALLENGE**

Copy and complete this magic square.

		$\frac{3}{8}$
$\frac{1}{2}$	$\frac{3}{4}$	1

MULTIPLYING FRACTIONS

Examples

a $3 \times \frac{3}{4}$

$= \frac{3}{1} \times \frac{3}{4}$

$= \frac{9}{4}$

$= 2\frac{1}{4}$

or   3 &boxed;× 3 &boxed;$a^b/_c$ 4 &boxed;=

b $\frac{3}{4} \times \frac{1}{2}$

$= \frac{3 \times 1}{4 \times 2}$

$= \frac{3}{8}$

or   3 &boxed;$a^b/_c$ 4 &boxed;× 1 &boxed;$a^b/_c$ 2 &boxed;=

EXERCISE 6A

Simplify the products in questions **1–5**.

1 a $8 \times \frac{1}{2}$ **b** $6 \times \frac{2}{3}$ **c** $5 \times \frac{1}{3}$ **d** $4 \times \frac{2}{5}$

2 a $\frac{1}{2} \times \frac{1}{4}$ **b** $\frac{1}{3} \times \frac{1}{2}$ **c** $\frac{3}{4} \times \frac{2}{3}$ **d** $\frac{1}{8} \times \frac{4}{5}$

3 a $\frac{1}{2}$ of $\frac{1}{2}$ **b** $\frac{1}{4}$ of $\frac{1}{3}$ **c** $\frac{1}{3}$ of $\frac{3}{4}$ **d** $\frac{2}{3}$ of $\frac{3}{8}$

4 a $3 \times \frac{2}{3}$ **b** $4 \times \frac{3}{8}$ **c** $2 \times \frac{3}{4}$ **d** $6 \times \frac{5}{8}$

5 a $\frac{1}{4} \times \frac{1}{4}$ **b** $\frac{1}{4} \times \frac{4}{5}$ **c** $\frac{2}{3}$ of $\frac{3}{10}$ **d** $\frac{1}{10}$ of $\frac{5}{8}$

6 a What fraction of square (i) below is shaded?
   b Multiply the length of the shaded rectangle ($\frac{1}{3}$ unit) by its breadth ($\frac{1}{2}$ unit). Do you get the same fraction as in part **a**?

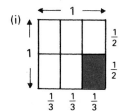 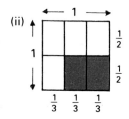

   c Repeat **a** and **b** for square (ii) above.

7 Repeat question **6** for the squares below.

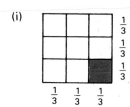 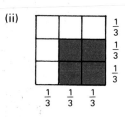

8 $\frac{2}{3}$ of a person's weight is water. Ahmed weighs 63 kg. How much of this is water?

9 On the moon, everything weighs $\frac{1}{6}$ of its weight on Earth. How much will a 72 kg astronaut weigh on the moon?

10 Henry eats $\frac{1}{3}$ of a tin of catfood daily. How many tins will he need in September?

HENRY

11 Henry also drinks $\frac{3}{4}$ pint of milk daily. How many pints will be bought for him in February 1999?

12 A bottle of orange juice contains $\frac{2}{3}$ litre. Calculate the number of litres of juice in:
   a (i) 3 bottles   (ii) 6 bottles   (iii) 2 bottles
   b (i) $\frac{1}{2}$ bottle   (ii) $\frac{1}{3}$ bottle   (iii) $\frac{3}{4}$ bottle

13 Could either of these be recorded on a 3-hour tape?
   a seven $\frac{1}{2}$-hour programmes
   b four $\frac{3}{4}$-hour programmes.

14 A 30 m length of carpet is needed for a stair $\frac{3}{4}$ m wide. Calculate the area of the carpet.

15 An aircraft flying at 1800 km/h reduces its speed by $\frac{1}{2}$, then by a further $\frac{2}{3}$ for landing. Calculate its landing speed.

16 Use this diagram to calculate C when F is:
   a 77   **b** 104   **c** 212.

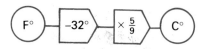

17 Mrs Samson chose a patterned material to make a dress for herself and a skirt for each of her twin daughters. She bought 6 m at £9.60 a metre, and used $\frac{2}{3}$ of it for her dress and the rest for her daughters' skirts. How much did the dress and each skirt cost?

MULTIPLYING MIXED NUMBERS

EXERCISE 6B

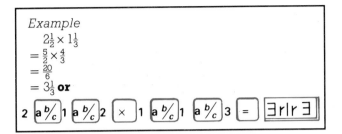

Example
$2\frac{1}{2} \times 1\frac{1}{3}$
$= \frac{5}{2} \times \frac{4}{3}$
$= \frac{20}{6}$
$= 3\frac{1}{3}$ **or**

Simplify the products in questions **1–3**.

1 a $1\frac{1}{2} \times 2$ **b** $1\frac{1}{4} \times 3$ **c** $2\frac{1}{2} \times 5$ **d** $3\frac{1}{3} \times 6$

2 a $1\frac{1}{2} \times 1\frac{1}{2}$ **b** $1\frac{1}{4} \times 1\frac{1}{5}$ **c** $1\frac{1}{3} \times 2\frac{1}{4}$ **d** $1\frac{3}{5} \times 2\frac{1}{2}$

3 a $4\frac{1}{2} \times 1\frac{1}{3}$ **b** $3\frac{1}{3} \times 2\frac{1}{4}$ **c** $1\frac{1}{8} \times 1\frac{1}{3}$ **d** $2\frac{2}{5} \times 3\frac{3}{4}$

4 Calculate the areas of this square and rectangle:

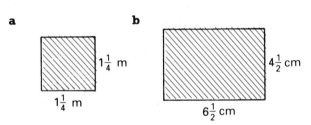

a $1\frac{1}{4}$ m, $1\frac{1}{4}$ m

b $4\frac{1}{2}$ cm, $6\frac{1}{2}$ cm

5 a $4\frac{1}{2}$ litres to the gallon. How many litres in $3\frac{1}{2}$ gallons?
b $2\frac{1}{2}$ cm to the inch. How many centimetres in $9\frac{1}{4}$ inches?
c $2\frac{1}{4}$ lb to the kilogram. How many lb in $6\frac{1}{2}$ kilograms?

6 A turntable makes $33\frac{1}{3}$ revolutions in a minute. How many turns will it make in:
a 3 minutes **b** $4\frac{1}{2}$ minutes?

7 Calculate the actual distance between places which are:
a 3 cm apart on the map **b** $4\frac{1}{2}$ cm apart.

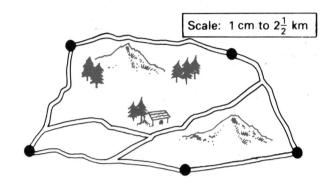

Scale: 1 cm to $2\frac{1}{2}$ km

8 Calculate the volumes of these cuboids.

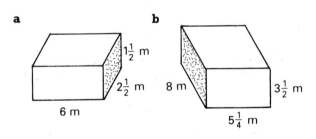

a $1\frac{1}{2}$ m, $2\frac{1}{2}$ m, 6 m

b 8 m, $3\frac{1}{2}$ m, $5\frac{1}{4}$ m

9 Deepa's tape recorder has speeds of $1\frac{7}{8}$, $3\frac{3}{4}$ and $7\frac{1}{2}$ inches per second.
a How many inches of tape will be used at each speed in 40 seconds?
b What is the connection between the three speeds?

10 For a cube with sides $1\frac{1}{2}$ cm long, calculate:
a the total length of the edges
b the total surface area
c the volume.

DIVIDING NUMBERS WITH FRACTIONS

Use your calculator for these calculations:

a $8 \div \frac{2}{3}$

$8 \boxed{\div} 2 \boxed{a^b/_c} 3 \boxed{=} \boxed{12}$

So $8 \div \frac{2}{3} = 12$

b $5\frac{1}{2} \div 1\frac{2}{3}$

$5 \boxed{a^b/_c} 1 \boxed{a^b/_c} 2 \boxed{\div} 1 \boxed{a^b/_c} 2 \boxed{a^b/_c} 3 \boxed{=} \boxed{3\,\lrcorner\,3\,\lrcorner\,10}$

So $5\frac{1}{2} \div 1\frac{2}{3} = 3\frac{3}{10}$

EXERCISE 7B

Calculate:

1 a $4 \div \frac{1}{2}$ **b** $5 \div \frac{1}{3}$ **c** $6 \div \frac{3}{4}$ **d** $8 \div \frac{2}{3}$

2 a $\frac{1}{2} \div \frac{1}{4}$ **b** $\frac{1}{2} \div \frac{1}{8}$ **c** $\frac{3}{4} \div \frac{1}{2}$ **d** $\frac{1}{3} \div \frac{1}{6}$

3 a $6 \div 1\frac{1}{2}$ **b** $15 \div 2\frac{1}{2}$ **c** $10 \div 1\frac{1}{4}$ **d** $7 \div 2\frac{1}{3}$

4 a $5\frac{1}{2} \div 2\frac{1}{2}$ **b** $3\frac{1}{3} \div 1\frac{1}{3}$ **c** $2\frac{1}{4} \div 1\frac{1}{4}$ **d** $3\frac{3}{4} \div 2\frac{1}{2}$

5 Calculate the length of each of these rectangles.

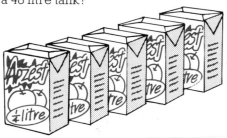

a 10 m² — $2\frac{1}{2}$ m
b 20 m² — $3\frac{1}{3}$ m

6 How many $\frac{1}{4}$ litre cartons of juice can be filled from a 48 litre tank?

7 How many $\frac{3}{4}$ hour programmes can be recorded on:
a a 3-hour tape   **b** a $1\frac{1}{2}$-hour tape
c a 4-hour tape?

8 A tip-up truck can hold $4\frac{7}{8}$ tonnes. Calculate the least number of trips needed to remove 25 tonnes of rubble.

9 $a = 8$, $b = 1\frac{1}{2}$ and $c = \frac{3}{4}$. Calculate the values of:
a ab **b** ba **c** $a \div b$ **d** $b \div a$
e bc **f** $b \div c$ **g** $c \div b$ **h** $a \div c$

BRAINSTORMER

Flags are placed every $\frac{1}{5}$ km along the route of a 'fun run'. The course is $4\frac{3}{5}$ km long. How many flags are needed, including the ones at the start and finish of the race?

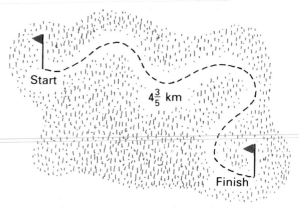

Start

$4\frac{3}{5}$ km

Finish

CHECK-UP ON FRACTIONS, DECIMALS AND PERCENTAGES

1 Three students in Sally's class are left-handed and twenty-one are right-handed. What fraction of the students, in simplest form, are:
a left-handed **b** right-handed?

2 Calculate:
a 10% of £46 **b** 17.5% of £840
c $\frac{1}{5}$ of £9 **d** $\frac{3}{4}$ of £63 **e** $\frac{2}{3}$ of £4500

3 At sea, 1 knot $\doteqdot$ 1.15 mph.
a Change to mph:
(i) 10 knots (ii) 25 knots
b Change to knots, correct to 1 decimal place:
(i) 10 mph (ii) 36 mph

4 Calculate:
a the discount on the calculator
b the sale price of the calculator.

5 In an exam, nine students out of 120 are awarded a grade A. What percentage of the students got an A?

6 Jim and George made £7.20 in an afternoon.

How much does each take if the shares are:
a 50% each **b** 40% to Jim, 60% to George?

7 Nicole invests £5000. She leaves the interest in her account each year. Calculate the amount she will have in her account at the end of:
a 1 year **b** 2 years

8 Copy and complete this table.

Fraction	$\frac{1}{2}$			$\frac{2}{5}$	
Decimal		0.25			0.07
Percentage			10%		72%

		$\frac{1}{8}$		$\frac{9}{10}$	
			0.65		2.75
			80%		101%

9 a Change to proper fractions:
(i) $1\frac{2}{3}$ (ii) $2\frac{1}{2}$ (iii) $3\frac{1}{7}$ (iv) $1\frac{7}{8}$
b Change to mixed numbers:
(i) $\frac{9}{4}$ (ii) $\frac{11}{3}$ (iii) $\frac{27}{10}$ (iv) $\frac{18}{5}$

10 Calculate:
a $\frac{3}{5}+\frac{2}{5}$ **b** $4-\frac{3}{4}$ **c** $\frac{3}{4}+\frac{1}{2}$ **d** $\frac{4}{5}-\frac{2}{3}$
e $1\frac{1}{3}+\frac{2}{3}$ **f** $1\frac{3}{8}+1\frac{1}{4}$ **g** $3\frac{1}{2}-1\frac{1}{4}$ **h** $2\frac{1}{3}-1\frac{2}{3}$

11 Calculate:
a $6\times\frac{1}{3}$ **b** $\frac{3}{5}\times10$ **c** $\frac{1}{2}$ of $\frac{3}{4}$ **d** $\frac{2}{3}\times\frac{4}{5}$
e $\frac{3}{4}\times\frac{2}{5}$ **f** $1\frac{1}{2}\times\frac{2}{3}$ **g** $2\frac{1}{4}\times\frac{2}{5}$ **h** $2\frac{1}{2}\times1\frac{1}{5}$

12 For this cuboid, calculate:
a the sum of all the edges
b the total surface area
c the volume.

13 Calculate:
a the length of a strip of 10 stamps
b the perimeter of one stamp
c the area of a stamp.

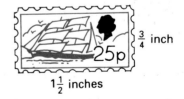

14 The curved wooden frame of the squash racket is $\frac{9}{16}''$ (inch) thick. Calculate d.

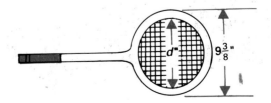

4 EQUATIONS AND INEQUALITIES

LOOKING BACK

1 Solve these equations:
  a $3x = 12$ **b** $y + 5 = 8$ **c** $z - 1 = 6$

2 Multiply out:
  a $2(x + 3)$ **b** $3(t - 1)$ **c** $5(2 + p)$

3 Make an equation for each of these, and solve it.

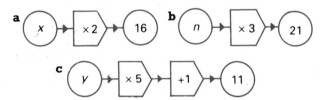

4 Make an equation for each balance, and solve it.

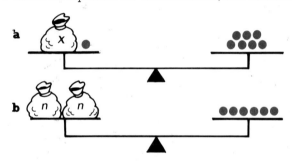

5 I think of a number (n), multiply it by 3 and add 1.
  The answer is 19. Make an equation, and solve it
  to find n.

6 I think of another number (m), multiply it by 4
  and subtract 3. The answer is 9. Make another
  equation, then solve it for m.

7 a Write down an expression for the area of this
  rectangle.

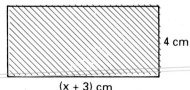

(x + 3) cm

b The area is 32 cm². Make an equation, and
  solve it for x.
  c Calculate the perimeter of the rectangle.

8 Make an equation for this balance, and solve it.

9 Solve:
  a $3x + 2x = 30$ **b** $4y - y = 12$ **c** $2(x + 1) = 8$

10 Say whether each of these is true (T) or false (F):
  a $2 < 1$ **b** $1 > 0$ **c** $0 > 5$ **d** $2 > -2$
  e If x is a whole number, and $x > 3$,
  then $x = 3, 4, 5, \ldots$

11 y can be chosen from the numbers marked on
  this line.

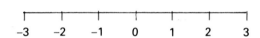

Write down the solutions of these inequalities:
  a $y > 0$ **b** $y \geqslant 2$ **c** $y < 0$ **d** $y \leqslant -1$

12 Write down an inequality for each picture
  below.

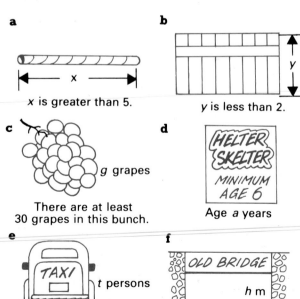

a x is greater than 5.

b y is less than 2.

c g grapes
There are at least
30 grapes in this bunch.

d HELTER SKELTER
MINIMUM AGE 6
Age a years

e TAXI t persons
Maximum 6 persons.

f OLD BRIDGE
h m
Height limit 3.5 m.

EQUATIONS

EXERCISE 1A

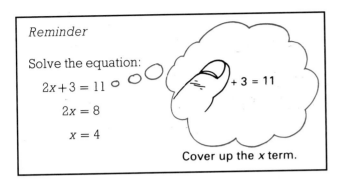

Reminder

Solve the equation:

$2x + 3 = 11$

$2x = 8$

$x = 4$

Cover up the *x* term.

Solve the equations in questions **1–5**:

1 a $x + 8 = 12$ **b** $y - 3 = 5$ **c** $z + 1 = 11$

2 a $2m + 1 = 7$ **b** $3n + 2 = 5$ **c** $4p + 3 = 19$

3 a $2x - 1 = 5$ **b** $3y + 4 = 10$ **c** $4z - 3 = 1$

4 a $7 + 3p = 13$ **b** $9 + 5t = 19$ **c** $3 + 4s = 23$

5 a $13 = a + 9$ **b** $17 = b + 8$ **c** $11 = c + 1$

6 Make an equation for each pair of equal straws, then solve it. In **a**, $3x - 3 = 18$.

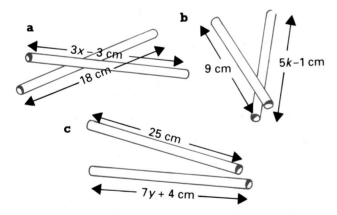

7 Match each of these equations with its solution.

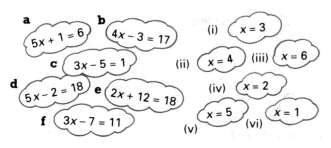

8 Write an equation for each balance, then solve it, to find how many weights are in each bag. In **a**, $2x + 3 = 15$.

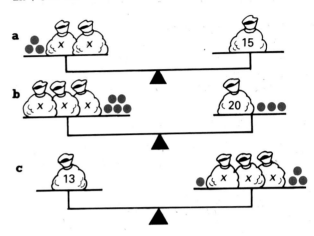

9 Write down an equation for each of these diagrams, then solve it.

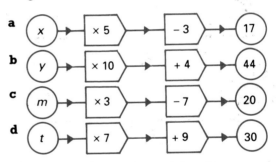

10 Make an equation for each diagram, and solve it.

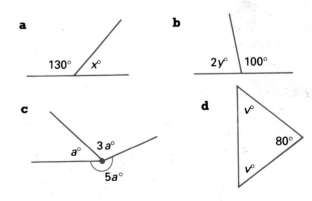

11 The *n*th term of the sequence 4, 7, 10, 13, ... is $3n + 1$.
Find *n* if the *n*th term is:
a 19 **b** 31 **c** 73 **d** 103

EXERCISE 1B

Reminder

Solve the equation:

$$5(y+1) = 20$$
$$5y+5 = 20$$
$$-5 \quad -5$$
$$5y = 15$$
$$y = 3$$

Reminder

Solve the equations:

a $2x-1 = 8$ **b** $3y+8 = 2$
$+1 \quad +1$ $-8 \quad -8$
$2x = 9$ $3y = 2-8 = -6$
$x = \frac{9}{2}$ $y = -2$
$ = 4\frac{1}{2}$

Solve the equations in questions **1–2**.

1 a $2(x-1) = 6$ **b** $3(y-2) = 9$
   c $4(z-3) = 12$ **d** $2(u+1) = 8$
   e $3(v+3) = 12$ **f** $5(w+2) = 20$

2 a $2(a-1) = 10$ **b** $3(b+2) = 6$
   c $5(c-2) = 0$ **d** $2(3p+1) = 14$
   e $4(2q-1) = 4$ **f** $3(2r+1) = 9$

3 Make an equation for each balance, and solve it.

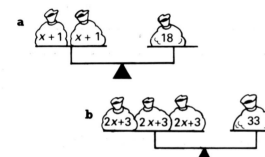

a

b

4 Make an equation for each set of straws, and solve it.

a

8 straws, each $3x+1$ cm long.
Their total length is 56 cm.

b

7 straws, each $2x-3$ cm long.
Their total length is 35 cm.

c

10 straws, each $5x-2$ cm long.
Their total length is 380 cm.

Solve the equations in questions **5–10**:

5 a $2x = 4$ **b** $2x = 5$ **c** $2x = 7$ **d** $2x = 11$

6 a $2y+1 = 4$ **b** $2y-1 = 8$ **c** $2y+3 = 4$
   d $3u+1 = 8$ **e** $4v-3 = 2$ **f** $2w+4 = 5$

7 a $2x = -6$ **b** $3y = -12$ **c** $4z = -4$
   d $5a = -10$ **e** $2b = -8$ **f** $3c = -9$

8 a $2x-1 = -7$ **b** $2x-3 = -5$
   c $3y+5 = 2$ **d** $4y+9 = 1$

9 a $2p-1 = -5$ **b** $3q-2 = -8$
   c $5r+8 = 3$ **d** $4s+9 = 1$

10 a $2(x+3) = 9$ **b** $3(y-1) = 1$ **c** $4(z+1) = 6$
    d $2(u-2) = -6$ **e** $3(v+2) = 0$ **f** $5(w+3) = 5$

CHALLENGE

A long time ago it was found that when two weights balance like this, then:

$$a \times b = c \times d$$

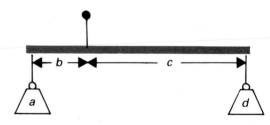

For example, the scale below balances because $4 \times 3 = 6 \times 2$.

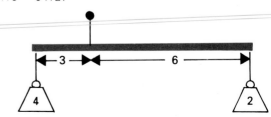

This one tilts down to the left because $5 \times 3 > 6 \times 2$.

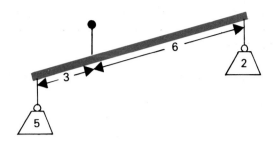

1 Explain whether each of these is balanced. If not, say which way the balance tilts.

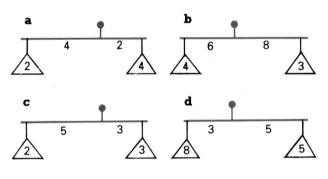

2 These beams are balanced. Make an equation for each, and solve it.

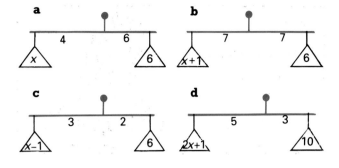

EXERCISE 2A

Reminders

Solve these equations:

a $4x = 2x + 5$	
$-2x \quad -2x$ (to get x terms	
$2x = 5$ on one side)	
$x = 2\frac{1}{2}$	

b $2y = 12 - y$
$+y \quad +y$
$3y = 12$
$y = 4$

c $5x - 3 = 2x + 12$
$-2x \qquad -2x$ (xs to one side)
$3x - 3 = 12$
$+3 \quad +3$ (numbers to one side)
$3x = 15$
$x = 5$

Copy the equations in questions **1–3**, and solve them.

1 a $2x = x + 4$ **b** $4y = 3y + 2$ **c** $3z = z + 6$
$\quad -x \quad -x \qquad -3y \quad -3y \qquad -z \quad -z$

2 a $9k = 5k + 40$ **b** $7n = 3n + 12$
$\quad -5k \quad -5k \qquad -3n \quad -3n$

$\quad$ **c** $2p = 6 - p$
$\qquad +p \quad +p$

3 a $2x - 3 = x$ **b** $5y - 4 = y$
$\quad -x \qquad -x \qquad -y \qquad -y$

$\quad$ **c** $4t = 10 - t$
$\qquad +t \quad +t$

Solve the equations in questions **4–8**.

4 a $5g = 4g + 7$ **b** $6h = 3h + 15$ **c** $2k = k + 6$

5 a $3y = y + 8$ **b** $4t = 9 + t$ **c** $3u = 8 - u$

6 a $6p = p + 5$ **b** $5q = q + 12$ **c** $8r = 18 - r$

7 a $2a + 1 = 3a$ **b** $b = 2 - b$ **c** $3c = 8 - c$

8 a $m + 16 = 5m$ **b** $6 + n = 4n$ **c** $10 + t = 6t$

9 Make an equation for each pair of equal straws, solve it and write down the lengths of the straws.

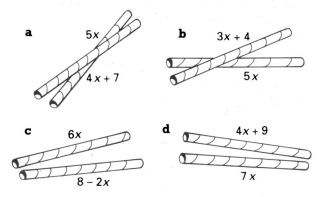

a 5x, 4x + 7   **b** 3x + 4, 5x
c 6x, 8 − 2x   **d** 4x + 9, 7x

10 The shelves in each pair are the same length. Make an equation for each, solve it, then write down the lengths of the shelves.

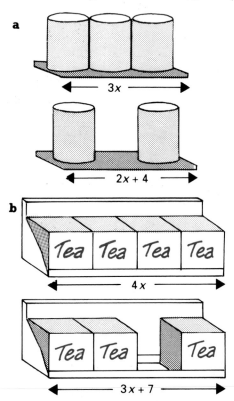

a 3x, 2x + 4
b 4x, 3x + 7

11 Make an equation for the perimeter of each triangle, solve it, and write down the lengths of the sides.

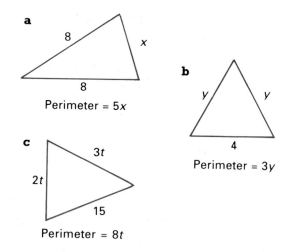
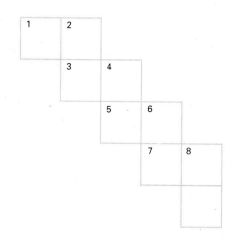

a 8, 8, x, Perimeter = 5x
b y, y, 4, Perimeter = 3y
c 3t, 2t, 15, Perimeter = 8t

12 Copy and complete this cross-number puzzle.

Across
1 $2x+12 = 3x$
3 $64+3x = 5x$
5 $4x = 54+x$
7 $8x = 7x+37$

Down
2 $10x = 6x+92$
4 $105+x = 6x$
6 $3y = 83+2y$
8 $8m+144 = 10m$

EXERCISE 2B

1 Solve these equations:
a $3x-1 = 2x+6$ **b** $4m+3 = 2m+7$
c $3n-2 = 14-n$ **d** $5y-1 = 8-4y$
e $3t-2 = t+1$ **f** $3+5u = 4+3u$
g $7p-1 = 5p-3$ **h** $4+6k = k-1$

2 Make an equation for each of these, and solve it:

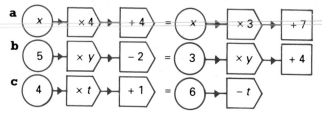

a $x \to \times 4 \to +4 = x \to \times 3 \to +7$
b $5 \to \times y \to -2 = 3 \to \times y \to +4$
c $4 \to \times t \to +1 = 6 \to -t$

3 Multiply out the brackets, and solve these equations:

  a $5(x-1) = 3x+11$ **b** $8x+1 = 3(x+2)$
  c $3(y-3) = 2(y-3)$ **d** $6(y-1) = 2(2y+1)$
  e $4(1+2u) = 5u+1$ **f** $2(3v-2) = 3v-4$
  g $3(t-1) = 1-t$ **h** $5(k-1) = 4-k$

4 Jacqui is organising a school trip to London and calculates she has enough people to fill seven A buses or five B buses.

  a Make an equation, and solve it.
  b How many people:
   (i) can each bus hold
   (ii) are going on the trip?

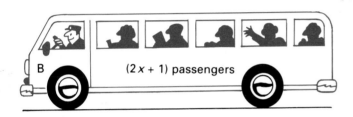

A   (x + 5) passengers

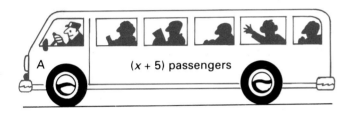

B   (2x + 1) passengers

5 The bowl can be filled by the liquid from six small jugs or two large jugs. Units are litres.

  a Make an equation, and solve it.
  b How much can:
   (i) each jug hold   (ii) the bowl hold?

6 The areas of the rectangles in each pair are equal.
  (i) Make an equation for each pair, and solve it.
  (ii) Write down the areas of the rectangles.
   In **a**, $5(n-3) = 2(n+3)$.

a

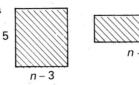

5   2
   n + 3
n − 3

b

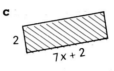

2x + 1   2x − 1
   3   5

c

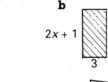

2   3
 7x + 2
   5x + 1

d

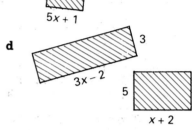

   3
3x − 2
5
   x + 2

CHALLENGE

Copy this cross-number puzzle, and solve it.

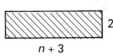

Across
 1 $5x-1 = 3(x+15)$
 3 $8(x-11) = 5(x+7)$
 5 $2(x-156) = x+144$
 7 $13x-139 = 3(3x+167)$
 9 $6(x-100) = 4(x-8)$
 10 $15(x-1) = 12(x+7)$
 11 $5(20+x) = 8(x-7)$

Down
 1 $10(x-41) = 8(x+9)$
 2 $3(4x+3) = 7x+184$
 4 $4(2x+15) = 5(x+72)$
 6 $x+200 = 2(x-209)$
 8 $7x-15 = 6(105+x)$
 9 $4(2x-21) = 5(x-3)$

INEQUALITIES

CLASS DISCUSSION

a  I'm taller than you.

b  You're heavier than me.

c We made over £500 for charity.

d He should break the 4-minute mile.

e More than 20 mm of rain fell yesterday.

f A current of more than 10 amps will blow the fuse.

g The freezer temperature should be between −18°C and −34°C.

h No items at the sale cost more than £10.

Do you agree that the idea of greater than or less than comes into all of these?
Can you think of more examples?

Greater than or less than

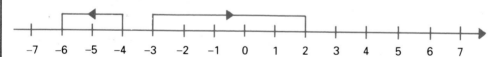

On the number line, 2 is to the right of −3, so 2 **is greater than** −3.
−6 is to the left of −4, so −6 **is less than** −4.

The greater number is always to the right of the smaller one on the number line.

 I know an easier way!

2 > −3 means '2 is greater than −3'.
−6 < −4 means '−6 is less than −4'.

WHICH IS WHICH?

EASY! The arrowhead points to the smaller number.

EXERCISE 3A

1 Write down the greater number in each pair. Use the number line if you wish.
  a 8, 6 **b** 4, 5 **c** −1, 2 **d** −3, 0
  e −7, 7 **f** 1, 0 **g** 0, −1 **h** −2, −3

2 Say whether each of the following is true (T) or false (F).
  a 1 > 2 **b** −1 < 2 **c** 0 < 3
  d 2 > 3 **e** 2 > −3 **f** −1 < −2
  g −1 > 0 **h** 1 < −10 **i** −3 < −2

3 Use > or < to connect the two numbers in each pair. For example, for −2, −1: −2 < −1
  a 3, 5 **b** 2, 0 **c** −1, 1 **d** −2, −1
  e −3, 3 **f** 4, −4 **g** 0, −1 **h** −1, 0

4 Use >, < or = to connect the weights in each pair of scales below.

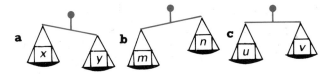

More useful symbols

≥ 'is greater than or equal to' . . .

Price (£*P*) at least £80 000: $P \geqslant 80\,000$

≤ 'is less than or equal to' . . .

30

Maximum speed (*S* mph) 30 mph: $S \leqslant 30$

Examples
Solve these inequalities, choosing *x* from the set {1, 2, 3, 4, 5}:
  a $x > 3$
    $x = 4, 5$
  b $x \geqslant 2$
    $x = 2, 3, 4, 5$
  c $x < 3$
    $x = 1, 2$
  d $x \leqslant 2$
    $x = 1, 2$

5 Choosing *x* from the set {1, 2, 3, 4, 5}, solve these inequalities:
  a $x > 4$ **b** $x \geqslant 4$ **c** $x < 3$
  d $x \leqslant 3$ **e** $x < 4$ **f** $x \geqslant 1$

6 Choosing *y* from the set {−2, −1, 0, 1, 2}, solve these inequalities:
  a $y > 0$ **b** $y < 0$ **c** $y \geqslant -1$
  d $y \leqslant -1$ **e** $y < 2$ **f** $y \geqslant -2$

7 Choosing *t* from the set {1, 2, 3, 4, 5, 6}, solve these inequalities:
  a $t + 1 > 4$ **b** $t + 1 < 3$ **c** $t + 2 \geqslant 3$

8 The bag on the left weighs less than the one on the right, so $x < 4$.

Choosing *x* from {1, 2, 3, 4, 5, 6, 7}, $x = 1, 2, 3$. Write down an inequality for each picture below, and its solution, choosing *x* from {1, 2, 3, 4, 5, 6, 7}.

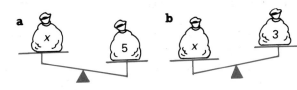

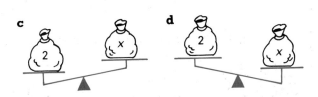

SOLVING INEQUALITIES

EXERCISE 3B

Example
Solve this inequality:

$$3x+2 \geqslant 8-x$$
$$+x \qquad +x$$
$$4x+2 \geqslant 8$$
$$\quad -2 \quad -2$$
$$4x \geqslant 6$$
$$x \geqslant 1\tfrac{1}{2}$$

Solve these inequalities, giving your answers in the form $x \geqslant 1\tfrac{1}{2}$, $x < 2$, etc.

1 a $x+1 > 2$ **b** $x+2 < 6$ **c** $y+3 \geqslant 5$

2 a $3x > 9$ **b** $5x < 10$ **c** $2x < 5$

3 a $2m-1 < 5$ **b** $3t+2 \geqslant 5$ **c** $5k+1 \leqslant 6$

4 a $2p-8 \leqslant 4$ **b** $4q > -4$ **c** $3r+7 > 1$

5 a $4(x-3) > 2x$ **b** $3(y+1) < 6$ **c** $5(z-4) < z$

6 a $3x-2 > x$ **b** $4y+6 > y$ **c** $4t-2 < 2t$

7 a $3u+2 \geqslant u+6$ **b** $4v-2 < v+4$

8 a $4t+5 \geqslant 3t+5$ **b** $7w+3 < 3w+15$

9 a $5a+7 > 3a+1$ **b** $8b+1 < 4b+7$

10 The area of rectangle (i) is greater than the area of rectangle (ii).
  a Make an inequality, and solve it.
  b What can you say about the length of the bottom side of each rectangle?

(i)
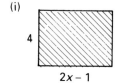
4

2x − 1

(ii)
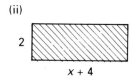
2

x + 4

11 Repeat question **10** if the *perimeter* of rectangle (i) is greater than the perimeter of rectangle (ii).

---

a *Copy the axes and shading on squared paper. The x-coordinate of every point in the **unshaded** region is less than or equal to zero, that is $x \leqslant 0$. Check this by plotting these points: $(-2, 0)$, $(-3, 3)$, $(-4, 3)$, $(2, 2)$, $(2, -1)$, $(-3, -4)$, $(0, 3)$.*

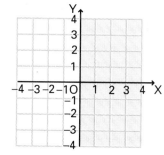

b *Draw similar diagrams for the regions given by these inequalities:*
(i) $x \geqslant 0$ (ii) $y \geqslant 0$ (iii) $y \leqslant 0$
(iv) $x \geqslant 0$ and $y \geqslant 0$ (v) $x \leqslant 0$ and $y \leqslant 0$
(vi) $x \geqslant 2$ (vii) $x \leqslant 2$ (viii) $-2 \leqslant x \leqslant 2$
(ix) $-2 \leqslant y \leqslant 2$ (x) $x \geqslant 2$ and $y \leqslant 2$

BRAINSTORMER

Mrs Manson has marked a test out of 20. She has written a flowchart for awarding grades A, B and C to her pupils.

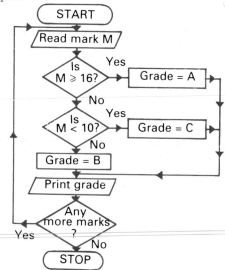

a *Use the flowchart for this data: 18, 8, 16, 12, 10.*
b *What was Mrs Manson's rule for awarding the grades?*

**CHECK-UP ON EQUATIONS AND
INEQUALITIES**

1 Solve these equations:
   a $3x = 15$ **b** $y+3 = 7$ **c** $z-1 = 6$
   d $2u+1 = 9$ **e** $3v-1 = 5$ **f** $8-w = 2$

2 Write an equation for each diagram, then
solve it:

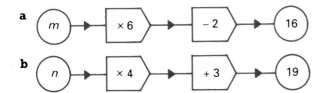

3 Write an equation for each balance, solve it, and
say how many weights are in each bag.

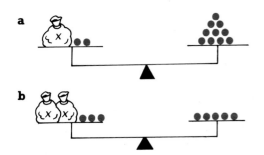

4 Solve these equations:
   a $3(x+1) = 12$ **b** $5(y-1) = 5$ **c** $8(t+2) = 16$

5 Make an equation for each picture, then solve it.

   a

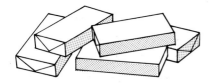

   5 packets, each weighing $(x+2)$ kg.
   Total weight 45 kg.

   b

   7 stamps, each worth $(2x+1)$p.
   Total value 49p.

6 Solve these equations:
   a $2x = 9$ **b** $3y = -15$ **c** $4k = 6$
   d $u+1 = -4$ **e** $v-1 = -2$ **f** $w+3 = 0$

7 Solve these equations:
   a $2y = y+2$ **b** $5p = 3p+10$ **c** $4t = t-6$

8 Solve these equations:
   a $10m-3 = 7m+3$ **b** $8k-9 = 6k+2$
   c $7(a-2) = 3a+2$ **d** $3(b-1) = 2(b+1)$

9 The areas of these two rectangles are equal.
   a Make an equation, and solve it.
   b Write down the lengths, breadths and areas of
   the rectangles.

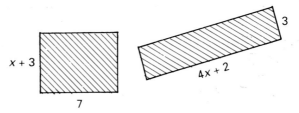

10 Say whether each of the following is true (T) or
false (F).
   a $3 > 2$ **b** $-3 < -2$ **c** $5 > -5$
   d $4+2 > 6$ **e** $4 \times 0 > -1$ **f** $4-6 > 2$

11 Choosing x from the set $\{1, 2, 3, 4, 5\}$, solve these
inequalities:
   a $x \geqslant 3$ **b** $x \leqslant 2$ **c** $x > 1$ **d** $x < 3$

12 Solve these inequalities, giving your answers in
the form $x > 2$, $x \leqslant 1\frac{1}{2}$, etc.
   a $5x+2 > 17$ **b** $4x-2 < 2x$ **c** $2x \geqslant 6-x$
   d $7x-3 \leqslant 3x+5$ **e** $8(x-1) > 5(x+5)$

13 Write an inequality for each picture, and solve it.

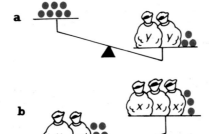

5 STATISTICS

LOOKING BACK

1 This pie chart shows how an average family spent its money weekly in 1992.

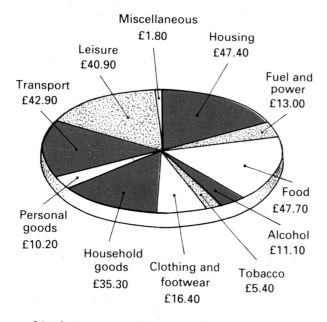

Miscellaneous £1.80
Housing £47.40
Leisure £40.90
Transport £42.90
Fuel and power £13.00
Food £47.70
Alcohol £11.10
Tobacco £5.40
Clothing and footwear £16.40
Household goods £35.30
Personal goods £10.20

a List the two main items in order, larger first.
b Calculate:
(i) the family's total spending
(ii) the percentage spent on clothing and footwear, to the nearest whole number.

2 Here are the heights, to the nearest cm, of a group of boys.

168 cm, 174 cm, 164 cm, 178 cm, 162 cm, 175 cm, 166 cm, 174 cm, 172 cm

a Write down:
(i) the greatest height (ii) the smallest height.
b Calculate:
(i) the range of their heights
(ii) their mean height, to the nearest cm.
c When the boys are lined up in order of height you can see the median (middle) height. What is this height?

3 Here are the times, to the nearest second, of 30 girls taking part in a 200 m race.

30, 33, 36, 28, 34, 37, 35, 32, 29, 38,
36, 44, 32, 35, 37, 32, 43, 35, 33, 32,
34, 38, 35, 32, 34, 34, 36, 32, 34, 35

a Make a frequency table, starting:

Class interval	Tally	Frequency
26–30	III	3
31–35		

b Write down the modal time interval.
c Describe the running abilities of the girls.

4 In farming research three fields of a crop were treated with different new fertilisers. The results are shown in these scatter diagrams.

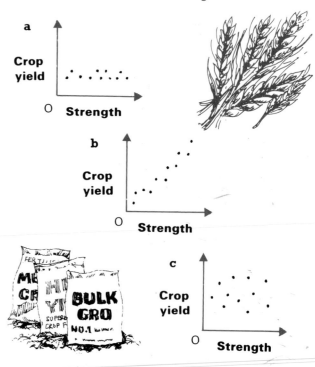

a Crop yield / Strength

b Crop yield / Strength

c Crop yield / Strength

Comment on the effect of each fertiliser. Which one would you recommend?

5 If you were drawing the pie chart for question **1**, what angle at the centre, to the nearest degree, would you use for household goods?

INTERPRETING AND DRAWING GRAPHS

EXERCISE 1

1 The bar chart shows the result of a survey of the number of adults who listen regularly to Radios 1 to 5.

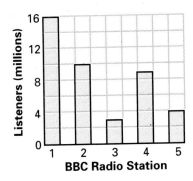

a Which station seems to be:
   (i) most popular   (ii) least popular?
b What is the total number of listeners?
c Which station has about 10% of the listeners?

2 This graph shows the changes in students' lunch habits from 1990–1994.

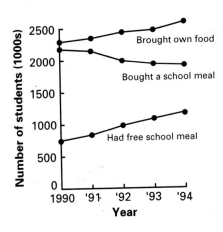

Explain what is happening (the trends), and suggest reasons for the changes, if you can.

3 The graph shows the percentages of men and women of several age groups in the population.

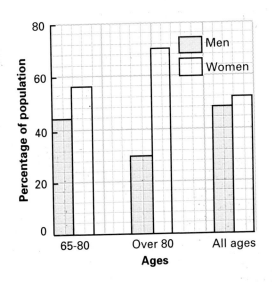

a Write down the percentages of men and of women who are aged:
   (i) 65–80   (ii) over 80.
b What conclusions can you make from all three pairs of bars on the graph?

4 A survey involving 720 people investigated the methods they used to travel to work in a city, before, and then after, a cycleway was opened.

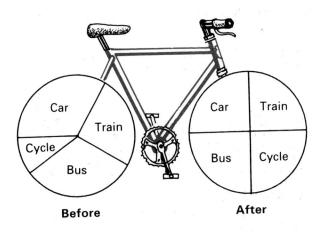

a Say whether more or fewer people used each form of transport after the cycleway was opened.
b Estimate the number in the survey who cycled to work, before and after.

5 A sample of the population was studied from age 40 to age 85 to compare the life-spans of smokers and non-smokers. The table shows the percentages in the sample who were still alive at ages 55, 70 and 85.

Age of people in sample	55	70	85
% of non-smokers alive	95	80	33
% of smokers alive	85	50	8

a Use these scales to draw line graphs of the data.

b Comment on the life expectancy of smokers and non-smokers.

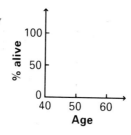

6 A report in 1994 about the employment of the population aged 16 and over in Britain gave these figures (in millions).

In full-time work	20.5
In part-time work	8
Unemployed	2.5
Retired or not seeking work	14

a Calculate:
  (i) the total number aged 16 or over
  (ii) the percentage in each group, correct to 1 decimal place.

b Draw a pie chart of the data, using angles to the nearest degree.

AVERAGES AND INTERPRETING DATA

EXERCISE 2A

1 Terry's temperature was taken daily while he was in hospital.

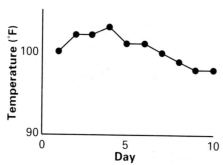

a What was his highest temperature? On which day?

b When did his temperature return to normal (98°F)?

c *Estimate* his mean temperature over the ten days.

d Calculate his mean temperature.

2 The number of visitors to four cathedrals in England in 1992 were:

York   2 250 000
Canterbury 2 250 000
St Paul's   1 400 000
Salisbury   550 000

Calculate the mean number of visitors (round your answer sensibly).

3 Tony noted the time he took to travel to work over a ten day period, to the nearest minute:

26, 29, 35, 30, 20, 120, 20, 32, 50, 40

a Calculate the mean time.

b Write down the modal and median times.

c Which average would you choose to represent the data? Why?

4 Amy and her friends have just completed a keep-fit course. To check their fitness they record the number of step-ups they could do in one minute, before and after the course.

Girl	A	B	C	D	E	F	G	H	I	J
Before	30	32	36	29	30	40	26	22	35	32
After	42	40	42	34	39	45	41	34	44	40

a Which girl increased her step-ups most?

b Calculate the mean and range of the data:
  (i) before the course   (ii) after the course.

c Comment on their performance.

5 Four brothers have an average age of 14. Alan is 8, David is 12 and Carl 16. How old is the fourth brother, Neil?

EXERCISE 2B

1 On Friday 8th November Mike recorded the number of pints of milk he delivered to houses in Glenfield Road.

Number of pints (n)	1	2	3	4	5	6
Number of houses (f)	12	36	23	19	8	2
n × f	12					

a List the number of pints in the third row of the table.

b How many pints did he deliver altogether?

c How many houses did Mike serve in Glenfield Road?

d Calculate the mean number of pints per house.

2 Road Rescue have a breakdown service for cars. This table shows one week's record of the time drivers had to wait for rescue.

Time (min)	1–10	11–20	21–30	31–40	41–50	51–60
Mid-interval (t)	5.5					
Frequency (f)	16	57	96	82	44	23
t × f	88					

a Copy and complete the table.

b The company aim for a mean waiting time of 30 minutes. How close to this did they come?

3 Laura hits 50 golf balls on the driving range. This is how they end up.

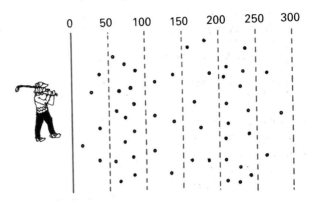

a Copy and complete the table.

Distance (d yards)	0 ≤ d < 50	50 ≤ d < 100
Mid-interval	25	75
Frequency	5	
Mid-interval × frequency		

b Calculate the mean distance, to the nearest yard.

c Which is the modal class interval?

d At the tenth hole of her local course, Laura has to drive over a stream 200 yards away. Has she a good chance of doing this? Explain.

/ **BRAINSTORMERS**

1 Sean's marks in five tests have a mean of 61. Three of the marks are 52, 62 and 62. The range of the marks is 39. Find his other two marks.

2 Sophie and Petra compare statistics of their schools' performance in the local hockey league over the season.

For Sophie's school, the mean number of goals scored per game is 2 and the range is 7.
For Petra's school, the mean is 5 and the range is 3.

   a Which team is likely to be higher in the league? Why?

   b Which team must have scored in every game? Why?

SCATTER DIAGRAMS

EXERCISE 3

1 As part of their pre-season fitness training the Rovers football team is given daily running exercises. Over a period of ten days, scatter diagrams were made of the players' average: **a** height **b** weight **c** distance run, against running time. Match **a**, **b** and **c** with (i), (ii) or (iii).

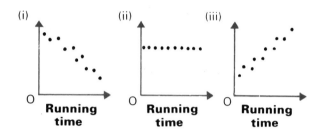

2 Sketch the kind of scatter diagrams you would expect for these headings.

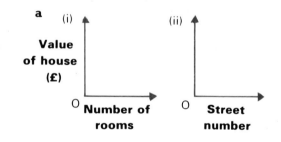

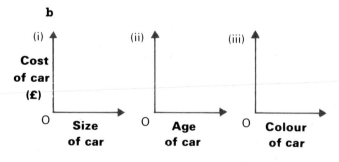

3 The Patels' central heating system uses a thermostat to maintain a steady room temperature. This table shows the number of hours per day the heating is on, and the maximum outside temperature that day.

Number of hours heating is on	8	12	11	3	5
Outside temperature (°C)	6	0	2	15	12

6	0	10	4	9
10	20	3	13	5

a Plot the points on a scatter diagram.
b Draw a line of best fit.
c What happens to the heating as the outside temperature rises?

4 a A group of students have their shoe sizes and heights measured. Sketch the kind of scatter diagram that you would expect.

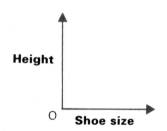

b Calculate the mean shoe size and the mean height for the data, correct to 1 decimal place.

Shoe size	5	11	7	10	$8\frac{1}{2}$	6
Height (cm)	158	179	166	173	170	160

7	$7\frac{1}{2}$	$6\frac{1}{2}$	8	6	9
164	165	161	170	163	172

c (i) Draw a scatter diagram.
   (ii) Plot the mean shoe size against the mean height, then draw a best-fitting straight line through the point. Was your answer to **a** correct?
d Jamie's height is 178 cm. Estimate his shoe size.

FREQUENCY POLYGONS

The frequency table and frequency diagram show the distribution of weights in a batch of melons.

Weight (w g)	$300 \leqslant w < 350$	$350 \leqslant w < 400$	$400 \leqslant w < 450$	$450 \leqslant w < 500$
Frequency	3	14	12	8

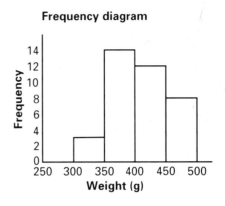

Frequency diagram

The second diagram shows the frequency polygon formed by joining the midpoints of the tops of the rectangles and the zero rectangles on either side.

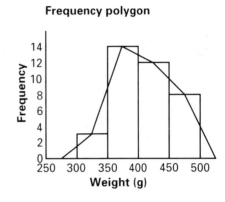

Frequency polygon

EXERCISE 4A

1 The table and the frequency diagram show the number of weeks for which some books have been out on loan from Hillside High School Library.

Number of weeks	1	2	3	4	5
Frequency (number of books)	15	23	29	21	12

a How many books are out on loan?
b Books should be returned within four weeks. What percentage of books are not yet overdue?
c Copy the frequency diagram on squared paper, and draw the frequency polygon.

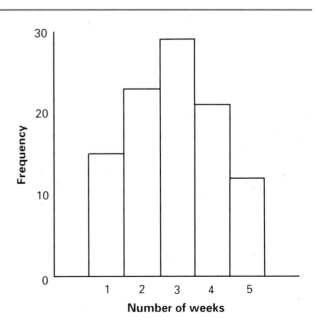

2 For his statistics project, Keith makes a survey of the travelling time to and from school of 150 students in his year.

Time (t min)	Frequency
$0 \leqslant t < 10$	21
$10 \leqslant t < 20$	25
$20 \leqslant t < 30$	30
$30 \leqslant t < 40$	40
$40 \leqslant t < 50$	24
$50 \leqslant t < 60$	10

a In which class interval is the modal time?
b On squared paper draw a frequency diagram and a frequency polygon of the data.

3 From plans of the school Marlene finds the floor area of every classroom.

Area (A m²)	$20 \leqslant A < 30$	$30 \leqslant A < 40$	$40 \leqslant A < 50$
Frequency	2	17	15

$50 \leqslant A < 60$	$60 \leqslant A < 70$	$70 \leqslant A < 80$
10	4	3

a Draw a frequency diagram and a frequency polygon for her data.
b The fifty-one rooms are numbered in order of size from 1 to 51.
  (i) What is the number of the middle-sized room?
  (ii) In which class interval is the middle-sized (median) room?

4 The spring medal competition at Greenvale Golf Club is always popular. This frequency table shows the distribution of scores.

Score	66 –70	71 –75	76 –80	81 –85	86 –90	91 –95	96 –100
Frequency	4	23	38	34	20	10	5

a Draw a frequency diagram and a frequency polygon of the data.
b Which is the modal class interval?
c In which class interval is the median score?
d Use mid-interval values to calculate the mean score, correct to 1 decimal place.
e How many golfers definitely scored less than the mean?

EXERCISE 4B

---

1 A research centre tests the growth of two types of grain, and shows the results in these frequency polygons.
  a Copy and complete this frequency table.

Height (h cm)	$0 \leqslant h < 20$	$20 \leqslant h < 40$	$40 \leqslant h < 60$
Type A frequency			
Type B frequency			

b How many plants were in each sample?
c Use mid-interval values to estimate, to the nearest cm, the mean height of each plant.
d Compare the information on the two types. Which would you recommend?

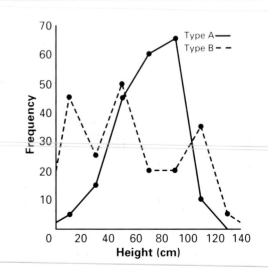

2 Suzanne compares the June temperatures in a British and a Greek holiday resort. Here are the maximum daily temperatures.

Britain: 14, 17, 16, 19, 21, 23, 24, 25, 29, 28, 28, 25, 24, 22, 20, 19, 19, 18, 19, 17, 17, 14, 13, 14, 13, 12, 14, 13, 16, 18

Greece: 26, 28, 28, 29, 29, 30, 31, 33, 32, 32, 29, 30, 28, 27, 24, 24, 22, 21, 27, 20, 19, 18, 18, 20, 21, 23, 23, 24, 26, 28

a Copy and complete this frequency table:

Temperature (t°C)		$10 \leqslant t < 15$	$15 \leqslant t < 20$
Frequency	Britain		
	Greece		

b Draw frequency diagrams and frequency polygons on the same sheet of squared paper.
c Use statistics to compare the temperature distributions.

3 Tough Tyres and Tireless Tyres check their manufacturing processes by measuring the distances that samples of 100 can cover before they are replaced.
a Draw a frequency diagram and frequency polygon on the same diagram.
b Which type of tyre would you choose? Justify your choice statistically.

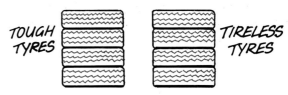

Distance (d 1000 km)	$0 \leqslant d < 10$	$10 \leqslant d < 20$	$20 \leqslant d < 30$	$30 \leqslant d < 40$	$40 \leqslant d < 50$	$50 \leqslant d < 60$
Tough Tyres' frequency	0	15	32	46	7	0
Tyreless Tyres' frequency	10	24	14	22	18	12

/‾‾‾‾‾‾‾‾‾‾‾‾‾‾‾‾‾‾‾‾‾‾‾‾‾‾‾‾‾‾‾‾‾‾‾/
CHALLENGE

This table gives weather data for Hastings and Aberdeen during one week in November.

Use graphs, scatter diagrams and averages to analyse, compare and report on the weather in the two towns.

Day	Sun (hours)		Rain (inches)		Minimum temperature (°C)		Maximum temperature (°C)	
	Hastings	Aberdeen	Hastings	Aberdeen	Hastings	Aberdeen	Hastings	Aberdeen
Sunday	4.4	0	0	0.11	0	−1	10	9
Monday	0	0	0	0.65	8	7	13	10
Tuesday	0.1	2.5	0.17	0.42	12	3	13	6
Wednesday	8.2	6.8	0	0	2	−1	9	5
Thursday	2.2	0	0.04	1.01	−2	−4	9	7
Friday	2.1	0	0.11	1.03	3	4	11	6
Saturday	0.3	2.1	0.79	0.12	4	1	8	3

CHECK-UP ON STATISTICS

1 This bar chart shows the number of UK cars sold at home and as exports.

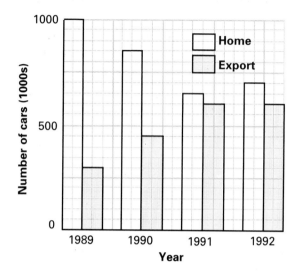

a Make a table which shows the number of cars sold each year:
(i) at home   (ii) as exports   (iii) in total.
b Write a report on the ways in which the sales varied over the four-year period.

2 Roger asked his friends: 'On average, how many hours a week do you spend watching TV, and how many doing homework?'
He made this table of replies.

TV (h)	16	18	10	5	11	9	9
Homework (h)	7	4	10	14	9	12	11

4	13	17	11	7
15	8	6	8	12

a Calculate the mean number of hours, correct to 1 decimal place, his friends spent on:
(i) TV   (ii) homework.
b (i) Draw a scatter diagram.
(ii) Plot the point M giving the mean number of hours of TV and homework, and draw the best-fitting straight line through it.
c Roger spends about 14 hours a week watching TV. Estimate the time he might spend on homework.

3 Annette made a survey of the ages of cars boarding a ferry, and recorded the results in a table.

Age (years)	0	1	2	3	4	5	6	7	8
Frequency	10	11	12	11	8	6	5	6	3

a Write down:
(i) the modal age   (ii) the range of ages.
b Calculate:
(i) the median age
(ii) the mean age, correct to 1 decimal place.
c Draw a frequency polygon of the ages.

4 In a motorway traffic check, the speeds of cars are measured to the nearest mph. The results are shown in this table.

Speed (mph)	31–40	41–50	51–60	61–70	71–80	81–90
Number of cars	8	27	44	68	26	2

a Show the results in a frequency diagram.
b What percentage of cars were exceeding the speed limit of 70 mph?

5 The line graph shows the daily number of hours of sunshine during July in Paradise Isle.

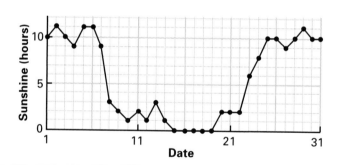

a Copy and complete this table:

Sunshine (h hours)	$0 \leqslant h \leqslant 2$	$3 \leqslant h \leqslant 5$	$6 \leqslant h \leqslant 8$	$9 \leqslant h \leqslant 11$
Number of days (n)		2		
Mid-interval (f)		4		
n × f		8		

b Use the table to calculate the mean number of hours of sunshine per day, to 1 decimal place.
c Which weeks would have been best for a holiday?

REVIEW: SHAPE AND SPACE

ANGLES AND TRIANGLES

1 Look at this rectangular flag. How many of these can you count?
  a right angles   **b** acute angles
  c obtuse angles **d** straight angles

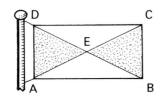

2 In the flag diagram above, name:
  a an angle which is:
    (i) the complement of $\angle$ BAC
    (ii) the supplement of $\angle$ AEB
    (iii) vertically opposite $\angle$ BEC
  b a line which is:
    (i) parallel to AD   (ii) perpendicular to AD.

3 Calculate the sizes of $x°$ and $y°$ on the clock.

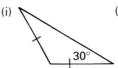

4 Calculate a, b and c in the diagrams below.

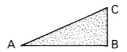

5 Calculate x in each diagram.

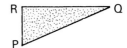

6 Sketch the diagrams below, and fill in the sizes of all the angles.

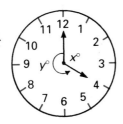

7 A bicycle wheel has 24 spokes. Calculate the size of the angle between a neighbouring pair of equally spaced spokes.

8 a Sketch these triangles, and fill in the sizes of all the angles.

(i)   (ii)   (iii)

  b What type of triangle is each—isosceles, equilateral, acute-angled, etc?

9 Triangles ABC and PQR are congruent. Name pairs of equal sides and angles.

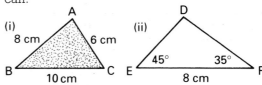

10 Calculate the area of the triangular end of each of these:

a   **b**

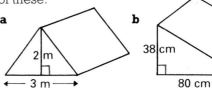

11 a Construct these triangles as accurately as you can:

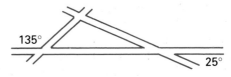

  b Measure the angles at A and D.

12 Copy this diagram of a network of roads and fill in the sizes of all the angles.

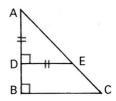

13 Copy the diagram.
  a Name the angle corresponding to $\angle$ AED.
  b Fill in the sizes of all the angles.
  c Why is $\triangle$ABC isosceles?

65

QUADRILATERALS

1 Sketch the square and the rectangle, and fill in as many lengths and angles as you can.
(Lengths are given to the nearest cm.)

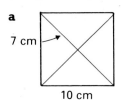 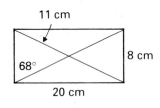

a   **b**

7 cm   11 cm   8 cm   68°   10 cm   20 cm

2 Mark all the axes of symmetry in a square and a rectangle like those in question **1**.

3 What types of quadrilaterals are these?

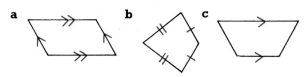

a   **b**   **c**

4 a On squared paper plot the points P(4, 0), Q(6, 2) and R(2, 6).
  b Plot the point S so that PQRS is a rectangle.
  c Write down the coordinates of:
  (i) S   (ii) the point where the diagonals of the rectangle cross.

5 a Sketch this parallelogram.

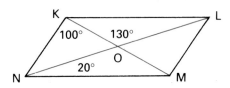

K   100°   130°   L   20°   O   N   M

  b Fill in the sizes of all the angles.
  c List four pairs of:
  (i) equal lines   (ii) congruent triangles.

6 The roads shown in this diagram run in a square and rectangular pattern.

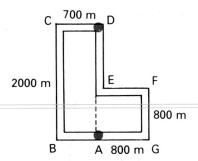

C   700 m   D   2000 m   E   F   800 m   B   A   800 m   G

Which route from A to D, ABCD or AGFED, is shorter? How much shorter?

7 a Sketch this kite, and fill in the sizes of all the sides and angles.

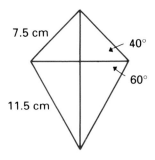

7.5 cm   40°   60°   11.5 cm

  b Calculate the perimeter of the kite.

8 a Construct a rhombus with diagonals 8 cm and 6 cm long, at right angles to each other.
  b Measure and mark the lengths of its sides and the sizes of its angles, to the nearest degree.
  c Draw its axes of symmetry as dotted lines.

9 a On squared paper draw x and y-axes, each numbered from −6 to 6.
  b Plot the points A(3, 1), B(6, 6) and C(1, 3), and draw the quadrilateral OABC, where O is the origin.
  c What shape is OABC?
  d Draw the reflection of OABC in:
  (i) the x-axis   (ii) the y-axis, and fill in the coordinates of all the vertices.
  e Draw the axis of symmetry of your diagram. Write down its equation.

10 Copy and extend these tiling patterns of quadrilaterals on squared paper.

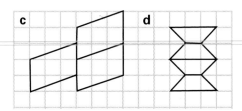

a   **b**

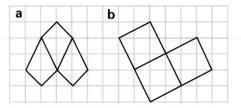

c   **d**

REFLECTION AND ROTATION

1 This shape is symmetrical about both *x* and *y*-axes. Write down the coordinates of vertices D, E, F, G and H.

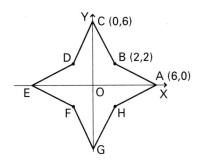

2 ABCDEF is a regular hexagon.

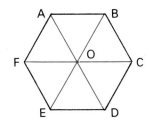

  a How many axes of symmetry does it have?
  b What is its order of rotational symmetry?
  c Calculate the size of:
    (i) ∠AOB
    (ii) an angle of the hexagon, for example ∠ABC.

3 Copy this diagram, and add one square to make the pattern symmetrical about the dotted line.

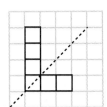

4 Copy the diagram below, and show the image of the shaded rectangle after reflection in:
  a the *x*-axis **b** the *y*-axis **c** the dotted line.

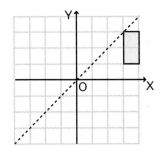

5 a On squared paper plot the points A(0, 4), B(-3, -2) and C(3, -2), and join up the points.
  b Under a half-turn about O, A → D, B → E and C → F. Plot D, E, F, and join up these points.
  c Draw dotted lines to show the axes of symmetry of the whole figure. Write down the equations of these axes.

6 This is part of the logo for Ace Products. Copy and complete it by giving the part shown a half-turn about O.

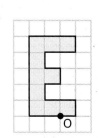

7 Electric Echo are designing their new album cover. It will consist of the letter E and its image under:
  a reflection in the dotted line, or
  b rotation of 180° about O (see diagram below). Draw both designs on squared paper. Which would you choose?

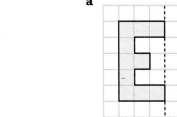

8 This diagram shows one of four tiles which form a pattern. The pattern has quarter-turn symmetry about corner O. Copy the square, and complete the pattern.

SCALE DRAWING

1 a Use the scale of 1 cm to 2 m to make a scale drawing of the Thomsons' back garden. Start with base-line AB.

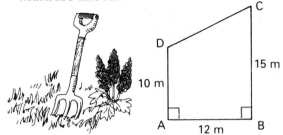

b What length is CD:
(i) on the scale drawing   (ii) in the garden?

2

a How far apart are A and B on the map?
b The scale of the map is 1:50 000.
Calculate the actual distance between A and B in: (i) cm   (ii) m   (iii) km.

3

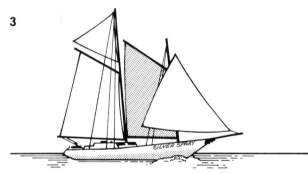

The *Silver Spray* sails eight miles west, then five miles south-west from the harbour.
a Show its voyage in a scale drawing.
b How far is the *Silver Spray* from the harbour now?

4 a Dipton is 70 miles from Peakton. Measure PD. What is the scale of the drawing?

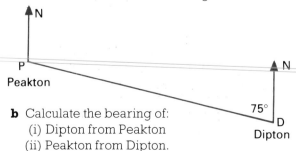

b Calculate the bearing of:
(i) Dipton from Peakton
(ii) Peakton from Dipton.

5 This diagram shows the course for a yacht race which starts and finishes at A.

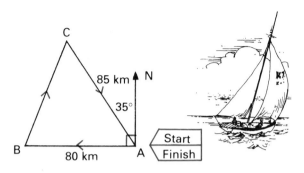

B is 80 km due west of A.
a Calculate the size of ∠BAC.
b Make a scale drawing of the course.
c Find:
(i) the distance BC   (ii) the size of ∠ABC
(iii) the bearing of C from B.

6 An aircraft flies 75 miles from Prestwick on a course 090°. It then alters course to 010°, and flies on to Dyce Airport at Aberdeen. The bearing of Dyce from Prestwick is 040°.

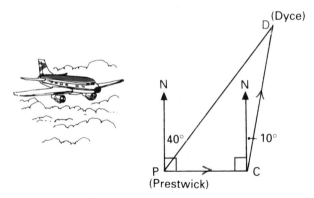

a Make a sketch, and fill in the given angles.
b Calculate the size of: (i) ∠CPD   (ii) ∠PCD.
c Make a scale drawing of △PCD, using a scale of 1 cm to 10 km.
d (i) Measure the length of PD on your drawing.
(ii) How far is it from Prestwick to Dyce in a straight line?

7 a Make scale drawings to solve these problems.
(i) A ladder is 4 m long, and its base is 2 m from the foot of a wall. What is the angle between the ladder and the ground?
(ii) The ladder is reset at 70° to the ground. How far up the wall does it reach?
b Now solve the problems using trigonometry.

PYTHAGORAS' THEOREM

1 Calculate x in each of these right-angled triangles.

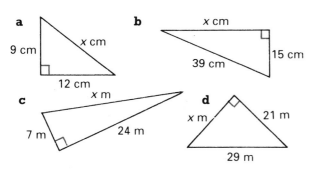

a 9 cm, x cm, 12 cm

b x cm, 39 cm, 15 cm

c x m, 7 m, 24 m

d x m, 21 m, 29 m

2 How far up the wall does each ladder reach, to the nearest centimetre?

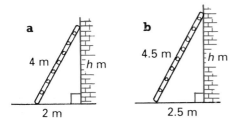

a 4 m, h m, 2 m

b 4.5 m, h m, 2.5 m

3 a Measure the length and breadth of the cover of this book, to the nearest tenth of a cm.

b Calculate the length of a diagonal, and check your answer by measurement.

4 Calculate:

a the lengths of the sides AB and CD of this kite

b the perimeter of the kite.

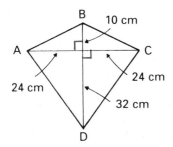

B, 10 cm, A, C, 24 cm, 24 cm, 32 cm, D

5 The shape of a fence post is made up of a rectangle with an isosceles triangle on top. Calculate the height of the triangular top.

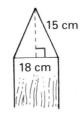

15 cm, 18 cm

6 The area of a square is 256 cm². Calculate the length of:

a a side of the square

b a diagonal, correct to 1 decimal place.

7

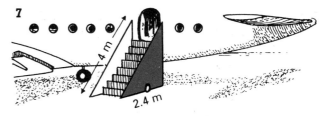

4 m, 2.4 m

Calculate:

a the height of the boarding ramp's rail

b the angle between the rail and the ground, to the nearest degree.

8 Roads are being built from Anton and Mossbank to join a new motorway at P. Calculate the total length of the two roads (AP + PM), correct to 1 decimal place.

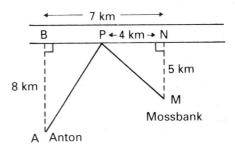

7 km, B, P ← 4 km → N, 8 km, 5 km, M, Mossbank, A Anton

9 Calculate, correct to 1 decimal place:

a the length of each supporting wire

b the angle between each wire and the ground.

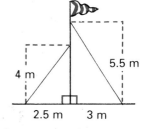

4 m, 5.5 m, 2.5 m, 3 m

10 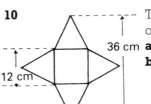 This is the net for a pyramid on a square base. Calculate:

36 cm **a** the height of each triangle

12 cm **b** the length of the sloping edge of each triangle, correct to 1 decimal place.

11 Calculate, correct to 2 decimal places, the length of the sloping floor of this swimming pool.

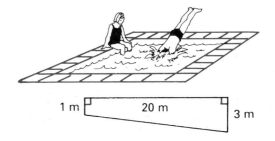

1 m, 20 m, 3 m

PYTHAGORAS' THEOREM

SIMILAR SHAPES

1 These two rectangles are similar. Calculate:
  a the enlargement scale factor from (i) to (ii)
  b the value of x.

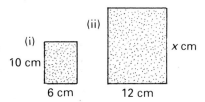

2 a Why are these triangles similar?
  b Calculate:
   (i) the reduction scale factor
   (ii) the value of y.

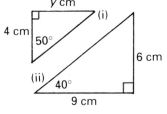

3 The rectangular edges of the picture frame are similar. Calculate:
  a the enlargement scale factor from the inner to the outer rectangle.
  b z.

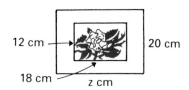

4 The two wooden support triangles are similar. Calculate:
  a the reduction scale factor from the larger one to the smaller one
  b x.

5 a Calculate the areas of the rectangles in question **1** ($x = 20$).
  b What is the enlargement scale factor for the areas in simplest form? Is it the square of the scale factor for lengths (2)?

6 a Calculate the areas of the triangles in question **2** ($y = 6$).
  b What is the reduction scale factor for the areas, in simplest form? Is it the square of the scale factor for lengths ($\frac{2}{3}$)?
  If the scale factor for lengths is n, the scale factor for areas is n^2.

7 For each pair of similar shapes, calculate the scale factor of lengths, the area and the scale factor of areas. Check that the area scale factor = (the length scale factor)^2.

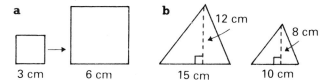

8 These two radiators are similar.

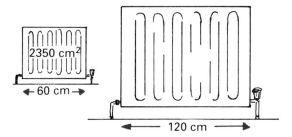

  a Calculate the enlargement scale factor for lengths.
  b Write down the enlargement scale factor for areas.
  c Calculate the area of the larger radiator.

9 Look at these two photographs. The enlargement scale factor of length is 3. Calculate the area of the larger photograph.

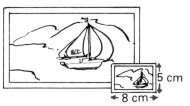

10 A full-size football pitch has an area of 8000 m^2. The reduction scale factor for the lengths of a 5-a-side pitch is 0.4. Calculate the area of the 5-a-side pitch.

11 a Why are the two triangles in this diagram similar?

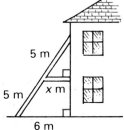

  b Calculate the enlargement scale factor of:
   (i) lengths   (ii) areas.
  c Calculate:
   (i) x (ii) the area of the larger triangle.

BRAINSTORMERS

A locus is a set of points defined by some rule. Here are two examples showing the locus of points:
a *1 cm from A*   **b** *1 cm from BC*

1 *On squared paper, sketch the locus of points:*
  a *1 unit from the x-axis (two lines)*
  b *1 unit from the y-axis*
  c *1 unit from the origin*
  d *the same distance from OX and OY.*

2 *Sketch the locus of points traced out by:*

  a *the descending lift*

  b *the weight on the swinging pendulum*

  c *a step on the escalator*

  d *the ball in flight*

  e *the tip of the rotating blade*

  f *the golf ball flying onto the green.*

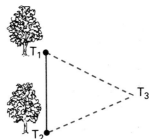

3 *Kirsty is a landscape gardener. She has to plant a tree T_3 which is the same distance from trees T_1 and T_2. Draw a line 4 cm long to represent T_1T_2, and mark all the places she could put T_3 (the locus of T_3).*

4

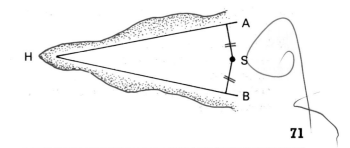

The master of the Silver Star (S) has to steer to the harbour H, keeping the same distance from the sandbanks HA and HB. Copy the diagram, and draw his course (the locus of S).

6 HOUSE AND CAR COSTS

LOOKING BACK

1 Calculate: **a** 5% of £40 **b** 80% of £25 000.

2 Jason has been saving up to buy a pair of binoculars. These cost £84 + VAT at 17.5%. How much:
a is the VAT
b has he to pay altogether?

3 The Astons pay £824 a year in Council Tax, in ten equal instalments. How much is each instalment?

4

4500 of the 5000 seats are taken at the ice hockey match.
a What fraction of the seats are taken?
b What percentage is this?

5 What interest would Alan receive on:
a £100 for one year
b £250 for one year
c £300 for six months?

SUPERSAVE BANK
INTEREST RATE
6% per annum

6 These hotel charges are for adults. Young people under 14 stay for half-price.

Hotel	7 nights		14 nights	
	May–Sept	Oct–Apr	May–Sept	Oct–Apr
Seaview	£280	£250	£550	£480
Clifftop	350	300	680	570
Oceanic	210	200	400	350

How much would these families pay?
a Mr and Mrs Simpson, 14 nights in November at the Clifftop.
b Mr and Mrs West, John (aged 18) and Julie (aged 12), 7 nights in August at the Oceanic.

7 Copy and complete:

16 books cost £120
1 book costs ...
5 books cost ...

8

Marchmont Power Station's annual output increased by 8% during the 1980s. The output was 13 million units in 1980. How many units were produced in 1989?

9 How much interest would Anwar pay on:
a £100 for one year **b** £100 for one month
c £1000 for one year?

SUPERSPEND BANK
• WE GIVE LOANS
• YOU PAY US 15% INTEREST PER ANNUM

72

BUYING A HOUSE

If you ever buy a house you will probably have to ask for a loan from a bank or a building society.

EXERCISE 1

1 Calculate the deposit you would need for each house in the table below.

House price (£)	40 000	60 000	75 000	32 000
Loan (£)	30 000	55 000	60 000	28 000
Deposit (£)				

2 Ann wants to buy a flat worth £50 000. The Homeguard Building Society offers her a loan of £38 000. How much money will she have to find (her deposit) to make up the price?

3 Ann's friend Karen is offered a loan of £27 000 for a flat costing £36 000. How much deposit will she have to find?

4 Homeloan offers loans of 90% of the house price. Copy and complete the table.

House price (£)	20 000	80 000	30 000	100 000
90% loan (£)	18 000			
10% deposit (£)	2 000			

5 Kate and Joel look at a flat valued at £35 000. The Home-owner Building Society offers them a loan of 80% of the value.
  a How much is the loan?
  b What deposit will Kate and Joel have to put down?

6 Mr Symon sees a house that seems just right. Its value is £150 000. The Union Jack Bank agrees to lend him 90% of the value, but he'll have to put down a deposit. How much?

7 Harry Hurst is interested in a house valued at £80 000. The Open Door Bank offers to lend him £60 000.
   a How much does he need to pay as a deposit?
   b (i) What percentage of the house value is the loan?
   (ii) So what percentage is the deposit?

8 Gerry has an £80 000 mortgage on his house. He has to pay £9 monthly for each £1000 borrowed. Copy and complete:

Mortgage   Monthly payment
£1000 ←————————→ £9
£80 000 ←————————→ £9 × $\dfrac{80\,000}{1000}$
                    = £ . . .

9 Calculate the monthly payments for these mortgages:

	Mortgage	Monthly payment (per £1000)
a	£20 000	£10
b	£50 000	£8
c	£80 000	£7.50
d	£125 000	£9

10 The Barlows borrow £60 000 from the Four Wells Building Society to buy a cottage. For each £1000 of the loan they pay £7.25 per month. Calculate how much they pay: **a** monthly **b** annually.

HOUSE AND CONTENTS INSURANCE

Thinking of buying or renting?
Be wise, insure the house contents and, of course, the building if it belongs to you.
Insurance policies cover loss or damage to buildings caused by fire, explosion, lightning, earthquake, storm, flood, impact by aircraft, vehicles, animals, aerials and trees, and, for contents, theft or damage.

Example
Vicky insured her house for £58 000.
Calculate her annual premium.

Value   Premium
£1000 ←————————→ £2.50
£58 000 ←————————→ £2.50 × $\dfrac{58\,000}{1000}$
                    = £145

SAFE AND SECURE
INSURANCE COMPANY
House Insurance Annual Rate —
£2.50 per £1000 value of your house

EXERCISE 2 (House BUILDINGS insurance)

1 Use Safe and Secure's house insurance rate in the advert on page 74 to calculate the annual buildings insurance premium for:
a a flat worth £35 000
b a semi-detatched villa valued at £60 000
c a house costing £110 000.

2 A rival company offers house insurance at the rate of £1.75 per £1000. Calculate the annual premiums for the properties shown below.

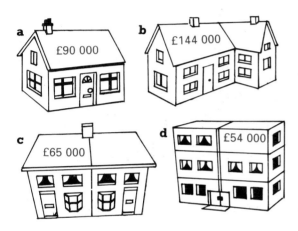

a £90 000
b £144 000
c £65 000
d £54 000

3 The Johnsons' bungalow is valued at £120 000, and is insured with Safe and Secure.

a Calculate their annual premium.
b How much is this, to the nearest penny:
  (i) per week
  (ii) per day?
c Does house insurance seem expensive? Explain your answer.

4 Mr and Mrs Amir increased their house value for insurance from £75 000 to £80 000. What is the increase in their annual premium with Safe and Secure?

5 Safe and Secure raise their rate by 10%.
  a What is their new rate per £1000?
  b Calculate the new annual premium for a house valued at £125 000.

EXERCISE 3 (House CONTENTS insurance)

This table shows the Safe and Secure Insurance Company's rates per £1000 for house **contents** insurance per year in different districts.

District	A	B	C	D	E	F	G	H
Rate for £1000	3.00	4.50	5.00	6.00	7.00	9.50	12.00	15.00

a Why do you think contents insurance costs more than buildings insurance?
b In which district above is insurance: (i) cheapest (ii) dearest? Why is there a difference?

1 Use the table above to calculate the annual insurance premiums for these house contents.

	a	b	c	d
Sum insured (£)	5000	12 000	30 000	9000
District	A	C	G	D

2 The Dixons live in district F. They reckon their house contents are worth £21 000. What would their annual premium be?

3 Mr and Mrs Arshad live in district H. Their house contents are worth £35 000.
  a Calculate their annual premium.
  b How much less would they have paid in district A?

4 The Kenneths live in district B, with house contents worth £32 000. The Connels live in district H, and their contents are worth £9000. Calculate the difference in the contents premiums that the two families pay.

5 Sue and Harry have saved hard for many years to buy the items in this room. They live in district D.
a Calculate their total annual premium for insuring all these items.

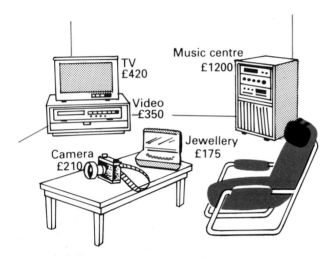

b They reckon the other items in the house should be insured for £16 000.
What premium have they to pay for them?
c Calculate their total premium:
(i) per year (ii) per month, to the nearest penny.

6 The King family live in district B. Calculate their total annual premium for house insurance (£1.90 per £1000) and contents insurance.

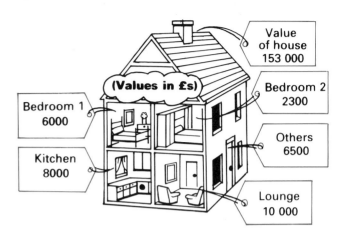

INVESTIGATIONS

1 List all the items in your own room, along with estimates of their value when new.

2 Find out about the insurance policies for your home and its contents. Are they up-to-date? Does anyone in your family have any extra insurance, for example for sports equipment? Have you a bicycle? Is it insured? Find out about insurance rates.

MOTOR CAR COSTS

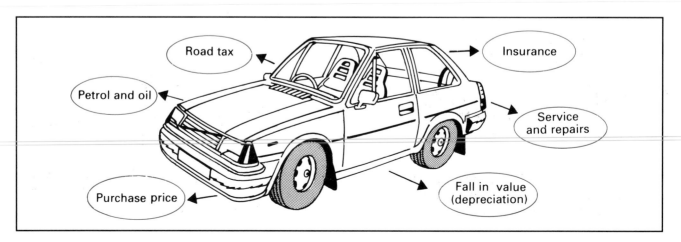

EXERCISE 4

1 a During the year, Mr Dixon used 180 gallons of petrol at an average cost of £2.25 per gallon. How much did the petrol cost?

b Here are his other car costs for the year. Calculate the total cost.

Road tax	£ 130
Insurance	£ 340
Service and repairs	£ 180
Fall in value of car	£1000
Petrol	£
Total cost	£

2 Mr Dixon's car covers an average of 30 miles to the gallon.

a Copy and complete to find how much petrol the car uses to travel 240 miles:

Distance   *Petrol*
30 miles ⟷ 1 gallon
240 miles ⟷ $1 \times \dfrac{240}{30}$ gallons
$= \ldots$ gallons

b How much petrol would it use to travel 9000 miles?

3 'We're using too much petrol' said Mr Dixon. So he changed his car for one which did 40 miles to the gallon.
On a year's mileage of 8000 miles, calculate:

a how many gallons of petrol he will buy

b the cost of the petrol at £2.30 a gallon.

4 Tony reckons that his old banger needs one litre of petrol every 12 km. Over a year he travels 15 000 km.

a How many litres of petrol does he use?

b At 53 pence per litre, how much does he spend on petrol?

5 Tony's car was worth £800 in January, but only £700 in December. Calculate its percentage fall in value, based on the January value.

6 Ann has a note of her car costs for the past year. Road tax £130, insurance £280, service and repairs £300, fall in value £600. She drove 12 000 km getting an average of 15 km per litre of petrol (costing 50p per litre). Calculate:

a her total car costs

b the cost in pence per kilometre, to the nearest penny.

BRAINSTORMER

In this car cost pie chart, the road tax cost £130. Calculate:
a *the total cost*
b *the cost of each item.*

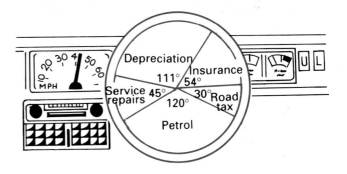

INVESTIGATION

Investigate the cost of buying and running a car. The picture shows you some of the things you'll have to think about.

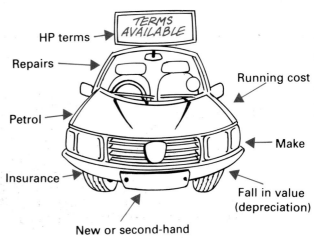

CAR INSURANCE

Car insurance premiums depend on the:

a size, age and type of car
b owner of the car—occupation, age, experience
c area where the owner lives and works
d type of insurance—comprehensive, or other
e use of car—for pleasure or business, etc
f no-claims record of the owner.

In what way do you think each of the above affects the insurance premium?

Car Care's table of annual insurance premiums (£)

Car group	District					
	A	B	C	D	E	F
1	347	437	507	615	770	832
2	357	447	520	630	784	845
4	427	532	620	735	895	970
6	510	620	720	842	910	980
8	540	725	833	942	990	1057
10	620	780	875	990	1085	1192
12	750	890	970	1050	1136	1288
14	925	1035	1147	1280	1465	1570

Examples of no-claims discounts:
30% discount if no claim in previous year
40% discount if no claim in previous two years
50% discount if no claim in previous three years
60% discount if no claim in previous four or more years.

Example
Alice has a Group 2 car and lives in District B. She has not made any claims in the past two years. Calculate her car insurance premium.
From the table, her annual premium is £447.
Her no-claims discount = 40% of £447 = £178.80
So her premium = £447 − £178.80 = £268.20

EXERCISE 5

1 List these annual premiums.

Car group	District	Premium
4	E	
8	C	
10	A	
14	F	

2 Harish lives in district D, and drives a sports car, Group 10. He receives no discount.
a Write down his annual premium.
b He thinks 'If I make no claims this year my premium will be less next year'. How much less?

3 Jamila lives in district B, and has a group 6 car.
a What is her premium, before discount?
b She has not claimed for four years. Calculate her no-claims discount.
c How much has she to pay this year?

4 Mr Hill lives in town (district E) and drives a large, group 12, car. He has 2 years no-claims discount.
   a What is his premium, before discount?
   b Calculate his no-claims discount.
   c How much has he to pay?

5 For the drivers in this table, calculate:
   (i) their insurance premium before discount
   (ii) any no-claims discount
   (iii) their annual premium.

	Name	Car group	District	Years without a claim
a	D. Barr	1	D	0
b	M. Munn	12	B	1
c	K. Burns	6	E	2
d	R. Race	4	C	3
e	A. Brand	10	B	4
f	I. Best	14	F	8

6 Ella Robinson drives a Mini 850 (Group 1). She lives in London (District F). Calculate her annual car insurance premium. (She has had one year without a claim.)

7 Ella (question **6**) had an accident, and lost her no-claims discount. She bought a new, group 2, car. What was the increase in her annual premium?

8 Gail is 21 years old and lives in district D. She has not claimed for two years, and her car is in group 10. Unfortunately the insurance company charges 10% extra for drivers under 25 years of age. Calculate her annual premium.

CHALLENGE

George Holmes' annual premium is £780, less a £234 discount (one year without a claim). You can see from the picture that he needs repairs now! The bill comes to £250, which he claimed from his insurance company.

   a *What is his annual premium for the following year?*
   b *His next door neighbour, Mr Know-All, said 'A mistake, George, you shouldn't have claimed'. How much did George lose the following year by making the claim?*

APPRECIATION AND DEPRECIATION

Houses tend to **appreciate**, or increase in value, year by year; cars usually **depreciate**, or decrease in value, year by year. Why?

Example
Liz paid £40 000 for her flat. In the following year it appreciated by 5% and in the year after that by 10%. Calculate its value each year.
First year   Value = £40 000
           Appreciation = 5% of £40 000 = £2000
Second year   Value = £42 000
           Appreciation = 10% of £42 000 = £4200
Value after two years = £46 200.

EXERCISE 6B

1 The Simpsons bought their house two years ago for £52 000. In the first year it appreciated by £5000 and in the second year by £2000. What is its value now?

2 Tony has just paid £1500 for a car. He estimates that it will depreciate by about £300 each year.
  a Estimate its value in two years from now.
  b How many years before its only value is for scrap?

3 A house costs £57 000. If it appreciates by 10% next year, how much will it then be worth?

4 Ali's car cost him £2000. How much is it worth a year later, allowing a 10% depreciation?

5 Peter and Ruth bought a house for £80 000. In each of the following two years its value went up by 10%. How much was it worth after:
  a one year **b** two years?

6 a By how much did the house below appreciate in the year?
  b Calculate the appreciation as a percentage of its value in 1994.

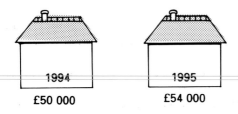

1994 — £50 000   1995 — £54 000

7 a By how much did this car depreciate in each of the two years?

| 1994 | 1995 | 1996 |
| £1200 | £1000 | £750 |

  b Calculate the percentage depreciation each year, to the nearest whole number.

8 Mr and Mrs Ngema bought their new house for £40 000 at the end of 1992.
  a Did their house increase in value in:
    (i) 1993   (ii) 1994   (iii) 1995?
  b Calculate the value of the house at the end of each of these years.

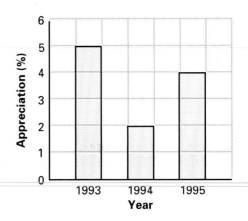

CHECK-UP ON HOUSE AND CAR COSTS

1 Mr and Mrs Fleming buy a house for £70 000. The Open Door Building Society lends them 85% of this value. Calculate:
a the amount the Building Society lends
b the deposit the Flemings have to pay.

2 For a mortgage of £20 000 Ms Grey has to pay £8 monthly on each £1000 borrowed. Calculate:
a her monthly payment
b the annual cost.

3 a Copy and complete this calculation of the monthly payments for an £18 000 mortgage over 15 years with the Safe and Secure Building Society. (See table below.)

Mortgage   Payment
£10 000 ⟷ £94.24

£18 000 ⟷ £94.24 × $\frac{\ldots}{\ldots}$

= £ . . .

Safe and Secure Building Society Monthly payments on a £10 000 mortgage			
15 years	20 years	25 years	30 years
£94.24	£83.69	£76.81	£72.70

b Calculate the monthly payment if the mortgage was paid over 30 years.

4 The Safety First Insurance Company charges an annual premium for house insurance of £1.80 per £1000 of the value of the house.
Calculate the annual premiums for house insurance for:
a a flat worth £20 000
b a semi-detached villa valued at £45 000
c a house worth £88 500.

5 Mr and Mrs Fleming insure their house for £75 000 and its contents for £15 000. The insurance rates are £1.90 per £1000 for the house and £9 per £1000 for the contents. Calculate their:
a house insurance premium
b contents premium
c total premium

6 Fred is a salesman for Sleepy Beds. One year he drove 16 000 miles, at an average 40 miles per gallon of petrol. His car costs included: insurance £450, road tax £130, service £400, petrol at £2.30 a gallon. Calculate:
a his petrol cost
b his total running costs for the year
c the cost in pence per mile, to the nearest penny.

7 June's car insurance premium is £890, less two years no-claims discount of 40%.
a Calculate her premium for the year.
b After another year without a claim, her discount rose to 50%, but she'd changed cars, and the new full premium was £1020.
How much more or less has she to pay than the year before?

8 A house increased in value from £64 000 in 1989 to £66 000 in 1994. Calculate the appreciation in its value:
a in £s   **b** as a percentage of its 1989 value.

9 A company spent £2 000 000 on computers. Their value depreciated by 12% annually. Calculate their value after:
a one year   **b** two years   **c** three years.

7 PAIRS OF STRAIGHT LINES AND EQUATIONS

LOOKING BACK

1 Jeff cycles at a steady speed. This graph shows his distance from a marker at certain times from 3 seconds after starting.

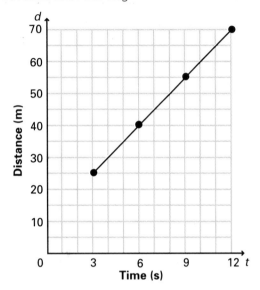

a Write down his distance from the marker after:
(i) 6 seconds   (ii) 9 seconds   (iii) 11 seconds.
b How long did he take to cycle a distance of:
(i) 35 m   (ii) 50 m   (iii) 60 m?

2 Copy and complete this table:

x	0	1	2	-2	-1
$2x$					
$x+4$					

3 Solve these equations:
a $2x = 12$ **b** $3x = 0$ **c** $5x = 5$ **d** $2x = -4$

4 a On squared paper, draw the lines with equations $x = 5$ and $y = 4$.
b Where the lines cross, the treasure is buried. Write down the coordinates of this point.
c Use Pythagoras' Theorem to calculate the distance, correct to 1 decimal place, from the treasure to the origin O.

5 When moist air rises, its temperature falls 5° per km. At sea level the temperature is 10°C.

a Copy and complete this table.

Height, H km	0	1	2	3	4
Temperature, T°C	10	5			

b Draw the graph of T against H, with H on the horizontal axis.

6 a On squared paper draw straight lines through the pairs of points:
(i) O(0, 0) and A(6, 6)   (ii) B(3, 0) and C(0, 6).
b Write down the coordinates of the point where the lines cross.

7 $2x + y = 8$. Write down the value of:
a x when $y = 0$ **b** y when $x = 0$.

8 $y = 3x - 6$. Calculate:
a x when $y = 0$ **b** y when $x = 0$.

9 Solve the equations:
a $2x = x + 3$ **b** $3x - 1 = x - 5$ **c** $3x - 1 = x$

10 Add:
a $3x$ **b** $2y$ **c** $5a$ **d** $-3b$
   $\underline{2x}$ $\underline{y}$ $\underline{-2a}$ $\underline{-3b}$

11 Subtract the lower term from the upper one.
a $3x$ **b** $3y$ **c** $-2u$ **d** $4v$
   $\underline{2x}$ $\underline{5y}$ $\underline{u}$ $\underline{-3v}$

12

> The sum of two numbers is 9. The difference between them is 2. What are the numbers?

CROSSING LINES

EXERCISE 1/CLASS DISCUSSION

1

Kim jumps, followed by Ian.

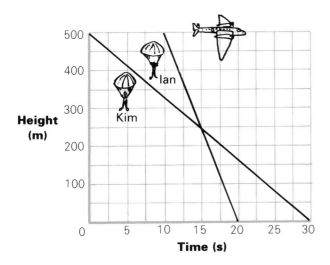

a What height do they jump from?
b How long does each take to reach the ground?
c How long after Kim jumps does Ian jump?
d Ian passes Kim on the way down.
  (i) At what height?
  (ii) How long after he jumped?

2 *The graph of* $y = x$

x	-5	-4	-3	-2	-1	0	1	2	3	4	5
y	-5	-4	-3	-2	-1	0	1	2	3	4	5

Using this table of values, we can plot the points, and draw part of the straight line with equation $y = x$.
Which of these points lie on the line?
a $(10, 10)$ **b** $(10, -10)$
c $(-10, -10)$ **d** $(-10, 10)$

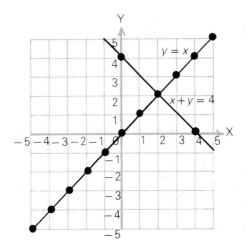

3 *The graph of* $x + y = 4$

This graph is also a straight line, so we only need to plot two points to draw it.
  (i) If $x = 0$, $y = 4$, so $(0, 4)$ is on the line.
 (ii) If $y = 0$, $x = 4$, so $(4, 0)$ is on the line.
The line joining these points is shown in the diagram above.
What are the coordinates of the point where the two lines cross?

At $(2, 2)$, $y = x$ **and** $x + y = 4$, so $(2, 2)$ is the solution of the equations $y = x$ and $x + y = 4$.

EXERCISE 2

1 Write down
the solution
of each pair
of equations.

a

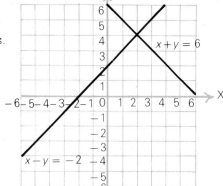

b

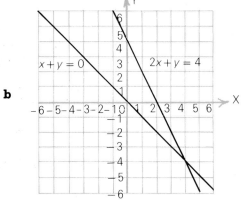

c

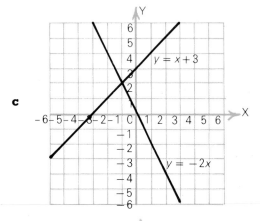

d

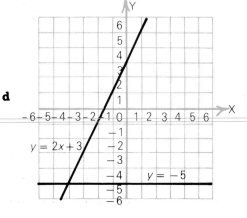

2 a Copy this graph of $y = x$ on squared paper.

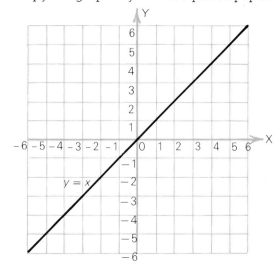

b To draw the graph of $x + y = 3$, copy and
complete:
If $x = 0$, $y = \ldots$. $(0, \ldots)$ is on the line.
If $y = 0$, $x = \ldots$. $(\ldots, 0)$ is on the line.
c Plot the two points on the diagram, and draw
the line through them.
d Find the point where the two lines cross, and
write down the solution of the pair of
equations $y = x$ and $x + y = 3$.

3 a Copy this graph of $y = -2x$ on squared paper.

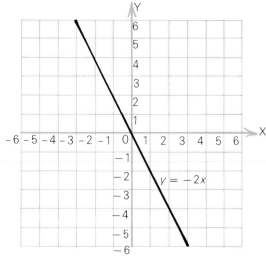

b To draw the graph of $x + y = 2$, copy and
complete:
If $x = 0$, $y = \ldots$. $(0, \ldots)$ is on the line.
If $y = 0$, $x = \ldots$. $(\ldots, 0)$ is on the line.
c Plot the two points on the diagram, and draw
the line.
d Write down the solution of the pair of
equations $y = -2x$ and $x + y = 2$.

Using the same axes and scales as in questions **1–3**, draw the graphs of each pair of equations below. Then write down the solution of each pair of equations.

4 $y = x$ and $x + y = 2$

5 $2x + y = 6$ and $x + 2y = 6$

6 $x + y = 6$ and $y = x + 2$

7 $x + y = 2$ and $y = x - 2$

8 $y = 2x + 6$ and $x + y = 0$ (for a second point, choose $x = 4$ for example)

9 $x - y = -3$ and $2x + y = 3$

10 $x - y = 0$ and $x + y = 0$

/ **ACCURATE DRAWING**

On 2 mm squared paper draw the graphs of these pairs of equations, and solve them, correct to 1 decimal place. Take 2 cm to 1 unit on each axis.
a $x + 3y = 6$ and $4x + y = 4$
b $2x + 3y = 12$ and $x - 2y = -2$

/ **CHALLENGE**

Newtown Youth Group are having a Treasure Hunt. Part of the football field is lined off in 10 metre squares.

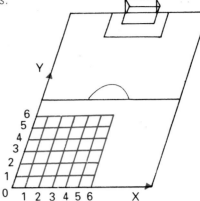

The treasure (a voucher for sports goods) is buried at one of the crossing points. The members are given these two clues to help them find the treasure:

$y = x$ $y = -x + 6$

1 *How many crossing points are there?*

2 *Copy the grid on squared paper. Imagine you are taking part in the Treasure Hunt. Can you find the treasure, using the two clues?*

3 *Can you think of any other ways to solve the pair of equations?*

GRAPHS AS MATHEMATICAL MODELS

To compare the car hire costs, make a table and draw a graph.

Number of days	0	1	2	3	4	5	6	7
Carplan cost (£)	50	60	70	80	90	100	110	120
Carloan cost (£)	0	20	40	60	80	100	120	140

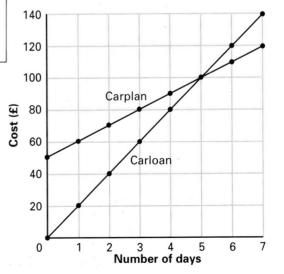

The graph shows that:
a Carloan is cheaper for up to four days.
b Both charge the same for five days.
c Carplan is cheaper for six days or more.

EXERCISE 3

1 a 'Maximiles' have motorbikes for hire. They
charge £20 deposit, and £5 a day.
(i) Copy and complete this table:

Number of days	0	1	2	3	4	5
Total cost (£)	20	25	30			

(ii) Copy and complete the graph.

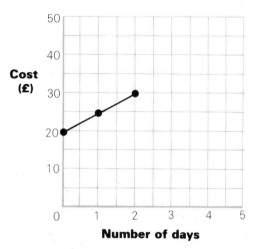

Cost (£)

Number of days

b 'Speedwheels' also hire out bikes. They charge
£10 a day, but no deposit.
(i) Copy and complete their table:

Number of days	0	1	2	3	4	5
Total cost (£)	0	10				

(ii) Draw their graph on the same sheet.
c After how many days is the total cost the same?
How much?
d Which would you choose for:
(i) a two–day hire (ii) a five–day hire?

2 a Make tables for Happy Hire and Fast Hire like
those in question **1**.

b Draw the two graphs of hire charges on the
same sheet.
c After how many days is the cost the same? How
much?
d Which firm would you choose for:
(i) two days (ii) four days?

3 a Make two tables like those in question **1** for 0, 1,
2, 3, . . . , 8 months TV rental under Star's two
methods.

b Draw graphs of the rentals on a grid like the
one below.

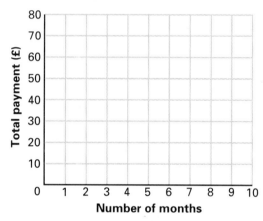

Total payment (£)

Number of months

c When are the total costs the same? How much?

4 Clear Drains have a call-out charge, and then an
hourly rate for their work.
a From the graph, write down:
(i) the call-out charge
(ii) the cost of five hours work.
b Calculate:
(i) the cost of five hours work without the call-
out charge
(ii) the hourly rate.

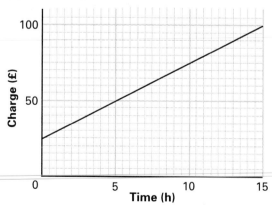

Charge (£)

Time (h)

c Nochokes have no call-out charge, but their
fixed charge is £75 per job. Put your ruler
along the line representing their charge. When
are the charges by the two firms the same?

5

Top Taxis charge £1 a mile. Quick Cabs have a fixed charge of £4 for any journey up to six miles, and then charge £2 a mile on top of the fixed charge.

a Copy and complete this table.

Distance (miles)	1	2	3	4		10
TT's total cost (£)	1					10
QC's total cost (£)	4	4				12

b Draw graphs of both sets of charges, using these scales:

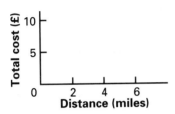

c For what distances are the total costs equal?
d For what distances are Top Taxis cheaper than Quick Cabs?

6 a North Gas Board has a standing charge of £10 per quarter, plus 10p per unit. Use the graph to copy and complete this table.

Number of units (N)	0	50	100	150	200
Cost (£C)	10	15			

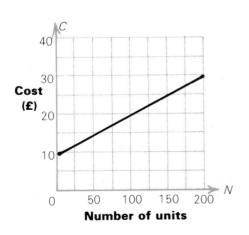

b South Gas Board has no standing charge, but each unit costs 20p. Copy and complete this table.

Number of units (N)	0	50	100	150	200
Cost (£C)	0	10	20		

c Draw graphs of C against N for both Boards on the same page.
d Where the two graphs cross, the Boards charge the same.
  (i) How much is this charge?
  (ii) For how many units?
e Lynn Taylor uses 150 units. Which Board would be cheaper for her? How much cheaper?

Superswift's tank holds 60 litres of petrol. In a race, the car averages 10 km per litre. Bluestreak's tank holds 40 litres, but it averages 20 km per litre.
a *Each car starts with a full tank of petrol. How much petrol does each have after 100 km?*
b *Using the axes shown, plot a pair of points for each car on squared paper—one for the start, one after 100 km.*

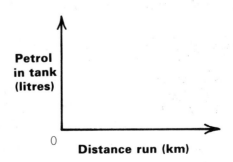

c *After how many kilometres will both cars have the same amount of petrol left?*
d *How far can each car travel altogether on a full tank of petrol?*

SOLVING PAIRS OF EQUATIONS BY SUBSTITUTION

Look at the two straight line graphs.

At A:

$$\left.\begin{array}{l} y = 2x \\ and \quad y = x+1 \end{array}\right\} \text{the } y\text{s are the same.}$$

So $2x = x+1$
$\quad 2x - x = x + 1 - x$
$\qquad x = 1$
$\qquad y = 2x = 2 \times 1 = 2$

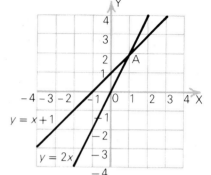

So the solution of the pair of equations is (1, 2). Check this from the graph.

Note: since $2x$ is substituted for y in the equation $y = x+1$, this method is called **substitution**.

EXERCISE 4

Solve each pair of equations by substituting the value of y from one equation into the other.

1 $y = 2x$
$\quad y = x+3$

2 $y = 3x$
$\quad y = x+4$

3 $y = 4x$
$\quad y = 2x+6$

4 $y = 2x$
$\quad y = x-1$

5 $y = 5x$
$\quad y = 3x-8$

6 $y = 10x$
$\quad y = x+9$

7 $y = 3x$
$\quad y = x+5$

8 $y = 4x$
$\quad y = 2x+3$

9 $y = 2x+1$
$\quad y = x+3$

10 $y = 2x-1$
$\quad y = x-2$

11 $y = 3x+4$
$\quad y = x+8$

12 $y = 6x+3$
$\quad y = 3x-6$

13 $y = 3x$
$\quad x+y = 10$

14 $y = x+1$
$\quad x+y = 4$

SOLVING PAIRS OF EQUATIONS BY ELIMINATION

A puzzle

The sum of two numbers is 20. Their difference is 4. Find the numbers.

Put $x = 12$ in the first equation:

Alison's solution

If the numbers are x and y,

$$x + y = 20$$
$$x - y = 4$$

Add $2x = 24$ . . . . (i)

$$x = 12$$
$$12 + y = 20$$
$$y = 20 - 12 = 8$$

The numbers are 12 and 8.

Check $12 + 8 = 20$, $12 - 8 = 4$

Note: y is eliminated in (i), so this method is called **elimination**.

EXERCISE 5A

Solve these pairs of equations by adding or subtracting them to eliminate x or y, etc.

1 $x + y = 12$
$x - y = 4$

2 $x + y = 16$
$x - y = 6$

3 $x + y = 20$
$x - y = 10$

4 $x + y = 15$
$x - y = 7$

5 $x + y = -5$
$x - y = 3$

6 $x + y = -6$
$x - y = -2$

7 $2x + y = 9$
$x - y = 3$

8 $3x + y = 7$
$x - y = 1$

9 $3x + y = 4$
$2x - y = 1$

10 $5x + y = 12$
$2x - y = 2$

11 $2x + y = 11$
$x + y = 7$
(Subtract!)

12 $3x + y = 10$
$x + y = 6$

13 $2x + y = 6$
$x + y = 4$

14 $4x + y = 12$
$2x + y = 6$

15 $2x + y = 6$
$x - y = 0$

16 $3x - y = 3$
$x + y = -3$

17 $2x - y = 3$
$x + y = 0$

18 $4x - y = -9$
$x + y = -1$

19 $6x + 2y = -8$
$x - 2y = 1$

20 $3x - 2y = 17$
$4x + 2y = 18$

/ CHALLENGE /

Two trains approach each other. Their passing speed is 60 mph.
   So $x + y = $ . . . .

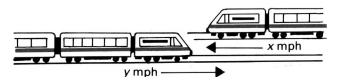

Next day one overtakes the other. Their passing speed is 10 mph.
   So $x - y = $ . . . .

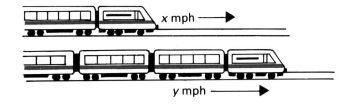

Find the speeds of the trains, by making two equations and solving them, using:
a *graphs, as shown in **Exercise 2***
b *elimination, as shown in **Exercise 5A**.*

EXERCISE 5B

Alison has a problem. This time neither adding nor subtracting eliminates x or y.
But there is a way.

Examples

a
$$2x+y=9 \quad \times 3 \quad 6x+3y=27$$
$$x-3y=1 \quad \times 1 \quad \underline{x-3y=1}$$
$$\text{Add:} \quad 7x \quad = 28$$
$$x=4$$
$$\text{So } 2\times 4+y=9$$
$$y=1$$
$$\text{and } x=4,\ y=1$$

b
$$3x+2y=13 \quad \times 1 \quad 3x+2y=13$$
$$2x+y=8 \quad \times 2 \quad \underline{4x+2y=16}$$
$$\text{Subtract:} \quad -x \quad = -3$$
$$x=3$$
$$\text{So } 3\times 3+2y=13$$
$$2y=4$$
$$y=2$$
$$\text{and } x=3,\ y=2$$

Solve these pairs of equations:

1 $x+2y=8 \quad \times 1 \quad \ldots\ldots$
   $2x-y=1 \quad \times 2 \quad \ldots\ldots$, then *add*

2 $3a+b=6 \quad \times 2 \quad \ldots\ldots$
   $a-2b=2 \quad \times 1 \quad \ldots\ldots$, then *add*

3 $4x-y=7$
   $x+2y=4$

4 $x+2y=6$
   $2x-y=7$

5 $a+3b=1$
   $2a-b=2$

6 $5u+v=4$
   $u-2v=3$

7 $3x+2y=4 \quad \times 1 \quad \ldots\ldots$
   $x+y=1 \quad \times 2 \quad \ldots\ldots$, then *subtract*

8 $4u+2v=2$
   $u+v=0$

9 $5a+b=1$
   $a+2b=2$

10 $2x-y=6$
   $x-2y=0$

11 $3x-2y=1$
   $x-y=0$

12 $3x-4y=14$
   $x+y=0$

13 $5u-2v=7$
   $u-v=2$

14 $2a+b=1$
   $a+2b=-1$

15 $2x-y=-2$
   $x-3y=-1$

16 $2p+3q=1$
   $p+q=1$

17 $2p+3q=4$
   $p-q=2$

BRAINSTORMERS

Make pairs of equations and solve them.

1

I'm thinking of two numbers.

Which numbers?

If I add the first number to double the second, I get 24. And if I double the first and add the second, I get 36.

Can you find the two numbers?

2
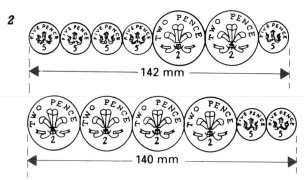

142 mm

140 mm

Use this information to find the diameter of a 5p coin and a 2p coin.

CHECK-UP ON PAIRS OF STRAIGHT LINES AND EQUATIONS

1 Ben jumps, followed by Rena. Describe, in a sentence or two, the main information these graphs give about their heights and times in the air.

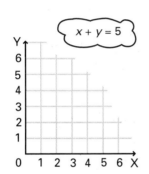

2 a Copy and complete.
   When $x = 0$, $y = \ldots$
   When $y = 0$, $x = \ldots$
   b Draw the graph of the equation $x + y = 5$ on squared paper.

$x + y = 5$

3 a Using the scales in question **2**, draw graphs of the equations $x + 2y = 8$ and $y = x + 1$.
   b Use your graphs to write down the solution of the pair of equations.

4

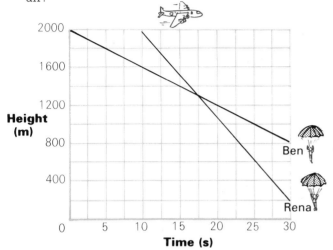

RENT A VIDEO
£20 at the end of every 3 months, or
£20 deposit and £10 at the end of every 3 months

a Copy and complete this table:

Number of months	0	3	6	9	12
Cost (£): 1st method	0	20			
Cost (£): 2nd method	20	30			

b Draw graphs for the two methods on a grid like the one shown at the top of the next column.

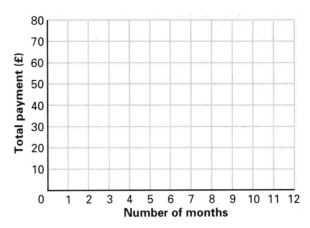

c Which method is cheaper if you plan to rent a video for: (i) 3 months   (ii) 12 months?
d When are the costs equal?

5 The small family firm Jones and Jones makes two components for the Hi-Fli TV Company. The daily production of 40 components is shown in the graph.

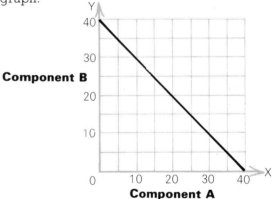

a Using the graph, copy and complete:

x	0	10	20	30	40
y	40				

b Write an equation, $x + y = \ldots$.
c Every Wednesday, three times as many B components are made as A components. Copy and complete: $y = \ldots$.
d Draw the graphs of $x + y = 40$ and $y = 3x$ on a grid like the one above, and find the number of each component made on Wednesdays.

Solve each pair of equations in questions **6** and **7** by calculation (not by graphs).

6 a $y = 2x$
      $y = x + 5$
   b $y = 5x$
      $y = 2x - 9$
   c $y = x + 1$
      $4x + y = 11$

7 a $2x + y = 10$
      $x - y = 2$
   b $3u + 2v = 9$
      $u + 2v = 7$
   c $3a + 2b = 1$
      $a + b = 0$

91

REVIEW: LETTERS AND NUMBERS

SIMPLIFICATION

1 Simplify:
  a $y+y+y$ **b** $2x-x$ **c** $4k+k$ **d** $t-t$
  e $m+n+m-n$ **f** $3+x+2+x$ **g** $u+v-u$

2 Find an expression for the total weight of each pair of cases.

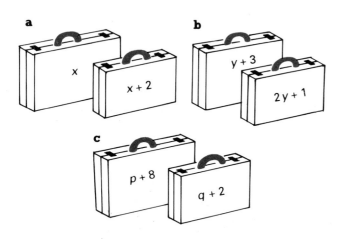

a x $x+2$
b $y+3$ $2y+1$
c $p+8$ $q+2$

3 Simplify:
  a $n+n$ **b** $n\times n$ **c** $2\times y$ **d** $3\times p\times p$

4 Find an expression for the total length of each cane.

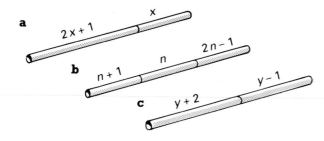

a $2x+1$ x
b $n+1$ n $2n-1$
c $y+2$ $y-1$

5 Multiply out these brackets:
  a $3(x+1)$ **b** $5(y-2)$ **c** $4(1-t)$ **d** $2(2-u)$
  e $3(2a+1)$ **f** $4(3b-1)$ **g** $6(4c-5)$

6 Find the common factor, and factorise each expression below. For example,
$3x+6y = 3(x+2y)$.
  a $2x+6$ **b** $3y+6$ **c** $4t-8$ **d** $5u+5$
  e $2u+2v$ **f** $3m+6n$ **g** $5p-5q$ **h** $10-5t$

7 Find, in its simplest form, an expression for the perimeter of each shape.

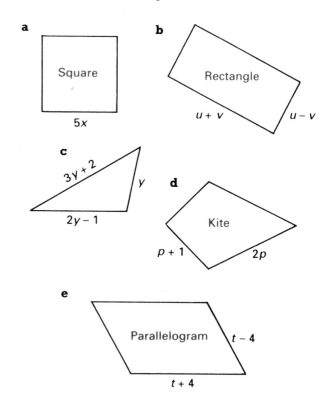

a Square $5x$
b Rectangle $u+v$ $u-v$
c $3y+2$ y $2y-1$
d Kite $p+1$ $2p$
e Parallelogram $t-4$ $t+4$

8 Multiply out the brackets, and tidy up:
  a $3(x+1)+6$ **b** $4+2(x+1)$
  c $2(y-1)+3y$ **d** $5n+3(2-n)$

9 Find the OUT expressions, with and then without brackets:

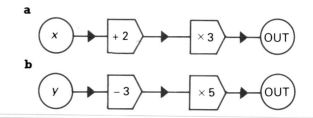

a x → $+2$ → $\times 3$ → OUT
b y → -3 → $\times 5$ → OUT

10 Factorise:
  a $2a+4$ **b** $2a+4b$ **c** a^2+ab **d** a^2+2a
  e $3a+6b+9c$ **f** $5x^2-5x-5$ **g** $y-y^2$

REPLACING LETTERS BY NUMBERS

1 How much money is in each of these bags?

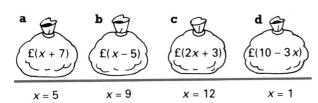

a £(x + 7)	**b** £(x − 5)	**c** £(2x + 3)	**d** £(10 − 3x)
x = 5	x = 9	x = 12	x = 1

2 $a = 7$, $b = 3$, $c = 2$ and $d = 1$. Calculate the value of:

a ab **b** $3c$ **c** $5 - d$ **d** $12 - a$
e a^2 **f** $2a^2$ **g** $a - b + c - d$ **h** $abcd$

3 Copy and complete these tables:

a

x	0	1	3	5
$4x$				

b

y	6	9	12	15
$y - 6$				

c
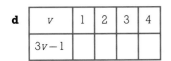

u	0	1	4	9
u^2				

d

v	1	2	3	4
$3v - 1$				

4 Calculate the first four terms of sequences with nth terms:

a $5n$ (Put $n = 1, 2, 3, 4$) **b** $\dfrac{1}{n}$ **c** $4n + 2$

d $n(n + 1)$ **e** $\dfrac{n}{n + 1}$

5 a $A = b^2$. Calculate A when $b = 8$.
  b $V = xyz$. Calculate V when $x = 10$, $y = 5$ and $z = 2$.
  c $S = \dfrac{D}{T}$. Calculate S when $D = 40$ and $T = 8$.
  d $x = \sqrt{A}$. Calculate x when $A = 49$.

6 Pastamac price their pizzas by size, using the formula $P = d^2 + 30$, where P pence is the price and d inches is the diameter of the pizza. Calculate the price of pizzas with diameters of:
  a 5 inches **b** 10 inches **c** 12 inches.

POSITIVE AND NEGATIVE NUMBERS

1 List these places in order, coldest first:

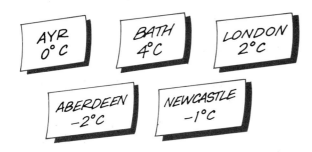

AYR 0°C

BATH 4°C

LONDON 2°C

ABERDEEN −2°C

NEWCASTLE −1°C

2 A, B, . . . , G show the positions of people's guesses in a 'Spot the Ball' competition.

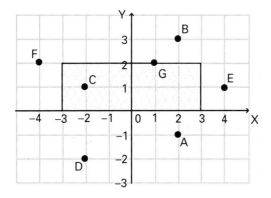

a List the coordinates of the points.
b The winning point lies on the line $x + y = -1$. Which point wins?

3 Here are the temperatures in five towns in Turkey on a winter day.

Izmar	Bursa	Konya	Samsun	Siras
−5°C	−7°C	−1°C	1°C	3°C

a Calculate the new temperatures if they all:
  (i) rise by 2°C   (ii) fall by 2°C.
b Which town is:
  (i) 2°C warmer than Bursa
  (ii) 4°C cooler than Konya?

4 Calculate:
  a $3 + (-1)$ **b** $-2 + 4$ **c** $-5 + 2$
  d $-3 + 3$ **e** $4 + (-3)$ **f** $4 + (-5)$
  g $-4 + 1$ **h** $-4 - 1$ **i** $7 + (-7)$
  j $-1 + (-1)$ **k** $-2 + (-1)$ **l** $8 - 10$

5 Jean Jackson has a craft shop. She lists her daily profits (positive) and losses (negative).

Day	Mon	Tue	Wed	Thu	Fri
Profit/loss (£)	200	500	−100	300	−200

  a By how much did her profit increase or decrease from:
    (i) Monday to Tuesday
    (ii) Tuesday to Wednesday
    (iii) Wednesday to Thursday
    (iv) Thursday to Friday?
  b Calculate:
    (i) her profit for the week
    (ii) her mean daily profit.

6 $a = -3$, $b = -6$, $c = 2$, $d = -1$ and $e = 4$.
  Calculate the value of:
  a $a + b$ **b** $c + d$ **c** $a + b + c + d + e$
  d $a - c$ **e** $d - e$ **f** $c - e$ **g** $a - e$
  h $2a$ **i** $5b$ **j** $10d$ **k** $-4 \times e$

EQUATIONS

1 Solve these equations:
  a $x - 2 = 7$ **b** $x + 6 = 17$ **c** $12 - x = 8$
  d $2y + 1 = 4$ **e** $3y + 4 = 1$ **f** $12 - 5y = 2$

2 Make an equation for each picture below, and solve it. Then write down the number of weights in each bag.

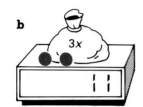

a $2x$ **b** $3x$

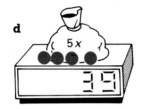

c $7x$ **d** $5x$

3 Make an equation for each diagram below, and solve it:

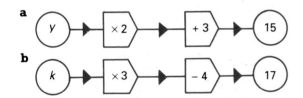

a y ▶ $\times 2$ ▶ $+ 3$ ▶ 15

b k ▶ $\times 3$ ▶ $- 4$ ▶ 17

4

I've thought of a number, multiplied it by 4 and added 3. The answer is 47. What was my number?

Let n stand for the number, make an equation, then solve it to find the number.

5 'I've thought of another number', said Louise. 'When I doubled it and added 11, I got 3. What was my number this time?'

6 (i) Make an equation for each triangle, and solve it.
   (ii) Write down the lengths of the sides of the triangles.

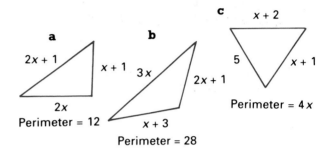

a $2x + 1$ $x + 1$ $2x$ Perimeter = 12

b $3x$ $2x + 1$ $x + 3$ Perimeter = 28

c $x + 2$ 5 $x + 1$ Perimeter = $4x$

7 Solve these equations:
  a $2(x + 3) = 8$ **b** $3(y - 1) = 12$ **c** $2(z + 3) = 9$

8 Solve these equations:
  a $3x = x + 2$ **b** $5x = 2x + 9$ **c** $6x = x + 15$
  d $7y - 2 = 5y$ **e** $5z - 8 = z$ **f** $4t = t - 9$
  g $3n - 2 = n + 6$ **h** $5k + 3 = 2k - 3$
  i $8p + 1 = 3p + 6$ **j** $6t + 5 = 5t - 1$

9 (i) Make an equation for each of these pictures, and solve it. In **a**, $3(x - 2) = \ldots$
   (ii) Write down the number of weights in each bag.

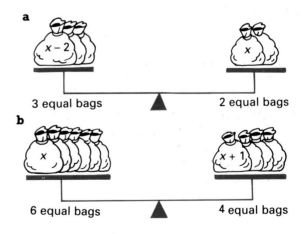

a $x - 2$ x
  3 equal bags   2 equal bags

b x $x + 1$
  6 equal bags   4 equal bags

FORMULAE

1 a Write down a formula for:
   (i) the area of the rectangle, $A = \dots$
   (ii) the perimeter, $P = \dots$
b Calculate A and P when $x = 8$ and $y = 12$.

y cm

x cm

2 a Write down a formula for the volume V cm³ of this cuboid.
b Calculate V when $l = 7.5$, $b = 8$ and $h = 9$.

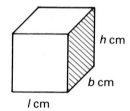

h cm

b cm

l cm

3 Make up a formula for each of these:
  a the cost, £C, of n books at £5 each; $C = \dots$
  b the change, £C, from £10 after spending £S; $C = \dots$
  c the number of pages, N, in b books, each of which has 100 pages; $N = \dots$
  d the number of windows, W, in y houses, each with x windows; $W = \dots$
  e the total time, T hours, for a three-act play, if the acts last x, y and z hours; $T = \dots$

4 $S = A + B$ and $P = AB$. Calculate S and P when $A = 12.5$ and $B = 7.5$.

5 $T = 2\sqrt{L}$. Calculate T when $L = 2401$.

6 $B = \dfrac{100}{L}$. Calculate B when $L = 32$.

7 $R = 5(P - 25)$. Calculate R when $P = 80$.

8 $H = \sqrt{(a^2 + b^2)}$. Calculate H, correct to 1 decimal place, when $a = 9.9$ and $b = 6.6$.

9 a Find formulae for the shaded areas, A, of these shapes, made of squares and rectangles.
b Calculate A for each when $x = 12$ and $y = 15$.

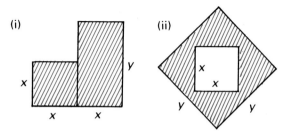

(i)

y

x

x x

(ii)

x

x

y y

10 Make a formula for:
  a the profit, £P, on a TV set which is bought for £C and sold for £S.
  b the cost £C of a carpet when a deposit of £25 is paid and then n monthly payments of £8.

11 The volume of a cone, V cm³, with area of base A cm² and height H cm, is given by $V = \dfrac{AH}{3}$.
  a Calculate the volume if the area of the base is 12 cm² and the height is 9.5 cm.
  b Could you fill it by softening a cube of ice-cream with 3.5 cm edges?

12 P cm = perimeter, A cm² = area and V cm³ = volume. x cm, y cm and z cm are lengths. Which of these formulae are possible?
  a $P = x + y + z$ **b** $A = x + y$ **c** $V = x + yz$
  d $A = yz$ **e** $P = y + z$ **f** $V = xyz$ **g** $P = xy$

SEQUENCES

1 (i) Write down the first four terms of the sequences with these nth terms.
   (ii) Describe the sequences in words.
   a n^2 **b** $2n$ **c** $5n$ **d** $2n-1$

2 Find a formula for the nth term of each sequence below, and check it for $n = 1, 2$ and 3.
   a $3, 7, 11, 15, \dots (4n - \dots)$
   b $6, 11, 16, 21, \dots (5n + \dots)$
   c $2, 5, 8, 11, \dots$ **d** $5, 11, 17, 23, \dots$
   e $4, 8, 12, 16, \dots$ **f** $10, 13, 16, 19, \dots$
   g $10, 11, 12, 13, \dots$ **h** $100, 200, 300, 400, \dots$

3 Copy and complete these differences:

a

b

4 Copy and complete the table for these patterns of coins:

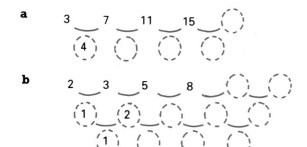

Pattern 1   Pattern 2   Pattern 3   ...

Pattern	1	2	3	4	12		n
Number of coins							

5 a Copy this sequence of dots, and draw the next two patterns.

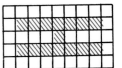

   b How many dots will there be in:
   (i) the sixth pattern
   (ii) the seventh pattern
   (iii) the nth pattern?

6 Copy and complete the table for this sequence of block patterns:

Pattern 1   Pattern 2   Pattern 3   ...

Pattern	1	2	3	4		8		n
Number of blocks								

7 a Copy this sequence of tables and chairs, and draw the next two patterns.

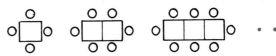

   b Find a formula for the number of chairs, c, for n tables.

8 At the school fête, desks are used for the stalls. The stall holders stand in the shaded areas. Copy and complete the table.

Number of shaded squares	1	2	3	4		10		n
Number of desks	8							

9 The helicopter landing pad is made of square slabs, with the letter **H** in the centre. Copy and complete the table.

Pattern	1	2	3	4		n
Number of slabs						
Number of grey slabs						
Number of white slabs						

INEQUALITIES

1 Rewrite the sentences, using the symbols $<$, $\leqslant$, $>$, $\geqslant$:
  a 2 is less than 6
  b 3 is greater than -3
  c x is less than or equal to y
  d $u+1$ is greater than or equal to v.

2
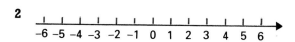

Say whether each of the following is true (T) or false (F):
  a $2 > -1$ **b** $-4 < -3$ **c** $0 > -1$ **d** $1 < -1$
  e $-4 > 2$ **f** $-1 < 0$ **g** $-2 > -1$ **h** $-3 < 3$

3 Write down an inequality for each picture.

  a   **b**

  The bag weighs more than 8 kg

  This present costs less than £10

  c   **d**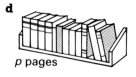

  p people

  p pages

  The maximum number of people carried is 17.

  The minimum number of pages per book is 250.

4 Choosing numbers from the set $\{-3, -2, -1, 0, 1, 2, 3\}$, solve these inequalities:
  a $x > 2$ **b** $x \leqslant 0$ **c** $x \geqslant -1$ **d** $-2 < x \leqslant 1$

5 Solve these inequalities:
  a $2x > 10$ **b** $3y < 3$ **c** $4z \geqslant -8$ **d** $5t \leqslant -5$
  e $t+1 > 5$ **f** $2n+1 \leqslant 7$ **g** $4p+5 < 1$
  h $2(x+3) < 16$ **i** $3(y-1) > 12$ **j** $5(1+z) \leqslant 20$

6 Write down an inequality for each picture, and solve it.

  a 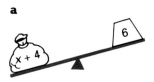 **b**

  c  **d**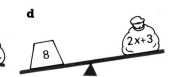

GRAPHS

Graphs come in all shapes and sizes, and every one tells a story. In questions **1–6** decide which graph fits each story best.

1 From the boundary Tom throws the cricket ball to the keeper.

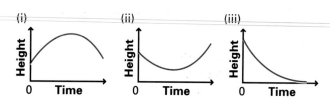

2 The car accelerates away from rest, then stops at crossroads.

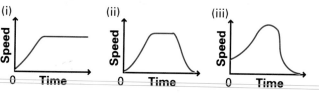

3 A bean is planted. It germinates and grows to its full height. Its height is measured daily.

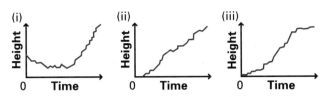

(i) Height / Time   (ii) Height / Time   (iii) Height / Time

4 The radiator is switched on in the room, and the temperature is measured hourly.

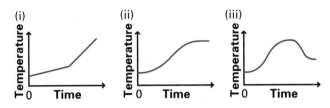

(i) Temperature / Time   (ii) Temperature / Time   (iii) Temperature / Time

5 Alice is blowing up a balloon.

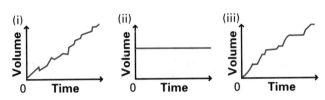

(i) Volume / Time   (ii) Volume / Time   (iii) Volume / Time

6 Carhire's charges: £50 deposit, then 50p per mile.

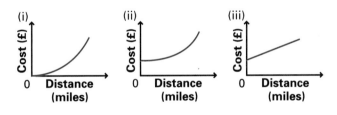

(i) Cost (£) / Distance (miles)   (ii) Cost (£) / Distance (miles)   (iii) Cost (£) / Distance (miles)

7 Water flows from the base of these containers at a steady rate. Match the graphs to the containers.

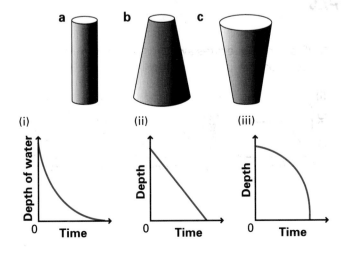

a   b   c

(i) Depth of water / Time   (ii) Depth / Time   (iii) Depth / Time

8 In this question, pair the equations with their graphs.

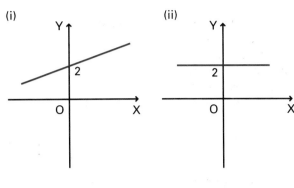

(i)   (ii)

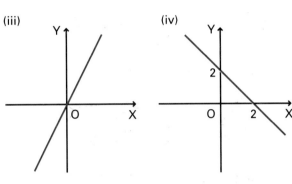

(iii)   (iv)

a $y = 2x$ **b** $x + y = 2$ **c** $y = 2$ **d** $y = \frac{1}{2}x + 2$

9 This graph shows Surendra's journey by car from Bristol to Reading via Swindon, and back to Bristol.

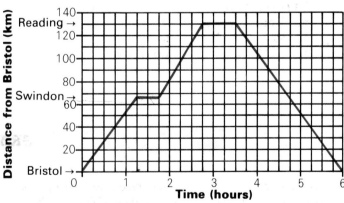

a What fraction of an hour does each square on the time scale represent?
b How long did the journey take from:
  (i) Bristol to Swindon   (ii) Reading to Bristol?
c For how long did Surendra stop at Swindon and Reading?
d How far is it from:
  (i) Bristol to Reading
  (ii) Bristol to Swindon
  (iii) Swindon to Reading?

99

8 PROPORTION IN PRACTICE

1 For these two bars of chocolate, write down, in simplest form, the ratio of their:
  a lengths $\left(\dfrac{\text{bar (i)}}{\text{bar (ii)}}\right)$ **b** breadths
  c weights **d** prices **e** areas

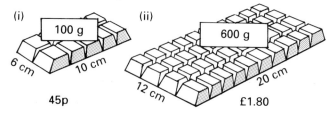

(i) 100 g
6 cm 10 cm
45p

(ii) 600 g
12 cm 20 cm
£1.80

2 $y = 5x$. Find the value of y when:
  a $x = 3$ **b** $x = 5$ **c** $x = 7$

3 Calculate the values of t^2 and $\sqrt{t}$ when:
  a $t = 4$ **b** $t = 9$ **c** $t = 25$

4 Solve these equations for k:
  a $10 = 2k$ **b** $24 = 6k$ **c** $36 = 4k$

5 Four calculators cost £24. Find the cost of:
  a one calculator **b** five calculators.

6 'When one quantity is directly proportional to another, doubling one doubles the other, and so on.'
  Which of these pairs of quantities are directly proportional?
  a the number of cans of cola and their cost
  b the numbers of hours worked and the pay
  c the average speed on a journey and the time taken to complete it
  d the weight of a person and his or her height
  e the circumference of a circle and its diameter.

7 The quantities in these tables are in direct proportion. List the missing entries.

a
Time (h)	2	3	4	5
Number of items made	12			

b
Speed (km/h)	10	20	40	70
Distance (km)	4			

8 a Write down the gradients $\left(\dfrac{\text{vertical}}{\text{horizontal}}\right)$ of OA and OB.

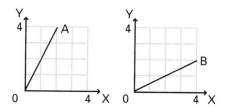

  b Write down the equations $y = \ldots x$ of OA and OB.

9 a Copy and complete this table.

Time passed (T min)	15	30	45	60
Angle ($A°$) turned through by the minute hand				

  b When the time passed is doubled, is the angle doubled?
  c Is the angle directly proportional to the time passed?
  d What angle does the hand turn through in five minutes?

10 a Plot the points in the table on squared paper, using the scales shown.

x	0	1	2	3	4
y	0	3	6	9	12

  b Draw the straight line through the points.
  c Write down:
    (i) the gradient of the line
    (ii) the equation of the line.

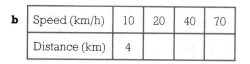

DIRECT PROPORTION CALCULATIONS

Reminders

Number of hours	Distance (km) at 20 km/h
1	20
2	40
3	60
4	80

Doubling the time doubles the distance.
Halving the time halves the distance.
The distance is directly proportional to the time.

EXERCISE 1

1 The cost of parking a car is directly proportional to the number of hours it is parked. Copy and complete:

a
Number of hours	Cost
1	50p
2	
3	
4	

b
Number of hours	Cost
1	75p
2	
4	
8	

2 List the entries in the second row of each table.
  a Cost of books at £6 each:

Number of books	1	2	3	4	5
Cost (£)	6				

  b Bicycle hire at £5 a day:

Number of days	1	2	5	7	14
Cost (£)					

3 Dave walks 12 km in three hours. At the same speed, how far would he walk in:
  a one hour   **b** two hours   **c** five hours?

4 Amy cycles 80 km in four hours. At the same speed, how far would she cycle in:
  a one hour   **b** two hours   **c** three hours?

5 Glynis pays £2.82 for 3 m of ribbon. How much would she pay for:
  a 1 m   **b** 2 m   **c** 7 m?

6 50 bricks make a wall 0.5 m long. How many bricks are needed for a wall of length:
  a 1 m   **b** 4 m   **c** 6 m?

7 Ian earns £60 in eight hours. To find how much he would earn in ten hours, copy and complete:

$$8 \text{ hours} \longleftrightarrow £60$$
$$1 \text{ hour} \longleftrightarrow £\tfrac{60}{8}$$
$$10 \text{ hours} \longleftrightarrow £\tfrac{60}{8} \times \ldots = £\ldots$$

8 Six books cost £27. Find the cost of eight copies of the book.

9 Four CDs cost £52. Find the cost of seven CDs.

10 30 m of carpet costs £540. How much would 24 m cost?

11 Bette drove 18 km in 15 minutes. How far would she travel in 20 minutes at the same speed?

12 £5 can be exchanged for $9 (dollars). How many dollars can be given in exchange for £21 at the same rate?

13 The height of the building is directly proportional to the number of storeys. Calculate the height of the right-hand part of the block of flats.

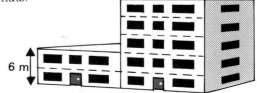

6 m

14 Mark is making scrambled eggs for two. He uses 2 eggs, 8 g butter and 50 ml of milk. How much of each should he use for:
a four people **b** six people **c** just himself?

15 The length of the shadow cast by an object is directly proportional to its height. A man 200 cm tall casts a shadow 50 cm long. Calculate:
a the length of the shadow of a house 10 m high
b the height of a tree which casts a shadow 120 cm long.

16 In which of the following can you say that one quantity is directly proportional to the other? Where they are proportional, use the symbol ∝ ; for example $y \propto x$.
a The height of a building (H m), and the number of identical floors (N).
b The height of a man (H m), and his age (A years).
c The thickness of a book (t mm), and the number of pages (n).
d The distance cycled (D km), and the speed (S km/h).
e The distance cycled (D km) at a steady speed, and the time taken (T h).

17 Can you think of two or three more examples of direct proportion between two quantities?

DIRECT PROPORTION GRAPHS

/ **CLASS DISCUSSION**

In chapter 1 you saw that the equation of a straight line through the origin is of the form $y = ax$, where a is the gradient of the line. Examples are $y = 2x$, $y = \frac{1}{2}x$, $y = -x$, and so on.
x and y behave in the same way—if you double one, you double the other; halve one, halve the other, etc.

So y is directly proportional to x, and we write $y \propto x$, or $y = kx$, where k is a constant.

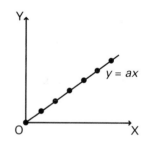

Example

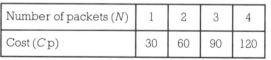

Number of packets (N)	1	2	3	4
Cost (C p)	30	60	90	120

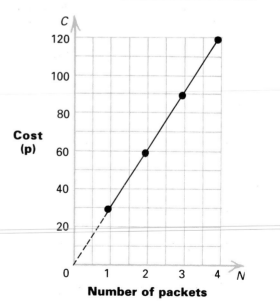

Number of packets

Emma can show that C is proportional to N, either by:
(i) plotting the points, and seeing that **they lie on a straight line through the origin,** *or*
(ii) checking that **all the gradient ratios are equal**: $\frac{30}{1} = 30, \frac{60}{2} = 30, \frac{90}{3} = 30, \frac{120}{4} = 30$.

So the formula for C is $C = 30N$ (compare $y = ax$).

EXERCISE 2

1 Sophie uses the table below to draw the currency conversion graph.

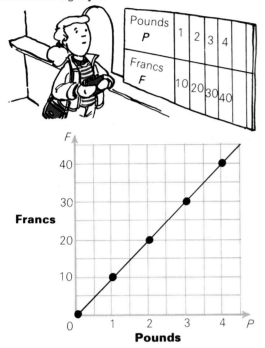

Pounds P	1	2	3	4
Francs F	10	20	30	40

a How does the graph show that the number of francs is directly proportional to the number of £s?

b Check that all gradient ratios, $\frac{10}{1}, \frac{20}{2}, \ldots$ are equal.

c Comparing '$y = ax$', copy and complete $F = \ldots P$.

2 The graph below shows the cost of yoghurts.

a Describe the graph.

b Is the cost directly proportional to the number of yoghurts?

c Write down the gradient of the line.

d Copy and complete the formula for C, $C = \ldots N$.

e Calculate the cost of five yoghurts.

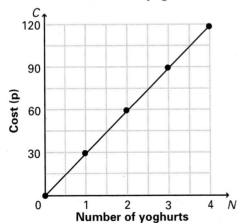

3 Karl hopes to raise funds for the school minibus by making greetings cards. He draws a graph to show his target.

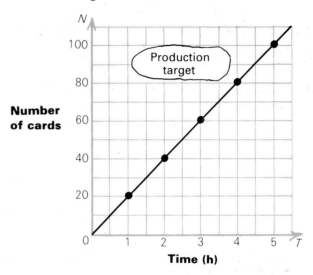

Production target

a Is N directly proportional to T? Why?

b Use the graph to help you copy and complete $N = \ldots T$.

c Estimate the number of cards made in 12 hours.

4 The graph below shows the annual interest the Western Bank gives on £100, £200, £300 and £400.

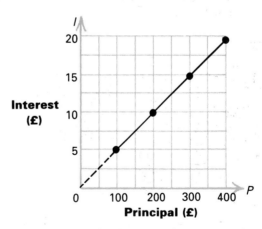

a Use the graph to copy and complete this table:

Money in bank (£)	100	200	300	400
Interest (£)	5			

b Check that all the gradient ratios are equal.

c Copy and complete:

(i) I is . . . . to P.

(ii) $I = \ldots P$.

d Calculate the interest on £750.

103

5

a Jim claims that his price (£P) is directly proportional to the height (H ft) of his Christmas trees. Do you agree? Give a reason.

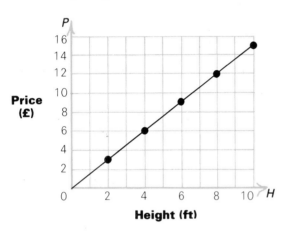

Height (ft)

b Write down the gradient of the line.
c Copy and complete the formula for P,
  $P = \ldots H$.
d Calculate the cost of a 22-foot tree.

6

Number of books (N)	5	10	15	20	25
Cost (£C)	25	50	75	100	125

a Check that C is directly proportional to N by:
  (i) calculating all the 'gradient ratios'
  (ii) drawing a graph, using the scales shown.

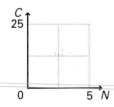

b Copy and complete:
  $C = \ldots N$.
c Calculate the cost of 38 books.

7

Ohm, a French scientist, claimed that in an electrical circuit, the current is directly proportional to the voltage. Viv and Sally got these results in an experiment.

Voltage (V volts)	0	1	2	3	4	5
Current (I amps)	0	3	6	9	12	15

a Draw a graph of I against V.

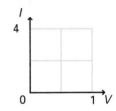

b Why can you say that the scientist was correct?
c Find a formula for I, $I = \ldots V$.
d Calculate I when $V = 3.8$.

8 Tom prints copies of the school newspaper on the duplicator.

Here is his record.

Time (t minutes)	2	4	6	8	12
Number printed (n)	50	100	150	200	300

a Draw a graph of n against t.

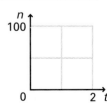

b Copy and complete:
  (i) $\ldots$ is directly proportional to $\ldots$
  (ii) $n = \ldots t$.
c How many copies had he printed after nine minutes?

DIRECT PROPORTION FORMULAE AND CALCULATIONS

The number of washing machines made (M) is directly proportional to the number of working days (D).
(Double the number of days, double the number of machines.)
So $M = kD$ (compare $y = ax$).
If 120 machines are made in three days, then
$120 = k \times 3$, and $k = 40$.
So the formula for M is $M = 40D$.

Note: **'y is proportional to x' and 'y varies as x' mean the same thing. In either case, $y \propto x$ or $y = kx$.**

Example
y varies directly as x, and $y = 10$ when $x = 2$.

a Find a formula for y.
b Calculate y when $x = 7$.

a $y = kx$
So $10 = k \times 2$, and $k = 5$.
The formula is $y = 5x$
b $y = 5 \times 7 = 35$

EXERCISE 3

1 y is directly proportional to x, so $y = kx$.
When $y = 20$, $x = 4$.
a Find a formula for y.
b Calculate y when $x = 5$.

2 s varies directly as t, so $s = kt$.
When $s = 30$, $t = 10$.
a Find a formula for s.
b Calculate s when $t = 8$.

3 y varies directly as x, and $y = 36$ when $x = 9$.
a Find a formula for y.
b Calculate y when $x = 1$.

4 p is directly proportional to q, and $p = 48$ when $q = 6$.
a Find a formula for p.
b Calculate p when $q = 25$.

5 The distance (d km) that Sally cycles varies directly as her speed (s km/h). So $d = ks$. She cycles 8 km at an average speed of 8 km/h.
a Find a formula for d.
b How far would she cycle at 9 km/h?

6 The number (n) of students served in the canteen varies directly as the time taken (t minutes). So $n = kt$. 200 students are served in 40 minutes.
a Find a formula for n.
b How many could be served in 50 minutes?

7 The mass of cement (c kg) varies directly as the mass of sand (s kg) in the mixture.
4 kg cement needs 1 kg sand.
a Find a formula for c.
b How much cement can be made from $2\frac{1}{2}$ kg sand?

8 The cost (£C) of glass varies directly as its area (A m²). The cost is £18 for 3 m².
a Find a formula for C.
b Calculate the cost of 8 m² of glass.

9 The number of dollars (d) varies directly as the number of £s (p) exchanged. You can get three dollars for £2.
a Find a formula for d.
b How many dollars would you get for £12?

10 Brian's pay (£P) varies directly as the number of hours (H) he has worked. His pay is £56 when he works for eight hours.
a Find a formula for P.
b Calculate his pay when he works for 20 hours.

11 Eastern Education Authority estimated that the number of teachers needed (t) varied directly as the number of students (s). There were 30 teachers in a school with 750 students.
a Find a formula for t.
b How many teachers are needed for 900 students?

DIRECT PROPORTION: $y \propto x^2$ AND $y \propto \sqrt{x}$

This new car is being tested. The distance it travels is noted every second.

Time (t seconds)	0	1	2	3	4
Distance (d metres)	0	2	8	18	32

d is *not* directly proportional to t; how can you tell?

The second table shows that d is directly proportional to t^2. How can you tell?

t^2	0	1	4	9	16
d	0	2	8	18	32

So $d = kt^2$
$2 = k \times 1^2$
$k = 2$, and the formula is $d = 2t^2$.

Example
The distance (d km) to the horizon varies as the square root of the height (h m) of the observer above sea level.
The distance is 5.2 km from a height of 4 m.
a Find the formula connecting d and h.
b Calculate the distance from a height of 9 m.

a $d = k\sqrt{h}$
$5.2 = k\sqrt{4}$
$5.2 = k \times 2$
$k = 2.6$
$d = 2.6\sqrt{h}$

b $d = 2.6\sqrt{h}$
$= 2.6\sqrt{9}$
$= 3 \times 2.6$
$= 7.8$
The distance is 7.8 km.

EXERCISE 4B

1 y varies directly as x^2, so $y = kx^2$.
When $y = 20$, $x = 2$.
a Find the formula connecting y and x.
b Calculate y when $x = 3$.

2 p varies as q^2, and $p = 16$ when $q = 4$.
a Find the formula connecting p and q.
b Calculate p when $q = 0.1$.

3 m varies as $\sqrt{n}$, so $m = k\sqrt{n}$.
When $m = 15$, $n = 25$.
a Find the formula connecting m and n.
b Calculate m when $n = 36$.

4 s varies as $\sqrt{t}$, and $s = 20$ when $t = 16$.
a Find the formula connecting s and t.
b Calculate s when $t = 100$.

5 a In one of these tables, $y \propto x$ and in the other $y \propto x^2$. Which is which?

(i)

x	1	2	3
y	2	8	18

(ii)

x	1	2	3
y	4	8	12

b Use the equations $y = kx$ and $y = kx^2$ to find the formulae connecting y and x in the two tables.

6 The mass (w grams) of a metal bar varies directly as the square of its diameter (d mm). The mass is 500 g when the diameter is 10 mm.
a Find the formula connecting w and d.
b Calculate w when $d = 12$.

7

The cost (c pence) of producing the *Millennium* magazine varies directly as the square root of the number of pages (n). 25 pages cost 35p to produce.
a Find the formula connecting c and n.
b Calculate the cost of producing a magazine with 36 pages.

8 The distance (s metres) through which a heavy body falls from rest varies as the square of the time (t seconds) taken. It falls 20 m in two seconds. How far will the body fall from rest in six seconds?

9 The safe speed (v m/s) at which a train can round a curve of radius r metres varies as $\sqrt{r}$. If the safe speed for a radius of 100 m is 20 m/s, calculate the safe speed for a radius of 121 m.

10 The time of swing (T seconds) of a pendulum varies as the square root of the length (L cm) of the pendulum. When the length is 81 cm the time of swing is 1.8 seconds. Calculate the time of swing for a pendulum 49 cm long.

11 Jenny's hobby is parachute jumping. This table shows the distance she falls in the first five seconds.

Time (t seconds)	1	2	3	4	5
Distance (d m)	4	16	36	64	100

a Show that $d \propto t^2$ by calculating ratios.
b Draw a graph of values of d against t^2.
c Write down:
   (i) the gradient of the graph   (ii) its equation.
d How far will she fall in ten seconds?

INVERSE PROPORTION

Pat's class are planning a 'Spot the Ball' competition for charity. The prize-money of £40 is to be divided among the winners.

What happens if there is more than one winner?

Each winner gets less. Look at the table.

Looks like inverse proportion, double one, halve the other.

Number of winners (N)	1	2	4	5	8	10	20	40
Prize for each (£P)	40	20	10	8	5	4	2	1

Check that for each pair of entries in the table $N \times P = 40$.

If y is inversely proportional to x, then:
(i) doubling x halves y (ii) halving x doubles y (iii) $x \times y = $ constant.

Example
At 40 words per minute, Margaret took nine hours to type a story.
How long would she take if she typed at 60 words per minute?

Doubling her speed halves her time, so this is inverse proportion.

40 words per minute ⟷ 9 hours
 1 word per minute ⟷ 9 × 40 hours
60 words per minute ⟷ $\frac{360}{6}$ = 6 hours

She would take six hours.   (*Common sense check*: Faster speed, so less time)

EXERCISE 5

1 In which table is *y* inversely proportional to *x* (doubling *x* halves *y*, or *x* × *y* = constant)?

a

x	1	2	4
y	5	10	20

b

x	1	2	4
y	12	6	3

2 *y* is inversely proportional to *x*. Copy and complete the tables below.

a

x	1	2	4	8
y	24			

b

x	20	10	5	1
y	3			

3 A £20 prize is shared out equally. How much is each share if there are:
  a two winners
  b five winners
  c ten winners?

4 Three winners each receive £12.
  a What is the total prize money?
  b How much would each winner receive if the money was shared equally between:
    (i) two   (ii) four   (iii) six winners?

5 At 6 m/s a journey takes 20 minutes. How long would it take at 10 m/s?
Copy and complete:
  6 m/s ⟷ 20 minutes
  1 m/s ⟷ 20 × 6 = . . . minutes

  10 m/s ⟷ $\dfrac{...}{10}$ = . . . minutes

(*Check:* Faster speed, shorter time.)

6 Three men turf a lawn in two hours.
  a Would one man take more or less time? How long?
  b How long would two men take? Set out your working as in question **5**.

7 Five pupils cleared the chairs after assembly in 12 minutes. Assuming that the number of pupils and the number of minutes are in inverse proportion, calculate the time four pupils would take.

8 Eight helpers deliver leaflets to an estate in 60 minutes. How long would the task take if there were two more helpers?

9 Six people win a competition and each receives £120. If there had been only five winners how much would each have received?

10 The librarian can buy 60 books costing £8 each. How many could she buy if they cost £12 each?

11 Clearview Double Glazing are posting adverts to local households. It took two staff six hours to put the adverts into envelopes. How many staff would be needed if the job had to be done in four hours?

12 The length of a rectangle of given area is inversely proportional to its breadth. For a length of 8 cm the breadth is 6 cm. Calculate the length for a breadth of 4 cm.

13 The waiting time in supermarket queues is inversely proportional to the number of check-outs which are open. For four check-outs the time was 10 minutes. How many check-outs are needed to reduce the time to 8 minutes?

14 For which of the following can you say that one quantity is inversely proportional to the other?
  a The time taken to deliver a batch of leaflets, and the number of people delivering them.
  b Company sales, and the money spent on advertising.
  c The distance walked at a steady speed, and the time taken.
  d The distance walked in a certain time, and the speed.
  e The number of people on a job and the time taken to do it.
  f The time and speed on a journey of fixed length.

CHECK-UP ON PROPORTION IN PRACTICE

1 The circumference of a circle is directly proportional to the diameter. What is the effect on the circumference if the diameter is:
a doubled   **b** halved?

2 List the values of y in the table if y is directly proportional to x.

x	2	4	6	8	10
y	12				

3 If he does eight hours overtime Ahmed earns £120. How much would he earn for eleven hours overtime?

4 In the seventeenth century, Isaac Newton studied the connection between the force on a body and its acceleration. A science class tried the same experiment, and drew this graph.

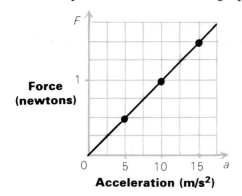

a Why can they say that the force is directly proportional to the acceleration?
b Calculate the gradient of the line.
c Copy and complete: $F = \ldots a$.
d Calculate the force for an acceleration of 40 m/s².

5 y is directly proportional to x, and $y = 14$ when $x = 7$.
a Find a formula for y.
b Calculate y when $x = 9$.

6 The weekly bonus (£B) at Sparks' factory varies directly as the weekly profit (£P). On a profit of £20 000, a bonus of £500 is paid.
a Find a formula for B.
b Calculate the bonus for a profit of £25 000.

7

A Youth Club hires a coach for an outing to the seaside. The cost (£C) varies directly as the square root of the time (T hours) it is hired. The cost for four hours is £60.
a Find the formula connecting C and T.
b Calculate the cost for nine hours.

8 The acceleration of this model train is inversely proportional to the number of coaches.

The acceleration is 20 units for five coaches. Calculate the acceleration for eight coaches.

9 Six cleaners can clean the school in two hours. How long would four cleaners take?

10 Harry makes wheels, and finds this table useful:

Number of spokes (N)	4	6	8	10	12
Angle between them ($A°$)	90	60			

a Copy and complete the table.
b Calculate the angle Harry will use for a wheel with 15 spokes.

11

Number of books (N)	5	10	15	20	25
Cost (£C)	15	30	45	60	75

a Check that C is directly proportional to N by:
  (i) calculating ratios
  (ii) drawing a graph.
b Find the formula connecting C and N.
c Calculate:
  (i) the cost of 35 books
  (ii) the number of books that can be bought with £54.

9 ANGLES IN A CIRCLE

1

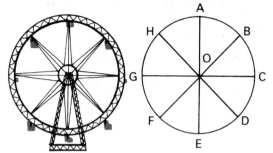

The spokes on the Big Wheel are equally spaced. So are the radii OA, OB, OC, ... in the circle, which has centre O.
a How many radii are there?
b What size is:
  (i) $\angle$AOC (ii) $\angle$BOC (iii) $\angle$BOD?
c The radius of the Big Wheel (OA) is eight metres. How long is its diameter (AOE)?

2 Calculate x.

a

b

3 Calculate a, b, c, d.

4 What is the sum of the three angles in a triangle—how many degrees?

5 Sketch these triangles, and fill in the sizes of all their angles.

a

b
Right-angled triangle

c
Isosceles triangle

d
Equilateral triangle

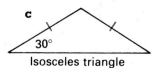

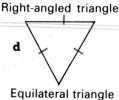

6 a Use Pythagoras' Theorem to complete
  $x^2 = \ldots + \ldots$
b Calculate x if $y = 8$ and $z = 6$.

7 Calculate the length, w metres, of the wire.

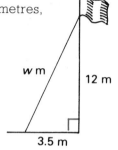

8 a Copy and complete:

  $\sin A =$ ——, $\cos A =$ ——, $\tan A =$ ——.

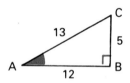

b Calculate angle A, correct to 0.1°.

9 Calculate the height, h metres, of the car ramp, to the nearest metre.

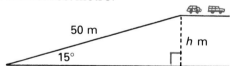

10 a Sketch this rectangle, and fill in:
  (i) all the right angles
  (ii) the lengths of all the lines.

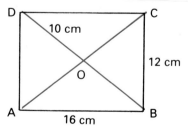

b Draw a circle, with centre O, passing through the vertices A, B, C and D of the rectangle. What is the length of the circle's:
  (i) diameter (ii) radius?

EXERCISE 1/CLASS DISCUSSION

1 Circles are all around us. Find some examples in these pictures.

2 List some other circular objects.

3 Copy this diagram, and label the centre, diameter and circumference, also a radius and an arc.

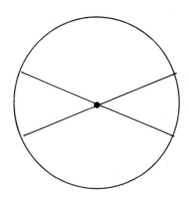

4 If the radius is 2.5 cm long, what length is the diameter?

5 *Trace* the circle. Turn it about the centre. Do you find that the circle always fits its outline?

6 In how many ways can each shape fit into the hole, without turning the shape over?

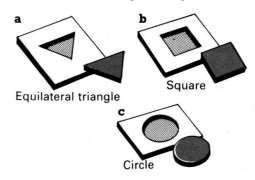

Equilateral triangle   Square   Circle

7 Which of these would make suitable wheels for a bicycle?

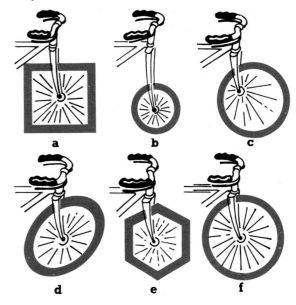

a   b   c

d   e   f

8 What can you say about all the spokes on a suitable wheel?

9 So what then can you say about all the radii in a circle?

10 Draw a diagram of this steering wheel, and mark the equal radius 'spokes'.

Steering wheel

111

ANGLES AND CHORDS

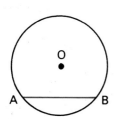

AB is a **chord** in the circle, centre O.

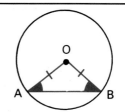

OA = OB (equal radii)

So △**OAB is isosceles**, and ∠OAB = ∠OBA.

Note In this chapter, O is the centre of each circle.

EXERCISE 2

1 In each circle below, name:
  (i) the equal radii
  (ii) the isosceles triangle
  (iii) the equal angles.

a 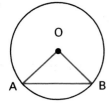   **b**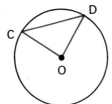

2 Calculate *a* and *b* in these diagrams.

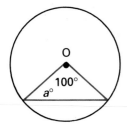

3 Calculate *c* and *d* below.

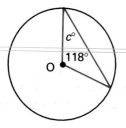   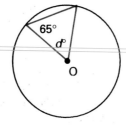

4 Calculate *e* and *f*.

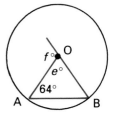

5 Calculate *g* and *h*.

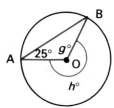

6 The angle at the centre of the steering wheel has to be 255° to give a clear view of the instruments. Calculate *m* and *n*.

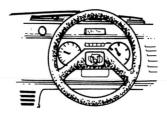

7 Calculate the angles *p*° and *q*° at the centre of the circle.

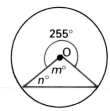   

8 The angle AOB of the lighthouse beam is 72°. Calculate the angles in the circle at A and B.

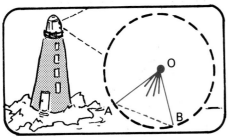

Lighthouse beam

9 Eight wedges of cheese spread fill the circular box. Calculate: **a** x **b** y.

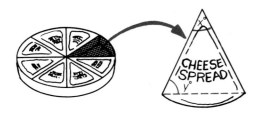

10 a In isosceles △OAC, calculate x.
b In isosceles △OBC, calculate y.
c What is the value of $x° + y°$?

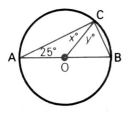

11 Sketch each of these four diagrams, and fill in the sizes of all the angles.

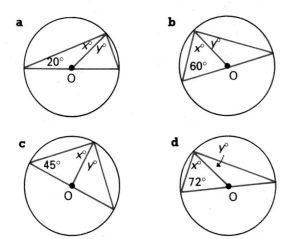

a   20° $x°$ $y°$ O

b $x°$ $y°$ 60°   O

c   45° $x°$ $y°$ O

d $y°$ $x°$ 72°   O

What is the value of $x + y$ for each circle?

---

1 a Draw a fairly large circle, and mark its centre.
b Use compasses to mark off two equal chords.

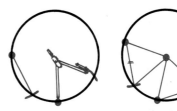

c Draw the angle at the centre facing each chord.
d Measure the two angles at the centre. What do you find?

2 a Think of a way to construct this square in the circle. Draw the square.

b Could you draw a hexagon with equal sides in the circle? Draw it.

3 To make a wheel disc, eight holes have to be drilled, equally spaced, in a circle of diameter 30 cm.
a Make a scale drawing to show this, using a scale of 1 cm to 5 cm. Find the distance between a pair of neighbouring holes in the disc.

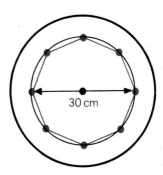

30 cm

b If you want a real challenge, use trigonometry to calculate the distance, correct to 0.1 cm. You'll have to join the two points to the centre, and then split the triangle into two right-angled triangles.

ANGLES IN A SEMICIRCLE

EXERCISE 3

1 *Practical*

  a Draw a semicircle, with radius at least 4 cm long.

  b Mark any point P on the circumference.

  c Join PA and PB.

  d Measure ∠APB.

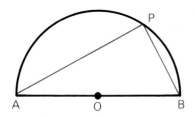

2 Try question **1** again for different sizes of semicircles, and different points on the circumference.

What do you find about the size of ∠APB each time?

3 O is the centre of the circle. What can you say about the lengths of:

  a the diameters AC and BD

  b the radii OA, OB, OC and OD?

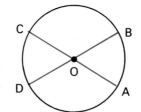

4 a What kinds of quadrilateral have equal diagonals that bisect each other?

  b What size are the angles at their corners?

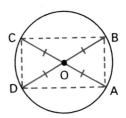

5 In the diagram below, ∠ABC is an angle in a semicircle, and BO meets the circle at D.

  a What do you know about the lines AC and BD?

  b What type of quadrilateral is ABCD?

  c What size is ∠ABC?

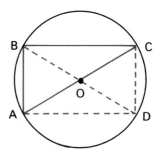

EXERCISE 4

Every angle in a semicircle is a right angle.

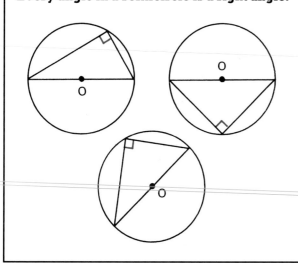

1 Calculate *x* in each diagram.

  a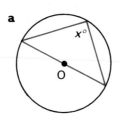

  b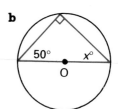

  c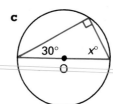

  d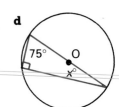

2 a Name the right angle.
  b Calculate *r* and *s*.

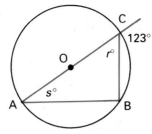

3 a Name the right angle in this diagram.
  b Calculate *t* and *u*.

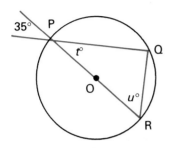

4 Sketch the diagrams below, and fill in the sizes of all the angles. (Mark the right angles in the semicircles first.)

a

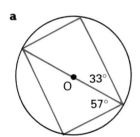

b

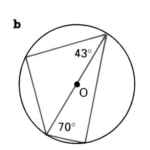

c

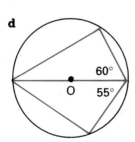

d

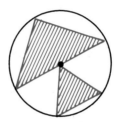

e

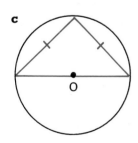

f

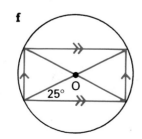

5 The semicircular roof of the tunnel needs repairs. Struts are put in to support it.

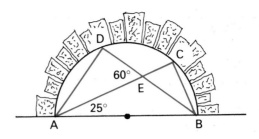

  a Name the two right angles.
  b Make a sketch, and fill in the sizes of all the angles.

6 The Orienteering Club have a logo which is based on a circle and two isosceles triangles. Make a sketch, and fill in all the angles.

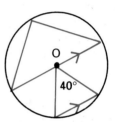

7 Sketch these diagrams, mark the right angles, and fill in the sizes of all the angles. In **a**, AC = CB.

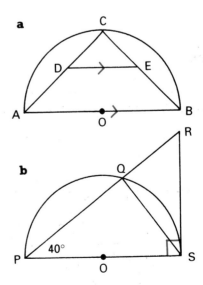

EXERCISE 5

Using Pythagoras' Theorem in 'semicircle triangles'.

Example
Calculate *d*.

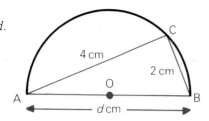

∠ACB = 90° (∠ in a semicircle)
$d^2 = 4^2 + 2^2$ (Pythagoras)
$d = 4.5$, correct to 1 decimal place.

1 In each diagram, name the right angle, then calculate *x*.

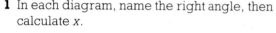

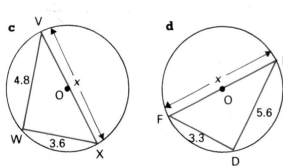

2 Again name the right angle, and calculate *s* (not the hypotenuse this time).

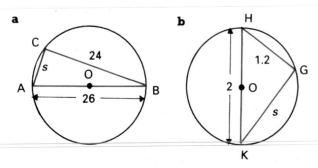

3 Calculate *y*, correct to 1 decimal place.

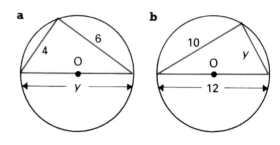

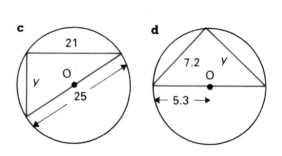

4 A row of semicircular cloches protects plants from frost. Each end is held on by a bent wire ABC. AB = 20 cm and AC = 52 cm. Calculate:
a BC   **b** the length of the wire.

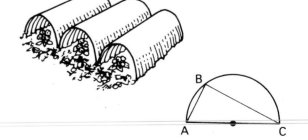

EXERCISE 6

Using trigonometry in 'semicircle triangles'.

Example
Calculate x.

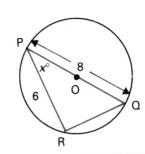

Reminder

SOH -
CAH -
TOA

$\angle PRQ = 90°$ ($\angle$ in a semicircle)
$\cos x° = \frac{6}{8}$
   $x = 41$, to the nearest whole number.

1 In each part of this question:
  (i) name the right angle and the hypotenuse
  (ii) calculate x, to the nearest whole number.

(In **a** use $\tan x°$, in **b** use $\sin x°$.)

a
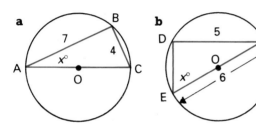

b

2 (i) Name the right angle and the hypotenuse.
  (ii) Calculate y, correct to 1 decimal place.

a
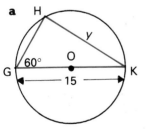

b
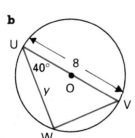

3 In each diagram calculate, correct to 1 decimal place: (i) d (ii) m.

a
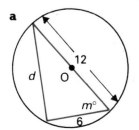

b
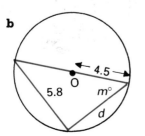

4 A modern rocking-recliner chair has semicircular ends. Calculate:
  a the length p metres of the arm-rest
  b the angle $x°$, to the nearest degree.

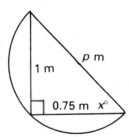

CHALLENGE

The sketch shows the end wall of a factory building.

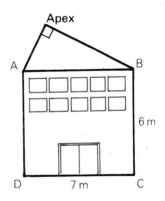

a *Make a scale drawing of the rectangular part ABCD, using a scale of 1 cm to 1 m. The angle at the apex of the roof has to be 90°.*
b *On your scale drawing, draw a semicircle with diameter AB. Why will the apex have to be somewhere on this semicircle?*
c *The longer side of the roof has to be 6 m. Complete your scale drawing.*
d *Measure the shorter side of the roof in your drawing as accurately as you can. What is its actual length? Check by calculation.*

TANGENTS TO A CIRCLE

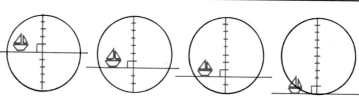

Looking through a telescope, Margot sees a yacht on the horizon. The vertical diameter is at right angles to the horizon.

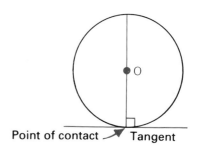

She tilts the telescope up, and the horizon appears to move down until it just touches the bottom of the circle. In this position, the horizon is a **tangent** to the circle.

A tangent is perpendicular to the radius at the point of contact.

Point of contact → Tangent

EXERCISE 7A

1 *Practical*
  a Use compasses to draw a circle, centre O.
  b Mark any point T outside the circle.
  c Draw a tangent TA, touching the circle at A.
  d Join OA, and measure ∠OAT.

2 Repeat question **1** for different tangents or different circles. What do you find?

AT is a tangent in each diagram below.

3 For these two diagrams, name the right angle, then calculate *x*.

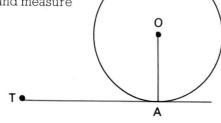

a

b

4 Sketch each diagram, then fill in the sizes of all the angles.

a

T ⟋ 44°
A
O

b

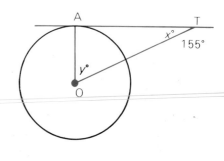

O
69°
T   A

5 In this diagram, name the right angle, then calculate *x* and *y*.

A   T
x°
155°
y°
O

6 Use Pythagoras' Theorem to calculate d, correct to 1 decimal place:

a

b

c

d

7 Use trigonometry to calculate the size of $\angle$ ATO in each diagram in question **6**, to the nearest degree.

8 a Write down:
  (i) the name of the right angle
  (ii) the lengths of OS and OT
  b Calculate:
  (i) the length of AT
  (ii) the size of angle AOT, to the nearest degree.

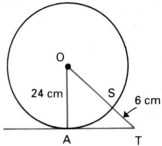

EXERCISE 7B

1 Time for a tea-break. Badi drops the shaft of the roller onto the ground. The shaft is 2.05 m long, and the *diameter* of the roller is 90 cm. Calculate PQ.

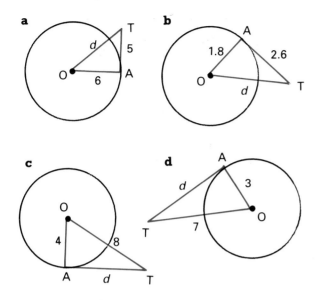

2 Jodi is drawing a plan for a large ice-cream sign. She makes the radius of the circle 25 cm long, and the length of the tangent BC 60 cm. Calculate:
  a OB
  b the distance from B to the top of the circle.

3 △ABC is isosceles, with AB = AC. Its sides are tangents to the circle.
  a Calculate angles ABC and ACB.
  b What size are angles OEC and ODC? Why?
  c Calculate $\angle$ DOE.

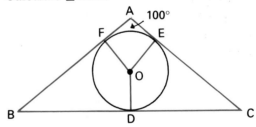

4 The twins have made a seesaw by bolting a plank to an old oil drum, centre O.
  a The plank is 4 m long. What is the length of AB, in centimetres?
  b The radius of the drum is 30 cm. Sketch △AOB, mark the lengths of AB and OB, then calculate OA, to the nearest cm.

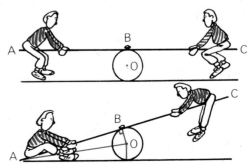

119

5 'Give me a place to stand, and I'll move the Earth',
said Archimedes (who lived in the third
century BC).
Calculate, to the nearest 100 km:
  a OB   **b** AB.

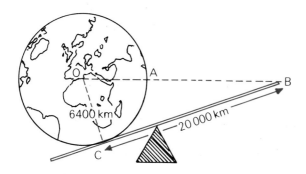

6 Sketch these diagrams, mark the right angles
between tangents and radii, then fill in all the
angles.

a   **b**

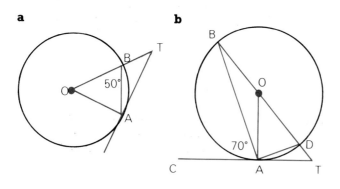

a *Draw △ABC with BC 3 cm long, ∠B = 50°,
∠C = 70° and ∠A = 60°.*

b *Draw pairs of lines at A, B and C which bisect the
angles at A, B and C. These lines meet at D, E, F
and G.*

c *Draw circles with centres D, E, F and G to touch
the sides of △ABC, or the sides produced.*

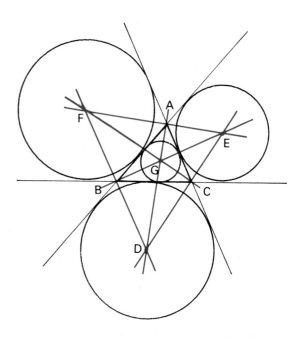

CHECK-UP ON ANGLES IN A CIRCLE

1 Draw a circle with centre O and radius 2 cm. In it draw a:

a radius OA   **b** diameter BOC
c chord AC   **d** tangent AT

2 Calculate *x* in each diagram below.

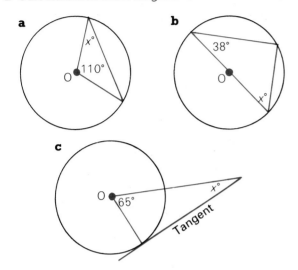

a

b   38°   *x*°

c   O   65°   *x*°   Tangent

3 a Make a sketch, and fill in all the angles.
b Calculate $x° + y°$. Why would you expect this answer?
c What is the length of the radius of the circle? Explain how you know.

O   60°   *x*°   *y*°   2.8 cm

4 (i) Name the right angle and hypotenuse in each triangle.
   (ii) Calculate *n*, correct to 1 decimal place.

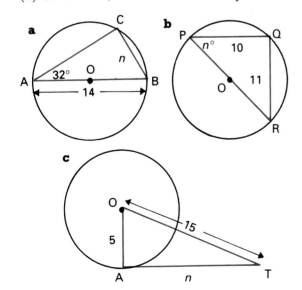

a   C   *n*   A   32°   O   B   14

b   P   *n*°   10   Q   O   11   R

c   O   5   15   A   *n*   T

5 Make a sketch, and fill in all the angles.

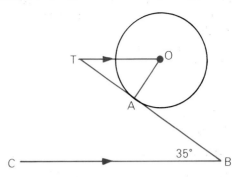

T   O   A   35°   C   B

6 One of Jack's tyres is punctured. He has left it in the garage for repair—it is leaning against the wall. The radius of the tyre is 30 cm.

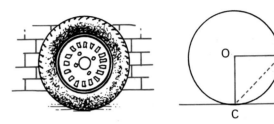

O   A   C   B

a Explain why each angle in OABC is a right angle.
b Calculate AC, to the nearest cm.

7 The aircraft is on a path parallel to the Earth's surface. The angle of depression of the horizon is 50°. Calculate the angle *x*° at the centre of the Earth.

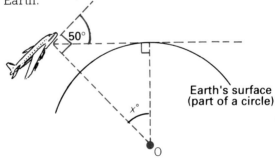

50°   Earth's surface (part of a circle)   *x*°   O

8 Hassan has organised a game of darts. He opens the close-fitting doors. The diameter of the dartboard is 44 cm. Calculate, to the nearest cm, the distance from O, the centre of the bull's eye, to:

a R   **b** Q   **c** P.

301   301   301   P   Q   R

LOOKING BACK

1 This bag contains nine discs, numbered 1, 2, . . . 9. One is drawn out at random. Calculate:

a P(1)
b P(odd number)
c P(square number)
d P(number less than 8).

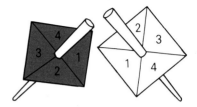

2 a When the spinner stops, what is:
(i) P(Win)   (ii) P(Lose)?

b Copy the number line below, and label P(Win) and P(Lose).

c How many times would you expect to win in 40 spins?

3 The tree diagram, based on national statistics, shows the probability of a student catching measles last year.

0.01 — P (catching measles)

P (not catching measles)

a Copy the diagram, and fill in the probability of not catching measles last year.
b In a school of six hundred students, how many would you expect to have had measles last year?

4 a What was the probability that a book would be overdue?
b In March, 6500 books were issued. How many were likely to be overdue on return?

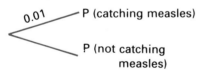

LIBRARIAN'S REPORT ON OVERDUE BOOKS
Last year, on average only 12 out of every 100 books issued were overdue.

5

The numbers on the two spinners are added to find the total score.

a Copy and complete the table.

Black spinner

+	1	2	3	4
1	2	3		
2	3			
3				
4				

Red spinner

b Calculate:
(i) P(total of 3)   (ii) P(total of 4)
(iii) P(total of 3 or 4).
c What is the connection between your answers in **b**?

6 Jane passes some traffic lights on her way to work.

a She has calculated that when she arrives at the lights, P(red) = 0.5, P(amber) = 0.3 and P(green) = 0.2.
How do you think she worked this out?
b Calculate:
(i) P(red or amber)
(ii) P(red or amber or green)
(iii) P(blue).

7 Draw a tree diagram for the traffic light probabilities in question **6**.

EXERCISE 1A

1

0	0.25	0.5	0.75	1

Copy the number line, and mark the positions of the probability that:

a
A number chosen at random from 1, 2, 4 or 8 is even

b
A coin comes up 'tails' when tossed

c
A year chosen at random is a leap year

d
A letter chosen at random from MATHEMATICS is N

e
This stone will fall when dropped

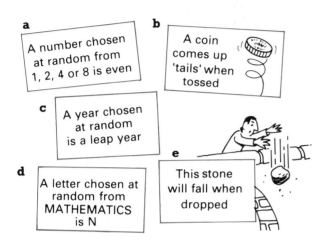

2 The probability of rain within the next twelve hours is 55%. What is the probability that it won't rain?

3

The probability that I'll beat Carol at chess is $\frac{1}{5}$.

If the girls play 20 games of chess, how many would Helen expect to:
a win   **b** lose or draw?

4 Sean finds that the probability that the postman delivers his mail before he leaves for work is 0.7. Estimate how often his mail will arrive before he leaves for work:
a in a week of six post days
b in a month of 26 post days.

5 One of these shapes is chosen at random. Copy and complete the tree diagram.

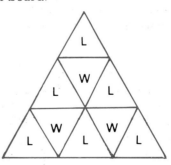

0.3

6 A dart is thrown, and lands at random on this triangular board.

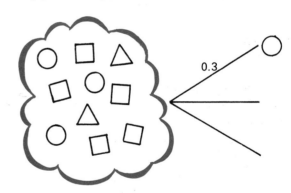

a Calculate:
(i) P(W)   (ii) P(L).
b If 30 darts strike the board at random, how many wins would you expect?

EXERCISE 1B

1 This spinner is unevenly weighted (biased), so that P(W) = 0.5 and P(D) = 0.1.
  a Calculate P(L).
  b In 60 spins, how many:
   (i) Ls   (ii) Ds
   would you expect?

2 Sam carries out electrical repairs. He claims that he can mend 85% of all faults. One month he works on 190 different faults. About how many can he:
  a repair **b** not repair?

3 These bags contain red and white marbles.

One marble is taken at random from each bag.
  a For each bag, draw a tree diagram to show the probabilities of drawing red and white marbles.
  b From which bag are you most likely to take a red marble?

4 A survey of 300 households in one town found that 210 had a car and 255 had a telephone.
  a Estimate the probability that one of the households, chosen at random, had:
   (i) a car   (ii) a telephone.
  b There are 10 000 households in the town. On the basis of the survey, estimate the number of households with:
   (i) a car   (ii) a telephone.

5 A machine makes head-set parts.

When it runs slowly, it makes only a few, all free from defects. When it runs quickly, more of the parts are faulty. The best speed gives P(defect) = 0.1. Should the machine be speeded up, left as it is, or slowed down if there are:
  a 20 defects in 100 parts
  b 20 defects in 300 parts
  c 30 defects in 300 parts?

COMBINED PROBABILITIES

EXERCISE 2

1 Bill passes two sets of traffic lights daily. They work independently, and red, amber and green each last the same time.
  a Copy and complete the table. R and r = red, A and a = amber, G and g = green.

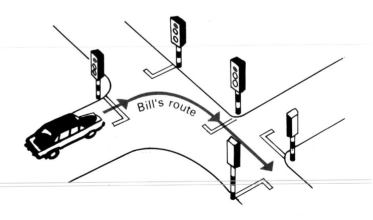

Bill's route

		Second lights		
		R	A	G
First lights	r	(r, R)		
	a			
	g			

  b How many possible outcomes are there?
  c Calculate the probability that:
   (i) both lights are green
   (ii) at least one is green
   (iii) one is amber and one is red.

2 Sedhar is equally likely to take the left or right road at each junction.

Axbury
Beeton
Carport
Darpool

a Copy and complete this tree diagram.

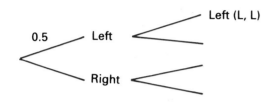

Left (L, L)
0.5   Left
Right

b Where does she arrive if she chooses:
   (i) Left, Left   (ii) Right, Left?
c Calculate the probability that she arrives at Beeton.

3 In a game, a disc is marked Home (H) on one side and Away (A) on the other, and a spinner is marked W, D, L. The disc is tossed and the spinner is spun.

	W	D	L
H			
A			

a Copy and complete the table.
b Calculate:
   (i) P(a Home Win)
   (ii) P(a Win at Home or Away).
c Two points are given for a Win and one for a Draw. Calculate P(at least one point).
d Copy and complete this tree diagram.

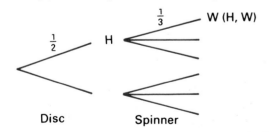

$\frac{1}{3}$ W (H, W)
$\frac{1}{2}$ H
Disc   Spinner

4 There are two drawers, each containing a knife, fork and spoon. Teresa takes one item at random from each drawer.
a In a table, list all the possible pairs she can take out.
b Calculate:
   (i) P(two knives)   (ii) P(both items the same)
   (iii) P(a knife and a fork).
c Construct a tree diagram.

5 Stuart's bike has three forward gears and six rear gears.

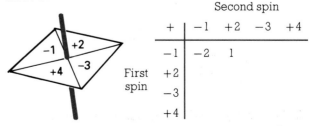

Rear gears
Forward gears

a Copy and complete the table.

		Rear gears					
		1	2	3	4	5	6
Forward gears	H	(H, 1)					
	M						
	L						

b If he selects gears at random, calculate the probability of having:
   (i) a low forward gear
   (ii) a high forward and rear gear 6
   (iii) a middle forward and rear gear 4 or less.

6 a Copy and complete this table for the rolling of two dice, one red and one blue.

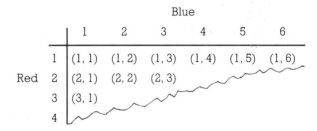

	Blue					
	1	2	3	4	5	6
Red 1	(1, 1)	(1, 2)	(1, 3)	(1, 4)	(1, 5)	(1, 6)
2	(2, 1)	(2, 2)	(2, 3)			
3	(3, 1)					
4						

b How many possible outcomes are there?
c Calculate:
   (i) P(6, 6)   (ii) P(at least one 6)
   (iii) P(red score is greater than blue score).

BRAINSTORMER

The spinner is spun twice, and the two scores are added.

		Second spin			
+		−1	+2	−3	+4
First spin	−1	−2	1		
	+2				
	−3				
	+4				

a *Copy and complete the table.*
b *Calculate:*
   (i) P(positive score)   (ii) P(score of +6)
   (iii) P(score of +6 or more).

RELATIVE FREQUENCY

EXERCISE 3

1 Joe and Terry each toss a coin a number of times. The results are in the table.

	Joe	Terry
Number of Heads	32	55
Number of tosses	80	100

For Joe the **relative frequency** of Heads
$= \frac{32}{80} = 0.4$.

a Calculate the relative frequency for Terry, as a decimal.

b Whose relative frequency is closer to P(H)?

2 Two surveys include questions about central heating in houses in a large town.

	Survey A	Survey B
Number with central heating	45	400
Number of homes in survey	60	500

a Calculate the relative frequency of homes with central heating in each survey.

b Which survey is likely to represent the situation in the whole town better?

3 Amy noted the number of 6s when she rolled a dice a number of times.

Number of 6s	3	6	12	17
Number of rolls	10	25	60	100
Relative frequency				

Calculate:
a the relative frequency of 6 each time
b the probability of 6, correct to 2 decimal places.

The larger the random sample, the closer the relative frequency is to the probability of the event.

4 The table shows results after every 50 spins of this spinner.

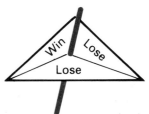

a Copy and complete the table.

Number of wins	16	28	39	50	125
Number of spins	50	100	150	200	500
Relative frequency					

b Is the spinner biased? Explain your answer.
c How many wins would you expect in 1000 spins of the spinner?

5 Statistics show that the probability of twins is 0.0125, correct to 4 decimal places. This table shows the number of sets of twins in three schools.

School	Parkside	Manor Park	Vale High
Number of sets of twins	10	12	14
Number of students	600	1500	1100

a Calculate the relative frequency of sets of twins in each school, correct to 4 decimal places.
b Which school's relative frequency is nearest 0.0125?
c How many sets of twins would you expect in 20 000 births in the areas around each school?

P(A OR B)

Example
A disc is taken at random from the bag.

P(black) = $\frac{3}{12}$, P(white) = $\frac{4}{12}$

P(black or white) = $\frac{3}{12} + \frac{4}{12} = \frac{7}{12}$

When two events are mutually exclusive (they cannot happen at the same time) you can add their probabilities.   P(A or B) = P(A) + P(B).

EXERCISE 4A

1 In the example above, calculate:
   a P(red)   **b** P(black)
   c P(red or black)   **d** P(red or white).

2 A pack of cards is cut at random. Calculate:
   a P(diamond)   **b** P(heart)
   c P(diamond or heart)
   d P(diamond or heart or spade)
   e P(diamond or heart or spade or club).

3 From past records, the probabilities for the highest temperature at Greenport on Christmas day have been worked out.

Temperature (°C)	Probability
<0	0.2
0 to 10	0.7
>10	0.1

Calculate the probability that the temperature on 25th December this year will be:
a 10°C or less   **b** 0°C or more
c < 0°C or > 10°C.

4 This spinner is biased. The table shows the probability of getting each score.

Score	Probability
1	0.15
2	0.25
3	0.4
4	0.2

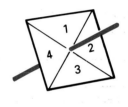

a Calculate:
   (i) P(3 or 4)   (ii) P(1 or 2)   (iii) P(2, 3 or 4).
b In 100 spins, how often would you expect to score:
   (i) 3 or 4   (ii) 1 or 2   (iii) 2, 3 or 4?

5 The winner of a quiz show spins this board to win a prize. All the sectors are equal.

a Calculate:
   (i) P(£100)   (ii) P(TV)   (iii) P(£100 or TV).
b The show takes place once a week. How many times would you expect a TV set or £100 to be won in a year?

EXERCISE 4B

1 Remember that you can add probabilities if the events are mutually exclusive, that is, if they cannot both happen at the same time.
Which of these pairs of events are mutually exclusive?

a Obtaining a Head and obtaining a Tail when a coin is tossed.

b Having a win and having a draw for the result of a football match.

c Getting a 6 and getting an even number when a dice is rolled.

d Getting a total of 6 and getting a total of 7 when a pair of dice are rolled.

e Getting two 6s when two dice are rolled, one after the other.

2 The organisers of a marathon used past data to predict the probability that runners will drop out during the 26 mile race.

Distance (D miles)	Probability
$0 \leqslant D < 10$	0.02
$10 \leqslant D < 15$	0.08
$15 \leqslant D < 20$	0.13
$20 \leqslant D < 23$	0.18
$23 \leqslant D < 26$	0.01

a Calculate the probability that a runner will drop out:
(i) in less than 15 miles
(ii) in less than 20 miles
(iii) at 20 or more miles.

b If 5000 runners start the marathon, how many are expected to finish?

3 a Copy and complete this table for the sums of all possible pairs of scores when two dice are rolled.

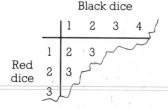
Black dice

b Which sum is:
(i) most likely   (ii) least likely?

c Calculate: P(2), P(3), P(4), . . . , P(12).

d Calculate: (i) P(10 or over)   (ii) P(4 or less).

4 To play Monopoly you need two dice, and you have to pay rent if your total score on the two dice is 7, 9 or 10. Use the table of totals for two dice you made in question **3** to calculate:

a P(you have to pay rent)

b P(you do not have to pay rent).

/**BRAINSTORMER**

The probabilities of the spinner stopping in the A, B, red or blue regions are shown below.

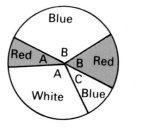

$P(A) = 0.4$
$P(B) = 0.5$
$P(RED) = 0.3$
$P(BLUE) = 0.4$

Calculate:

a   *(i) P(C)   (ii) P(WHITE)*
(iii) P(RED or BLUE)   (iv) P(A or B).

b *Explain why P(BLUE or C) is not 0.5.*
What is P(BLUE or C)?

/**PRACTICAL PROJECTS**

1 a *Roll two dice at least 120 times, and make a bar chart of the sums of the two scores. Compare the results with those you would expect to find by calculation.*

b *Repeat **a** for the differences between the two scores.*

c *Design experiments of your own with two dice. Compare theory with practice.*

2 *A board for a game is numbered 1 to 23.*

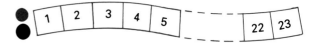

To finish, you must end up on 23. If you throw too many to finish, you do not move.

You need to design a dice for this game.
Why would this be a bad design?

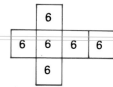

Design your own dice, and try it out by playing against a friend. Try to improve your design.

P(*A* AND *B*)

Look at the table of outcomes when these two spinners are spun.

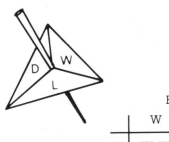

For the red spinner, P(W) = $\frac{1}{3}$.

For the black spinner, P(W) = $\frac{1}{3}$.

From the table, P(W, W) = $\frac{1}{9}$.

Notice that P(W, W) = $\frac{1}{9} = \frac{1}{3} \times \frac{1}{3}$

= P(W) × P(W).

Check that P(W, D) = P(W) × P(D).

	Black spinner		
	W	D	L
W	(W, W)	(W, D)	(W, L)
Red spinner D	(D, W)	(D, D)	(D, L)
L	(L, W)	(L, D)	(L, L)

It seems that P(*A* and *B*) = P(*A*) × P(*B*). Obtaining a win with the first spinner does not affect the outcome on the second spinner. The two events are **independent**.

For two independent events *A* and *B*, P(*A* and *B*) = P(*A*) × P(*B*)

EXERCISE 5

1 A 2p and a 5p coin are tossed.
  a List all possible outcomes.
  b Write down:
   (i) P(H) for the 2p
   (ii) P(H) for the 5p   (iii) P(H, H).
  c Check that P(H, H) = P(H) × P(H).

2 a List all possible outcomes when these spinners are spun.

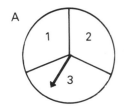 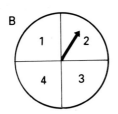

  b Write down:
   (i) P(2) for A   (ii) P(2) for B   (iii) P(2, 2).
  c Check that P(2, 2) = P(2) × P(2).

3 Two regular tetrahedron dice, numbered 1–4, are rolled.

  a List all possible outcomes.
  b Write down:
   (i) P(4) for the first dice
   (ii) P(4) for the second dice   (iii) P(4, 4).
  c Check that P(4, 4) = P(4) × P(4).

4 A coin is tossed and a dice is rolled.

  a List all possible outcomes.
  b Write down:
   (i) P(H)   (ii) P(6)   (iii) P(H, 6)—Head, then 6
   (iv) an equation connecting P(H), P(6) and
      P(H, 6).

5 Ben plants two daffodil bulbs. The probability that each one flowers is 0.9. Calculate the probability that both will flower.

6 Linkup Ltd make metal cables. Tests show that the probability of one breaking when it is tested is 0.2. Calculate the probability that the next two cables to be tested:
a both break   **b** both pass the test.

7 In the Sunshine Maternity Unit, P(boy) = 0.48.
a Write down P(girl).
b Calculate, correct to 2 decimal places, for the next two births:
(i) P(boy, boy)   (ii) P(girl, girl).

8 The wheel is spun. Each sector is the same size.

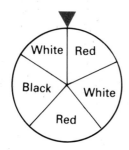

a Calculate P(Red).
The wheel is spun again.
b Calculate P(Red).
c Calculate the probability that two successive reds turn up.

9 Calculate the probability that two people chosen at random were both born:
a on a Sunday   **b** in the first week of January.

10 In a TV game show, contestants have a chance of winning prizes by spinning two wheels, each divided into equal sectors.

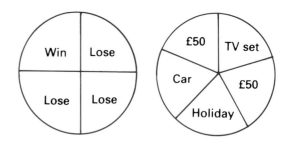

Calculate the probability of winning, in one attempt:
a a car—P(Win and Car)   **b** £50.

BRAINSTORMER

These bags contain red and white discs. A disc is taken at random from each bag. Calculate:
a *P(W, W)*   **b** *P(R, R)*
c *P(both have the same colour).*

CHECK-UP ON PROBABILITY

1 Ryan's five-a-side football team draw lots to see who will be the goalkeeper. What is the probability that Ryan:
a will be in goal   **b** will not be in goal?

2 a For a single spin of this wheel, which has equal sectors, calculate:
(i) P(Lose) (ii) P(£50) (iii) P(£100) (iv) P(£200).

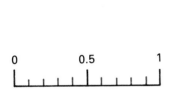

b Copy the scale, and mark the positions of the probabilities.

3 The three cards are placed face down. One is chosen at random, noted and replaced. The cards are shuffled, and another is chosen at random.

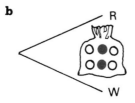

a Copy and complete the tree diagram.

J (J, J)

J

b Calculate the probability of picking:
(i) a pair of cards which are the same
(ii) a King and a Queen, in either order
(iii) at least one King.

4 Red and white counters are mixed up in the bags, and one is chosen at random. Copy and complete the tree diagrams.

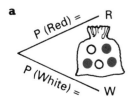

a P (Red) = ___ R
P (White) = ___ W

b R
W

5 The two spinners are spun, and the scores are added.

a Show all possible totals in a table.
b Calculate:
(i) P(4)   (ii) P(4 or 5)   (iii) P(4 or 5 or 6).
c How many totals of 8 would you expect in 400 pairs of spins?

6 Supersafe Insurance use these probabilities to predict the cost of car accidents.

Claim (£)	Probability
< 500	0.15
500–999	0.25
1000–1499	0.20
1500–1999	0.15
≥ 2000	0.25

a Calculate the probability that a claim will be:
(i) less than £1000
(ii) between £1000 and £2000.
b Out of 200 claims, how many would you expect to be under £1000?

7 In this game, players try to get a matching pair with two spins. Calculate:
a P(Rye, Rye)
b P(Corn, Corn)
c P(Wheat, Wheat)
d P(Barley, Barley)
e P(Rye, Corn).

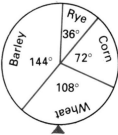

REVIEW: AREAS AND VOLUMES

Reminders

Square
$$A = l^2$$
$$P = 4l$$

l

l

Rectangle
$$A = lb$$
$$P = 2l + 2b$$

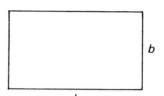

b

l

Triangle
$$A = \tfrac{1}{2}\,\text{base} \times \text{height}$$
$$= \tfrac{1}{2}bh$$

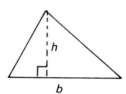

h

b

h

b

Circle
$$A = \pi r^2$$
$$C = \pi d$$

d

r

Parallelogram
$$A = \text{base} \times \text{height}$$
$$= bh$$

h

b

Rhombus
$$A = \tfrac{1}{2}d_1 \times d_2$$

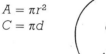

d_2

d_1

Kite
$$A = \tfrac{1}{2}d_1 \times d_2$$

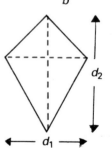

d_2

d_1

In this chapter give answers correct to 1 decimal place where necessary.

EXERCISE 1A

1 Calculate the areas and perimeters of the square and the rectangle.

2 Calculate the area of each triangle below.

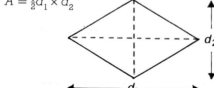

a

6 cm

6 cm

b

5 cm

8 cm

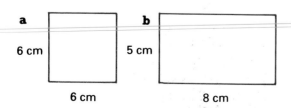

a

4 cm

6 cm

b

3 cm

4 cm

3 Calculate the areas of the rhombus and kite.

a

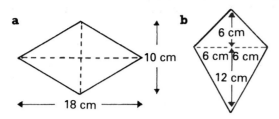

b

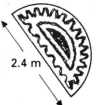

6 cm
6 cm 6 cm
12 cm

4 Calculate the area of the parallelogram below.

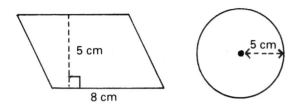

5 cm

8 cm

5 cm

5 Calculate:
  a the area of the circle above
  b the circumference of the circle.

6 Look at the square and the rectangle below.
Which has the greater: **a** area **b** perimeter?

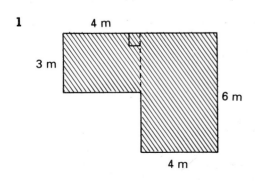

7 cm   7 cm

8 cm

6 cm

7 The diameter of this semi-circular rug is 2.4 m.
Calculate:
  a the length of its curved edge
  b its area.

2.4 m

8 Calculate the area of each of these six shapes.

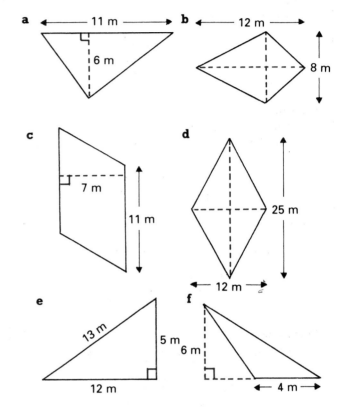

a — 11 m — 6 m

b — 12 m — 8 m

c 7 m 11 m

d 25 m 12 m

e 13 m 12 m

f 5 m 6 m 4 m

EXERCISE 1B

Calculate the shaded areas in questions **1–6** by
adding or subtracting areas of rectangles, triangles
or circles.

1

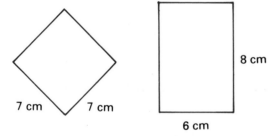

4 m
3 m
6 m
4 m

2

15 m
8 m
4 m
6 m

3

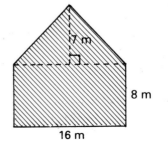

7 m
8 m
16 m

133

4

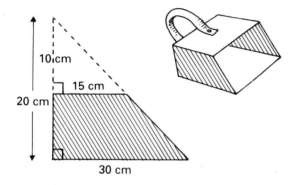

5 | **6**

9 m | 7 m | 3 m

8 m | 2 m | 6 m

7 A dustpan is made of metal. Each side is made by cutting a small triangle from a large triangle, as shown.

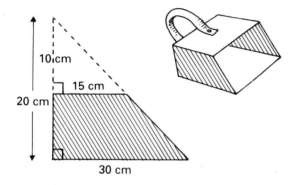

10 cm

15 cm

20 cm

30 cm

Calculate the area of:
a the large triangle
b the small triangle
c the shaded side of the dustpan.

8 A bracket to hold a gutter is made by cutting a semicircle from a rectangle of plastic.

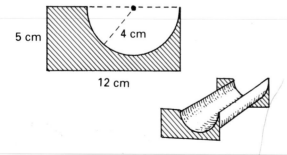

5 cm

4 cm

12 cm

Calculate the area of:
a the rectangle of plastic
b the semicircle
c the area of the bracket.

9 The side of a breadbin is based on a square and a quarter circle.

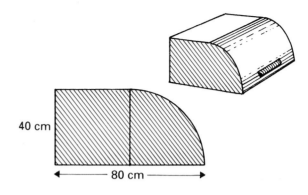

40 cm

80 cm

Calculate the area of:
a the square
b the quarter circle
c the side of the breadbin.

10 Concrete blocks, like the shaded one, are used to make garden walls. The four holes in the blocks are rhombuses, like the one shown.

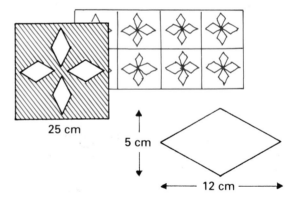

25 cm

5 cm

12 cm

Calculate the area of:
a the square outline of the block
b each hole in the block
c the shaded side of concrete.

VOLUMES

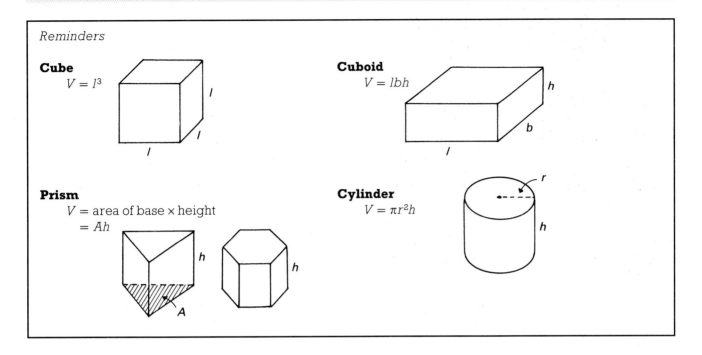

Reminders

Cube
$V = l^3$

Cuboid
$V = lbh$

Prism
$V = $ area of base $\times$ height
$\quad = Ah$

Cylinder
$V = \pi r^2 h$

EXERCISE 2A

1 Calculate the volumes of these six objects:

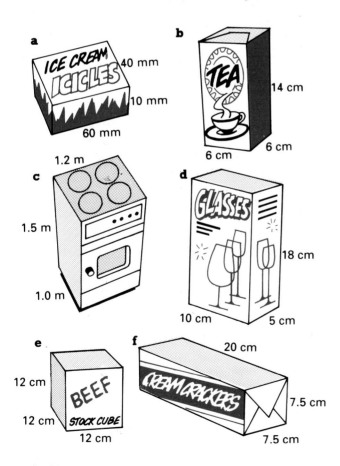

a ICE CREAM ICICLES 40 mm, 10 mm, 60 mm

b TEA 14 cm, 6 cm, 6 cm

c 1.2 m, 1.5 m, 1.0 m

d GLASSES 18 cm, 10 cm, 5 cm

e BEEF STOCK CUBE 12 cm, 12 cm, 12 cm

f CREAM CRACKERS 20 cm, 7.5 cm, 7.5 cm

2 A fish tank is 60 cm long, 40 cm broad and 25 cm high.
  a Calculate its volume:
    (i) in cm³   (ii) in litres (1 litre $= 1000$ cm³).
  b The tank contains 24 litres of water. What depth of water is in the tank?

3 Calculate the height of each cuboid:

a Volume 40 cm³, 4 cm, 5 cm

b Volume 120 cm³, 6 cm, 8 cm

4 Calculate the volumes of these prisms:

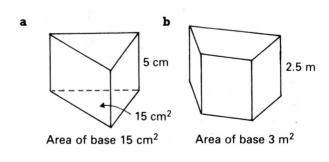

a 5 cm, 15 cm², Area of base 15 cm²

b 2.5 m, Area of base 3 m²

5 Calculate:
  a the area of the triangular end of the prism below
  b the volume of the prism.

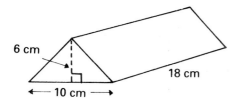

6 Calculate the volumes of these cylinders:

a   **b**

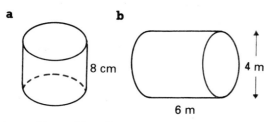

Area of base 75 cm²

7 The inside diameter of this pipe is 6 cm.

10 metres

  a Calculate the volume of the pipe.
  b How many litres of water does it hold when it is full?

8 This cuboid of modelling clay can be made into a number of other shapes.

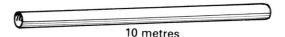

  a Calculate the volume of clay.
  b The clay is reshaped as a cuboid with a base 10 cm by 10 cm. Calculate its height.
  c The clay is used to make 50 identical cubes. Calculate the length of their edges.
  d It is then rolled into a cylinder shape 16 cm long. Calculate the area of a circular end of the cylinder.

EXERCISE 2B

1 The cost of heating a space is proportional to the volume of the space.

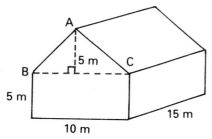

  a Calculate:
    (i) the area of the triangular shape ABC
    (ii) the volume of the roof space
    (iii) the volume of the whole house.
  b What fraction of heating is wasted on the roof space?

2 Chicken feed is poured into this trough.

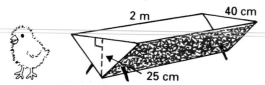

Calculate the volume of the feed (in cm³) when the trough is three-quarters full.

3 a Calculate the volume of liquid this cylindrical container can hold, in:
      (i) cm³   (ii) litres, to the nearest litre.

  b For safety, it should never be more than 80% full. Would a load of 16 000 litres be safe?

4 A free mug is given with each carton of Orchard Apple Juice.
  a Calculate the volume of the mug.
  b How many mugs can be filled from one carton of juice?

5 A concrete foundation consists of a cuboid with a slice below it as shown.

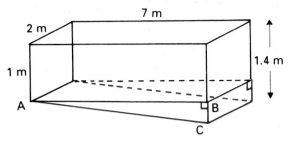

Calculate:
a the area of the triangular part ABC
b the volume of the triangular slice
c the total volume of concrete.

6 A waterwheel scoops up water to irrigate a field. Each scoop is shaped like a half cylinder.

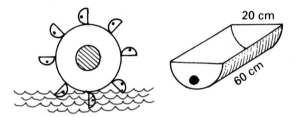

Calculate:
a the volume of a scoop
b the whole number of litres the wheel can deliver in 25 turns, assuming each scoop is filled with water, and no water is wasted.

7 Cubical cartons, with edges 10 cm long are packed into this box.

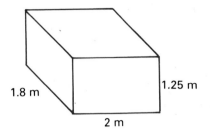

a How many cartons can the box hold?
b How much space in the box is wasted?

8 TV cables have an inner cylinder of fibres and an outer layer of insulation.

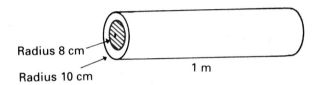

In one metre of cable, what is the volume, to the nearest cm^3, of:
a the whole cable
b the inner core of fibres
c the outer insulation?

SURFACE AREAS OF SOLIDS

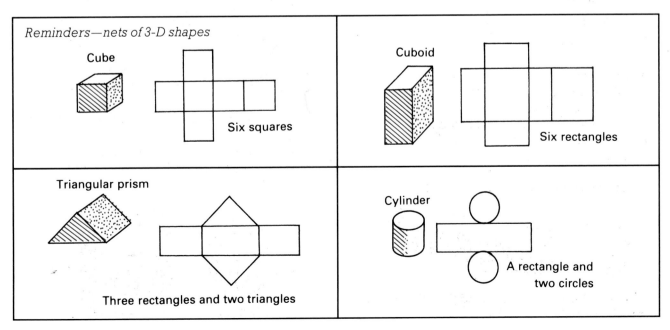

EXERCISE 3

1 The net for this dice is like the one for the cube in the box on page 137.
Calculate:
a the area of one face
b the total surface area of the dice.

2 cm

2 This net of squares can make an open-topped box.

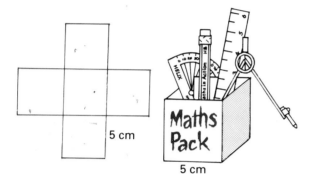

5 cm

5 cm

Maths Pack

Calculate:
a the area of one side of the box
b its total outer surface area.

3 This open sleeve has four square sides.
a Draw a net for it.
b Calculate the area of:
(i) each side
(ii) the whole outer surface.

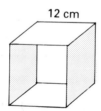

12 cm

4

26 cm

5 cm   12 cm

The net for this box is like the one for the cuboid shown on page 137.
a Copy the net, and fill in the lengths of its sides.
b Calculate the area of the net. What is the total surface area of the box?

5 a Draw a net for this video tape sleeve.
b Calculate the total outer surface area of the sleeve.

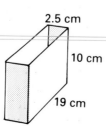

2.5 cm

10 cm

19 cm

6 The net for this triangular prism is like the one shown on page 137.

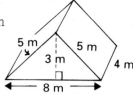

5 m   5 m
3 m
8 m   4 m

a Copy the net, and fill in the dimensions.
b Calculate the area of:
(i) each rectangle   (ii) each triangle
(iii) the whole surface of the prism.

7 A net is shown for this bookshelf.

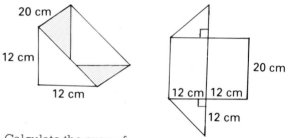

20 cm
12 cm
12 cm
20 cm
12 cm   12 cm
12 cm

Calculate the area of:
a each rectangle   **b** each triangle
c the whole bookshelf (outer area).

8 The net for this tin of beans is like the one for the cylinder shown on page 137.
a Copy the net, and calculate the length of the rectangle.
b Calculate the area of:
(i) the rectangle
(ii) each circle
(iii) the tin.

8 cm

BRILLIANT BEANS   8 cm

9

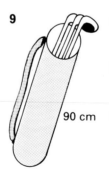

90 cm

a The net for this golf bag is the same as the one for question **8**, but with only one circle. Why?
b Draw the net, and fill in the dimensions—the radius of each end is 9 cm.
c Calculate the total outer surface area of the bag.

10 A rectangular sheet of plastic is curved to make a plant cover with open semicircular ends.
Calculate the area of the plastic.

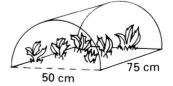

50 cm   75 cm

TOPICS TO EXPLORE

1 Paying for postage

Make a list of all the postage rates up to £1 which can be paid for with 20p and 24p stamps only. Arrange your work systematically.

2 Seeing red

A wooden cube is painted red, and is then cut into eight identical small cubes.

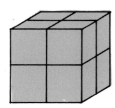

a How many red faces does each small cube have?
b Investigate the same problem if the original cube is cut into twenty-seven smaller cubes.

3 Multiple measures

These jars hold 2 measures and 3 measures of liquid. Explain how you could use them to pour 1, 2, 3, . . ., 7 measures of liquid.

4 Star shapes

a Draw a circle, and divide the circumference into five equal parts. (What size is each angle at the centre?)

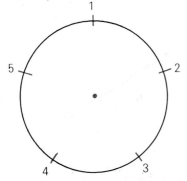

b Join $1 \rightarrow 3 \rightarrow 5 \rightarrow 2 \rightarrow 4 \rightarrow 1$ to make a 5-point star.

c Construct a star like the one below.

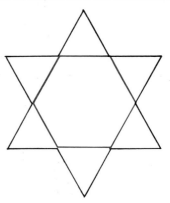

d Start with different numbers of points on the circumference, and draw more star shapes.
e What kinds of polygons can you see in them?

5 Areas and perimeters

Squares are made from small squares of side 1 cm, like this:

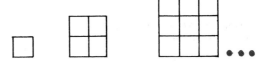

a Copy and complete this table:

Length of side (cm)	1	2	3	4	5	6		n
Perimeter (P cm)	4							
Area (A cm²)	1							
$P \div A$	4							

b For which square is $P = A$?
c Investigate the values of P, A and P/A for four 1 cm squares placed together to make different shapes, two squares always having a side in common.

6 Tabletennis balls

Tabletennis balls (diameter 4 cm) are to be sold in packs of six. The Packem Box Company has been asked to make boxes for them. They decide that cuboids, cylinders and triangular prisms are all possible shapes. Investigate this problem, including the dimensions of possible boxes, ways of packing the boxes in containers for sending to shops, and so on.

7 The long and short of it

a On squared paper make a careful copy of this corner, using ruler and protractor.

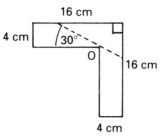

b Draw a line through O, like the one shown dotted, at 30° to the sides, and measure its length, to the nearest mm.

c Copy and complete this table, drawing and measuring the lines one by one.

Angle	20°	30°	40°	50°	60°	70°
Length of line						

d (i) What angle do you think would give the shortest line?
  (ii) Draw the line at this angle, and measure its length.

e Draw a graph, taking angles (20°, 30°, ..., 70°) on the horizontal axis and lengths (10 cm, 11 cm, ..., 17 cm) on the vertical axis.
Join the points with a smooth curve, and check your answer to part **d**.

8 Design a business reply letter

The Crafty Correspondence Company has to design a reply-paid, folding business letter.

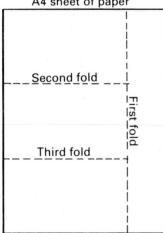

Start with an A4 sheet of paper, and make the folding letter shown. Put an address on the front, and fill in folding instructions. Include a message or information inside, with name and address for a reply.

9 Leaning towers

a This is the famous leaning tower of Pisa, in Italy. Draw a right-angled triangle, and calculate the angle of tilt from the vertical, correct to 1 decimal place.

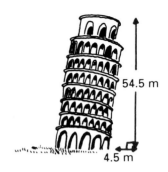

b When do you think the box shown below will topple over? Sketch its position then.

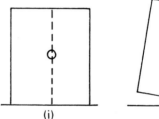

c Calculate the angle, to the nearest degree, when the book below will topple. Check your answer by tilting your maths book about one corner, and measuring the angle with a protractor held against the corner.

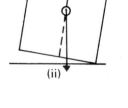

d Calculate the angle of tilt of the empty crate about edge AB when it is about to topple over.

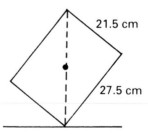

10 Polydiags and the 'Mystic Rose'

a (i) Carefully count the number of diagonals in the square, pentagon and hexagon.
(ii) Continue for polygons with 7, 8 and 9 sides.
(iii) Check that the formula $N = \frac{1}{2}n(n-3)$ gives the number of diagonals N in an n-sided polygon, as far as you have gone.

b To make a Mystic Rose you draw all possible lines from every vertex. That means all the sides *and* diagonals.
How many lines would be drawn for polygons with 3, 4, 5, . . . sides?

11 Number sequences

Marion is trying to remember how to find a formula N for the nth term of this sequence.

Add 2 to get the next term.

Compare multiples of 2:
2 4 6 8 . . . 2n
The sequence terms are 3 greater, so $N = 2n + 3$.
Again, for: 2 5 8 11 . . ., $N = 3n - 1$.
               3 3 3

a Find a formula for the nth term N of each of these five sequences:

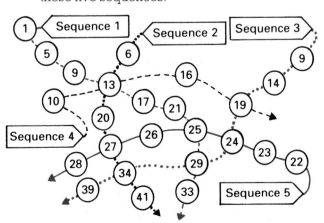

b Make up some sequences on your own, and find a formula for the nth term of each.

12 At the design centre

Have a go at making some tiling patterns.

TILING CENTRE

ALL SHAPES AND SIZES AVAILABLE   PATTERNS TO ORDER

As well as rectangles, try:

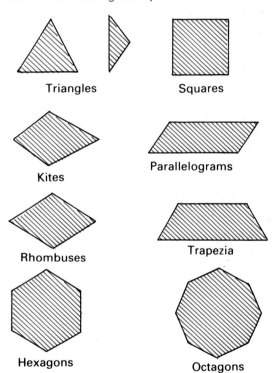

Triangles   Squares

Kites   Parallelograms

Rhombuses   Trapezia

Hexagons   Octagons

—or even a mixture of shapes.
Experiment with picture designs.

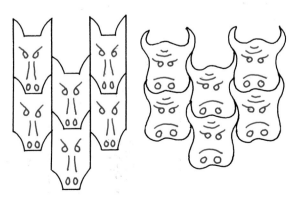

141

13 A house of cards

Mike is building a house of cards. For one storey he uses two cards, and makes one triangle of 1 unit.

For two storeys he uses five *more* cards, a total of seven. He makes four triangles of 1 unit and one triangle of 4 units.

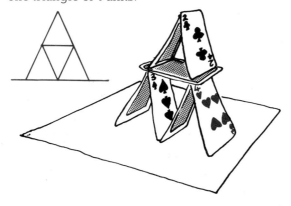

a For three storeys, how many:
   (i) more cards
   (ii) cards altogether
   (iii) 1-unit triangles
   (iv) 4-unit triangles
   (v) 9-unit triangles?

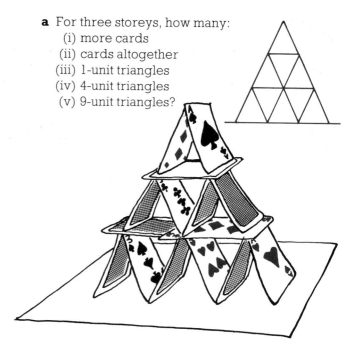

b Arrange all the data in a table, and extend it to four or five storeys.

c Find the formulae for:
   (i) the number of 1-unit triangles in n storeys
   (ii) the number of extra cards needed for the nth storey.

d How many storeys can Mike build with two packs of cards (52 in each)?

CHAPTER REVISION EXERCISES

1 Calculate the gradient of each line below.

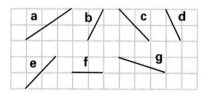

2 List the gradients of the lines in question **1** in order, giving the greatest positive one first.

3 a Draw these lines on squared paper:
   (i) from (0,1), gradient $\frac{1}{2}$
   (ii) from (4, 0), gradient 2.
   b Write down the coordinates of the point where they cross.

4 a Calculate the gradients of the sides of these quadrilaterals.
   b What type of quadrilateral is each one?

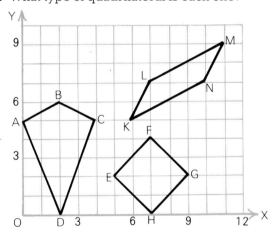

5 Find the gradients of the lines joining:
   a P(3,1), Q(7, 3) **b** R(0, 5), S(3, 4)

6 a Copy and complete this table for $y = 5x$.

x	-2	-1	0	1	2
y					

   b Plot the points on squared paper, and draw the straight line through them.
   c Write down the gradient of the line.

7 A road rises 5 m over a horizontal distance of 125 m. A railway line rises 1 m in a horizontal distance of 80 m. Sketch a triangle for each, mark the measurements and calculate the gradients of the road and railtrack.

8 Write down the gradient and equation of each of these straight lines.

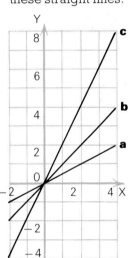
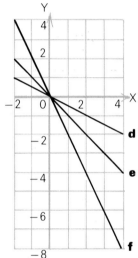

9 Stan hires a hedge-cutter. The hire charges are shown by the graph.

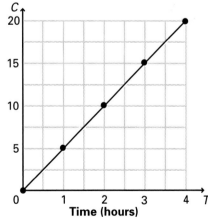

   a What will he pay if he hires it for:
      (i) 2 hours (ii) $3\frac{1}{2}$ hours?
   b A straight line through the origin has an equation like $y = ax$, here $C = aT$.
   Write down:
      (i) the gradient of the line (ii) its equation.

REVISION EXERCISE ON CHAPTER 2: TRIGONOMETRY

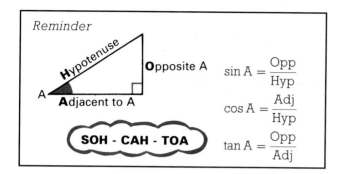

Reminder

$$\sin A = \frac{Opp}{Hyp}$$

$$\cos A = \frac{Adj}{Hyp}$$

SOH - CAH - TOA

$$\tan A = \frac{Opp}{Adj}$$

1 For each triangle below, write down which you would use—sin, cos or tan—then calculate *d*.

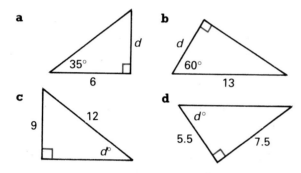

2 Calculate the width, *w* metres, of each river.

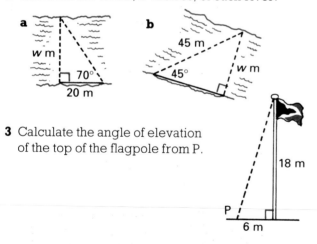

3 Calculate the angle of elevation of the top of the flagpole from P.

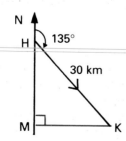

4 The *Silver Spray* sails 30 km from harbour H on a course 135°. Calculate how far she has sailed:
a south **b** east.

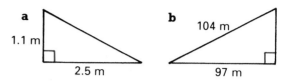

5 The slope of the ramp must not be more than 22°. Are these ramps too steep?

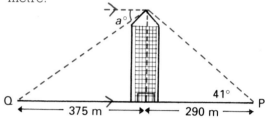

6 Claire measures the angle of elevation of the top of the Canary Wharf Tower in London from a point P 290 m away.
a Calculate the height of the tower, to the nearest metre.

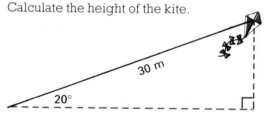

b Calculate the angle of depression *a*° of a point Q 375 m from the centre of the base.

7 It's a good breezy day, and Jill is flying her kite from a hook in the ground.
a She lets out 30 m of string, and this is taut at 20° to the ground.
Calculate the height of the kite.

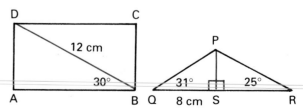

b The wind drops, and the kite falls to a point 5 m above the ground, with the string still taut. What angle does the string now make with the ground?

8 Calculate the area of rectangle ABCD below, to the nearest cm².

9 In △PQR above, calculate:
a PS **b** SR
c the area of △PQR, to the nearest cm².

REVISION EXERCISE ON CHAPTER 3: FRACTIONS, DECIMALS AND PERCENTAGES

1 Calculate entries A, B and C in this phone bill.

PHONE BILL	for 000-111-9999
£53.81	Call charges
£23.66	Rental charges from 1 March to 31 May
A	Total charges
B	Vat at 17.5%
C	**Total amount now due**

2 Sit Yin's monthly salary is £1600. She puts 5% of it into her pension fund. How much goes into her pension fund in: **a** a month **b** a year?

3 Change to fractions in their simplest form:
a 0.3 **b** 0.4 **c** 0.06 **d** 75% **e** 24%

4 Change to percentages:
a 0.03 **b** 0.375 **c** $\frac{9}{10}$ **d** $\frac{7}{20}$ **e** $\frac{17}{50}$

5 The ages and numbers of pedestrians injured in road accidents in Strathclyde in 1993 were:

0–4	5–15	16–25	26–65	65+
165	938	324	696	274

Calculate:
a the total number of people injured
b the percentage of those injured who were in age group 5–15, to the nearest whole number.

6 Mrs Morgan will need 17 m² of carpet.

£7.65 per m²

a Calculate the cost.
b She is given a discount of $\frac{1}{3}$. How much is:
(i) the discount (ii) the actual cost?

7 The price of a stamp increases from 25p to 28p. Calculate:
a the increase in price
b the percentage increase in price, based on the original price.

8 Write as mixed numbers:
a $\frac{11}{2}$ **b** $\frac{7}{5}$ **c** $\frac{4}{3}$ **d** $\frac{32}{3}$ **e** $\frac{35}{10}$

9 Write as proper fractions:
a $3\frac{3}{4}$ **b** $2\frac{7}{10}$ **c** $1\frac{1}{5}$ **d** $6\frac{1}{3}$ **e** $3\frac{7}{8}$

10 Prakash is absent for eight days out of 64. Write his absence:
a as a fraction, in its simplest form
b as a percentage.

11 Here is a recipe for Steak and Kidney Hotpot for four:

$1\frac{1}{2}$ lb steak	1 medium onion
$\frac{1}{2}$ lb kidney	1 tablespoon flour
$1\frac{1}{2}$ lb potatoes	1 tablespoon dripping
$1\frac{1}{4}$ oz butter	$\frac{3}{4}$ pint stock
$\frac{1}{4}$ lb mushrooms	Salt and pepper

What quantities would you need for sixteen people?

12 a Eagle computers had exports of £1 500 000 in 1993. These increased by 4% in 1994. Calculate the value of exports in 1994.
b In 1995, the increase was 5% of the 1994 value. Calculate the value of exports in 1995.

13 How much wider is:
a a $\frac{5}{8}$ inch spanner than a $\frac{1}{4}$ inch one
b a $\frac{3}{4}$ inch spanner than a $\frac{7}{16}$ inch one?

14 Look at the picture frames below, then calculate:
a how much wider one frame is than the other
b the perimeter of each frame
c the area of each picture and frame, correct to 1 decimal place.

20.75 cm

15.75 cm

17.5 cm

25.5 cm

15 James Johnston's salary is £18 000. He allocates 15% to food, 25% to house expenses, 10% to insurance, 10% to holidays, 22% to income tax, and saves the rest.
How much does he save, and how much does he spend on each part of his expenses?

REVISION EXERCISE ON CHAPTER 4: EQUATIONS AND INEQUALITIES

Solve the equations in questions **1–4**.

1 a $x+7 = 12$ **b** $y-2 = 10$ **c** $t+6 = 5$

2 a $3x+6 = 21$ **b** $4y-2 = 6$ **c** $3t+9 = 6$

3 a $2u-8 = 12$ **b** $3v+4 = 10$ **c** $2w-1 = 0$

4 a $5(t-2) = 40$ **b** $3(m-1) = 6$ **c** $7(n+1) = 7$

5 Make an equation for each picture and solve it.

a Six bricks, each weighing $3x+1$ kg. Total weight: 42 kg.

b Seven books, each with $5x+6$ pages. Total pages: 427.

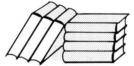

c Eight marbles, each costing $12-x$ pence. Total cost: 24p.

Solve the equations in questions **6–8**.

6 a $6a = a+5$ **b** $2b = b+1$ **c** $3c+4 = c$

7 a $8t-2 = t+5$ **b** $12m-2 = 2m+18$

8 a $3(x+2) = x+18$ **b** $3(y+1) = 2(y-1)$

9 The areas of the rectangles in each pair are equal.
  (i) Make an equation for each pair, and solve it.
  (ii) Write down the length, breadth and area of each rectangle.

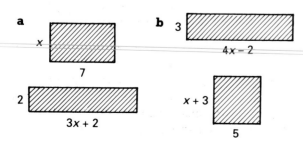

10 The nth term of the sequence 6, 9, 12, . . . is $3(n+1)$. Find n if the nth term is
a 36 **b** 81 **c** 123

11 Make an equation for each picture below, solve it, and find the cost of each packet.

a

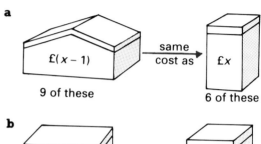

b

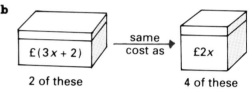

12 Choose x from the set $\{0, 1, 2, \ldots, 7, 8\}$ and solve these inequalities:
a $x \leqslant 3$ **b** $x > 3$ **c** $x \geqslant 6$ **d** $x > 6$
e $2x \leqslant 4$ **f** $x+5 > 12$ **g** $2x+3 \leqslant 19$

13 Solve these inequalities:
a $3m > 6$ **b** $4n < 12$ **c** $2n \geqslant 5$
d $3n+4 \geqslant 10$ **e** $5p-6 \leqslant 14$ **f** $3n-2 < 2n$
g $4(x+2) \geqslant 3x+10$ **h** $7(x+3) \leqslant 5(x+1)$

14 Write an inequality for each picture and solve it.

a

b

REVISION EXERCISE ON CHAPTER 5: STATISTICS

1 Phil starts a small business, making and selling filing cabinets. The graphs show his production and sales over a six-month period.

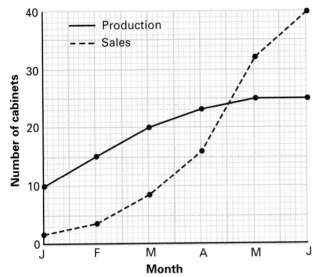

a Make a table which shows his production and sales figures month by month.

b Describe the graphs.

2 A survey of the book borrowing habits of 5000 people in Weston had these results:

How often?	Weekly	Monthly	Every 6 months	Once a year	Never
Percentage	25	30	15	10	20

a Illustrate the data in a pie chart.

b How many of the 5000 people borrow books: (i) every week   (ii) never?

3 In a science experiment, as the resistance in a circuit was changed, the current was measured. Hold your ruler along the best-fitting line, and estimate the resistance for a current of:

a 55 amps

b 25 amps.

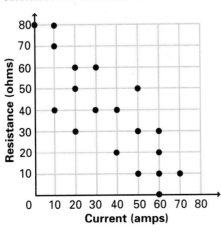

4 a Make a frequency table for this set of marks, using class intervals 1–5, 6–10, . . .

15	17	20	10	16	25	8	22	12	19
23	18	19	20	13	21	21	14	18	20
17	19	15	21	14	20	5	10	15	22

b Use mid-interval values to calculate the mean, correct to 1 decimal place.

c Draw a frequency polygon of the marks.

5 The table summarises Emma's performance in class tests over the year.

a In which subject was her performance:
  (i) best
  (ii) worst?

Subject	Range	Mean
Maths	12%	68%
English	6%	84%
Science	40%	52%

b Describe her performance in the science tests.

6 Top Toys make children's games. To improve sales, they increase their advertising. Here is a record of their sales for an eight-month period.

Advertising (£)	0	600	1000	1400
Sales (£)	17 000	18 000	22 000	28 000

2200	2600	3400	4000
26 000	34 000	36 000	38 000

a Is their advertising campaign successful?

b Calculate the mean monthly amounts of money involved in: (i) advertising   (ii) sales.

c Draw a scatter diagram, and the line of best fit through the mean point, M.

d Estimate the sales for £2400 advertising.

7 Here are the times of 200 runners in a marathon.

Time (t hours)	$2 \leqslant t < 2\frac{1}{2}$	$2\frac{1}{2} \leqslant t < 3$	$3 \leqslant t < 3\frac{1}{2}$
Number of runners	3	19	28

$3\frac{1}{2} \leqslant t < 4$	$4 \leqslant t < 4\frac{1}{2}$	$4\frac{1}{2} \leqslant t < 5$	$5 \leqslant t < 5\frac{1}{2}$	$5\frac{1}{2} \leqslant t < 6$
47	43	39	16	5

a Which is the modal class interval?

b In which class interval is the median time?

c Use mid-interval values to calculate the mean time to 1 decimal place.

d Construct a frequency polygon of the data.

REVISION EXERCISE ON CHAPTER 6: HOUSE AND CAR COSTS

1 Calculate the deposit needed to buy each of these houses:

Price (£)	35 000	64 000	48 000	130 000
Loan (£)	20 000	58 000	80% of price	95% of price
Deposit (£)				

2 Mary has her offer of £34 000 for the flat at 2 Braeside Avenue accepted. Her bank will give her a loan of £28 000. What deposit will she need?

3 The Smiths want to purchase a house valued at £80 000. Their building society offers a loan of £65 000.
a How much is the Smith's deposit?
b What percentage is the deposit of the house value?

4 This table shows Newtown Building Society's monthly charges for mortgages.

Monthly payments per £1000		
15 years	20 years	25 years
£13	£12.50	£10

Jan Brown borrows £50 000 for 25 years.
Calculate:
a her monthly payment
b the total amount she would pay over 25 years
c the total interest she would pay.

5 Perry insures his house, worth £55 000, at £2.50 per £1000. He also insures the contents, worth £15 000, at £8.20 per £1000.
Calculate his premium for:
a house **b** contents **c** house and contents.

6 House Alert Insurance Company offer buildings insurance at £2.25 per £1000, and contents insurance at rates per £1000 shown in the table.

District	A	B	C	D	E	F	G
Rate per £1000	£4	£5.50	£6	£7.50	£9	£10	£11.20

Calculate the total premiums for each of these:
a Address in district C; house worth £77 000, contents £20 000.
b Address in district G; house worth £115 000, contents £35 000.

7 Evan's car covers 32 miles for every gallon of petrol in town, and 44 miles per gallon on the motorway.
a How far can he travel on 10 gallons:
(i) in town   (ii) on the motorway?
b How much petrol, correct to 0.1 gallon, would he use in driving 100 miles:
(i) in town   (ii) on the motorway?

8 Here is part of Car Care's annual motor car insurance premium table.

Car Group	District					
	A	B	C	D	E	F
1	347	437	507	615	770	832
12	750	890	970	1050	1136	1288

Calculate the annual premiums for:
a Bill, group 1 car, district E, 30% no claims discount
b Moira, group 12 car, district B, 40% no claims discount.

9 Mr Thomson's house is worth £90 000, and his car has a value of £8000. The house value increases each year by 5% and the car's value decreases each year by 10%. How much is each worth after: **a** one year **b** two years?

10 List events in the picture below which should be covered by insurance.

REVISION EXERCISE ON CHAPTER 7: PAIRS OF STRAIGHT LINES AND EQUATIONS

1 A spaceship heads towards the moon. At the same time a meteor approaches the Earth.

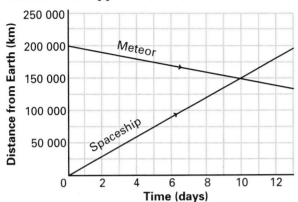

a (i) After how many days are the meteor and the spaceship the same distance from Earth? (ii) What is this distance?

b Which is farther from the Earth after:
(i) 2 days (ii) 11 days?

2

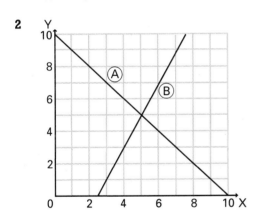

a This graph shows the lines with equations $x + y = 10$ and $2x - y = 5$. Which is which?

b Write down the solution of the pair of equations.

3 a On squared paper draw the graphs of the equations $x + y = 9$ and $y = 2x$.

b Use your graphs to write down the solution of the pair of equations.

4 David and Gillian are timing two water clocks. As the clocks empty, they measure the height of water in each.

C1   C2

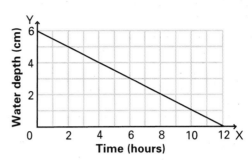

a The graph for C1 is shown. Its equation is $x + 2y = 12$. Draw the graph on squared paper.

b The equation for C2 is $2x + y = 12$. Draw this graph also, on the same diagram.

c (i) When is the height of water the same for each clock?
(ii) What is this height?

d How long does each clock 'run'?

5

PEDAL POWER Hire a bike for only £1 a day

SOFT SADDLE BIKE HIRE £5 deposit plus 50p a day

a Copy and complete this table:

Number of days	0	1	2	3	4		12
Pedal Power's cost (£)	0	1					
Soft Saddle's cost (£)	5	$5\frac{1}{2}$					

b Draw graphs of the two sets of charges on a grid like the one in question **2** with 'Number of days' on the horizontal axis and 'Total cost (£)' on the vertical axis.

c When are the total costs equal?

d Which would you choose for:
(i) a 5-day hire (ii) an 11-day hire?

6 Solve each pair of equations by substituting one expression for y in the other equation:

a $y = 2x$
  $y = x + 3$

b $y = 3x$
  $y = x - 2$

c $y = x - 1$
  $x + y = 5$

7 Solve, by eliminating x or y:

a $x + y = 11$
  $x - y = 3$

b $3x + 2y = -1$
  $x + 2y = 1$

c $x - 2y = 1$
  $2x + y = 2$

8 Solve the pairs of equations in questions **2**, **3** and **4** by calculation.

9 Use the graph in question **1** to estimate when the meteor will strike Earth.

149

REVISION EXERCISE ON CHAPTER 8: PROPORTION IN PRACTICE

1 Is y directly proportional to x in either of these tables?

a

x	2	4	6	8
y	5	10	15	20

b

x	2	4	6	8
y	12	6	4	3

2 Five pens cost 90p. Calculate the cost of eight pens.

3 In which graph is $y \propto x$?

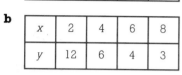

4 s varies as t, so $s = kt$. When $t = 6$, $s = 30$.
  a Find a formula for s in terms of t.
  b Calculate s when $t = 8$.

5 The quantity of tarmac (T tonnes) needed to resurface the Nayars' driveway varies directly as the area (A m²) covered. 1.5 tonnes can cover 30 m². What weight is needed to cover 48 m²?

6 The County Parks Department use this rule: The number (N) of rose bushes to be planted in a circular flower bed varies directly as the square of the diameter (D m) of the bed.
72 bushes fill a bed of diameter 6 m. Calculate the number needed for a bed with a 5-metre diameter.

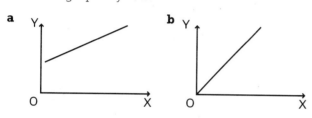

7 Here are the results of an experiment about the tension and extension of a spring with different weights on it.

Tension (T)	0	1	2	3	4	5	6
Extension (E)	0	6	10	14	20	26	30

a Plot the points, using these axes and scales.
b Draw the best-fitting line through the origin.
c Write down:
  (i) the gradient of the line
  (ii) its equation $E = \ldots T$.
d Calculate E when $T = 3.4$.

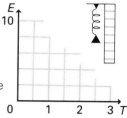

8 a Copy and complete the table for sharing out the pieces of chocolate in this bar.

Number sharing (S)	1	2	3	4	6	8	12
Number of pieces (P)							

b Write down the value of $S \times P$.
c Copy and complete: P is . . . . to S.

9 Five men paint a block of classrooms in 16 days. How long would eight men take? (More or less time?)

10 A photocopier can run off 100 copies in 40 seconds. How long will it take to do 135 copies? (More or less time?)

11 Sid is testing a new car's engine, and reads off the engine's revolutions per minute (rpm) and the car's speed in third gear.

rpm (R)	1000	2000	3000	4000
Speed (S mph)	13	26	39	52

a Check that $S \propto R$ by:
  (i) calculating ratios
  (ii) drawing a graph.
b Find a formula for S in terms of R.
c Calculate the car's speed at 5000 rpm.

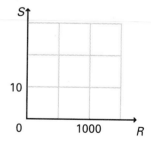

12 Hussein is designing a booklet. The area (A cm²) of each page is inversely proportional to the number of pages (N). He calculates that for an 8-page booklet each page will have to be 120 cm². Calculate the area of each page if he has to increase the number of pages by two.

REVISION EXERCISE ON CHAPTER 9: ANGLES IN A CIRCLE

O is the centre of each circle.

1 a What kind of triangle is AOB?
  b Calculate the size of:
    (i) ∠ABO (ii) ∠AOB.

2 If, in question **1**,
  ∠AOB = 130°,
  what size would
  ∠OAB be?

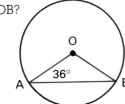

3 a Sketch this diagram.
  b Mark the three equal radii.
  c Fill in all the angles.

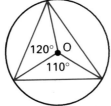

4 The coin sits symmetrically in the slot machine.
  Calculate x, y and z.

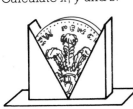

5 This wheel clamp is an isosceles triangle. Copy
  the diagram, and fill in all the angles.

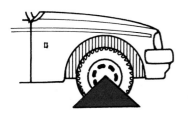

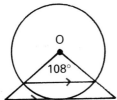

6 AOC is a diameter in the circle.
  a Why are angles ABC and
    ADC right angles?
  b Calculate:
    (i) ∠ACB
    (ii) ∠ACD.

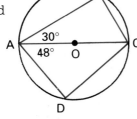

7

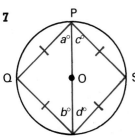

  a What size are angles PQR
    and PSR?
  b Calculate a, b, c, d.
  c What kind of quadrilateral
    is PQRS?

8 a Copy the diagram, and fill
  in the angles.
  b Check that the two angles
  you have marked at C
  add up to 90°.

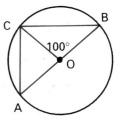

9

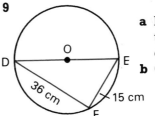

  a Name the right angle and
    the hypotenuse in this
    diagram.
  b Calculate the length of DE.

10 Use trigonometry to calculate, correct to 1
  decimal place, ∠D in question **9**.

11 a AT is a tangent to
    the circle. Why is
    ∠OAT = 90°?
  b Calculate:
    (i) ∠AOT
    (ii) OA, to the
      nearest 0.1 cm.

12 SAT is a tangent.
  Calculate x and y.

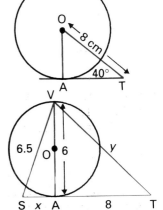

13 The model engine's boiler sits in a cradle,
  shown by ABC. ∠ABC = 110°. Calculate:
  a ∠POB **b** OB, correct to 1 decimal place.

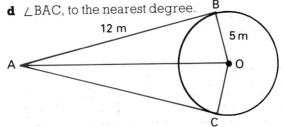

14 AB and AC are tangents. Calculate:
  a AO **b** OC **c** AC
  d ∠BAC, to the nearest degree.

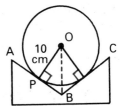

REVISION EXERCISE ON CHAPTER 10: PROBABILITY

1

One card is chosen at random.
a Calculate the probability that it:
   (i) has three letters
   (ii) begins with 'F'
   (iii) contains at least one 'E'
   (iv) contains exactly one 'E'
   (v) has six letters
   (vi) has more than two letters.
b Copy this scale, and mark all the probabilities on it.

```
|  |  |  |  |  |  |  |  |  |  |
0           0.5            1
```

2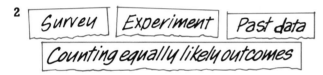

Which of the above methods would you choose to estimate or calculate these probabilities?
a Galloping Fury will win the 3 o'clock race.
b A Sparky matchbox will contain exactly the average number of matches shown on the box.
c Evelyn will pick a letter T at Scrabble.
d A shoe will land on its sole when dropped.

3 Which of these dice are likely to be biased?

Dice	A	B	C	D	E
Number of 6s	10	10	12	19	30
Number of throws	60	30	60	120	120

4 A Clothes Collection is made up of six different articles of clothing, which can be mixed and matched. Outfits can be purchased as pairs of items.
a Copy the table, and complete all the pairings.

	Blouse	T-shirt	Jumper
Shorts	(Sh, B)		
Skirt			
Leggings			

b Calculate the probability that an outfit chosen at random:
   (i) does not contain a skirt
   (ii) contains a blouse, but not leggings
   (iii) does not contain a T-shirt or shorts.
c Make a tree diagram to show all the probabilities.

5 Tireless Tyres test a random sample of tyres. This table shows the resulting data.

Number of miles	Fraction of tyres
< 10 000	0.06
10 000–14 999	0.24
15 000–19 999	0.36
20 000–24 999	0.22
⩾ 25 000	0.12

a Calculate:
   (i) P(less than 15 000 miles)
   (ii) P(15 000 or more miles).
b In one month they make 12 000 tyres. How many would they expect to last:
   (i) less than 15 000 miles
   (ii) 15 000 miles or more?

6 Railway records on the time of arrival of the Intertown Express shows that:
P(early arrival) = 0.5 and P(arrival on time) = 0.3
a Calculate:
   (i) P(arrival early or on time)
   (ii) P(late arrival).
b Calculate the probability that both today's and tomorrow's Express will arrive:
   (i) early   (ii) late.

7 A card is taken at random from each of two packs of cards. Calculate:
a P(Heart, Heart)   **b** P(Ace, Ace)
c P(Ace of Hearts, Ace of Hearts).

GENERAL REVISION EXERCISES

1 Hanif has sales of £1800 in his first week. What are his total earnings for the week?

> ***VIRTUAL REALITY SALES***
> *Earn £350 a week plus
> 5% commission on all sales*

2 Write down two more terms in each sequence.
  a 7, 14, 21, 28, . . .   **b** 1, 2, 4, 7, 11, . . .

3 The time taken to run a 1500 m race is recorded on this tape.

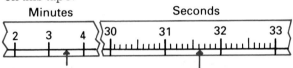

Write down the time in minutes and seconds.

4 Kirsty saw this car number plate in her rear-view mirror. Write down the car's number.

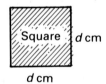

5 a Write down a formula for:
    (i) the perimeter P cm
    (ii) the area A cm².
  b Calculate P and A when
    $d = 13$.

Square | d cm

d cm

6 a Add the square of 7 to the square root of 16.
  b Express $\frac{1}{5}$ as: (i) a decimal   (ii) a percentage.

7 Frank calculated that 235×65 was 15 257.
  a Why must he be wrong?
  b What is the correct answer?
  c Calculate $235 \div 65$, correct to:
    (i) 2 decimal places   (ii) 2 significant figures.

8 What do these five scores add up to?

9 a Sketch an equilateral triangle and its axes of symmetry.
  b What is its order of rotational symmetry about its centre?
  c Fill in the sizes of all the angles in your figure.

10 This graph shows the maximum daily temperatures for a week in April.

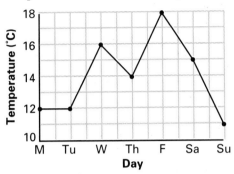

  a (i) What was the highest temperature?
    (ii) On which day?
  b Calculate: (i) the increase in temperature from Tuesday to Wednesday
    (ii) the percentage increase in temperature from Tuesday to Wednesday
    (iii) the mean temperature for the week.

11 Kirsty's car is always serviced every 9000 miles. She checks her mileage: 38 121. Calculate the number of miles: **a** since her last service
  b till the next service.

12 a On squared paper plot the points A(-1, 4), B(5, 4) and C(5, -2).
  b Mark D so that ABCD is a square, and write down the coordinates of D.

13 Jan is recording a programme which starts at 7.30 pm and lasts for $1\frac{1}{2}$ hours. What 24-hour times should she set?

14 Copy this diagram, and fill in all the angles.

15 Mr Ferguson insures his house for £75 000 at £2.45 per £1000. Calculate his annual premium.

16 On squared paper:
  a enlarge shape (i) by scale factor 3
  b reduce shape (ii) by scale factor $\frac{1}{2}$.

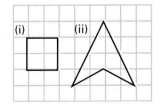

GENERAL REVISION EXERCISE 1B

1

OUR ADVERTISEMENT RATES
1-4 lines: £3.50 a line
Each extra line: £2.75

Calculate the cost for:
a four lines **b** eight lines.

2 Find the smallest whole number n for which $3^n > 30$.

3 What angle does the minute hand turn through from 8 am to:
a 8.15 am **b** 8.20 am?

4 In the clock in question **3**, how many degrees are there in:
a the obtuse angle between the hands
b the reflex angle between the hands?

5 a Express a population of 54 000 000 in standard form, $a \times 10^n$.
b Write 2.5×10^{-3} in full.

6 Copy and complete, given $y = 2x - 1$:

x	3	2	$\frac{1}{2}$	0	-1
y					

7 a Copy this triangle of numbers, and fill in the fourth row.
b Calculate:
  (i) the sum of the numbers in each of the first four rows
  (ii) the mean of the numbers in each of the first four rows.

8 Draw this cuboid on squared paper after enlargement by scale factor 2.

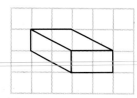

9 The cuboid in question **8** represents a brick 4 cm by 2 cm by 6 cm. Calculate the volume and surface area of the brick.

10 There are 15 girls and 17 boys in 4B. On Monday, 14 girls and 14 boys are present.
a What fraction of the students are absent?
b What percentage is this?

11 This graph shows the effect of two chemicals, A and B, on a plant's height. The U curve shows the growth of an untreated plant.

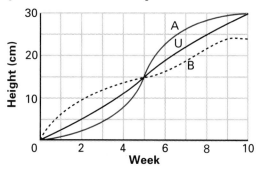

a When did all three plant samples have the same height? What height?
b Which chemical was more effective in:
  (i) weeks 1–5 (ii) weeks 5–10?
c Which method gave the greatest increase in growth in:
  (i) weeks 3–5 (ii) weeks 8–10?

12 In this isosceles triangle, calculate:
a its perimeter
b h
c its area.

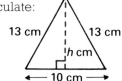

13 The money in Alan's building society account increases each year by 8%. Starting with £150, how much has he after:
a one year **b** two years?

14 a Describe the reflection or rotation which takes shape A to:
  (i) B (ii) C (iii) D.
b Write down the order of rotational symmetry of the pattern about O.

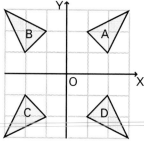

15 The area of each triangle in question **14** is $1\frac{1}{2}$ squares. If a dart is dropped at random onto the diagram, what is the probability that it strikes a triangle?

GENERAL REVISION EXERCISE 2A

1 a Lynn sees a bargain. How much is the price reduction?

b Mr James in the Furniture Department says this is a 20% reduction on the original price. Is he correct?

2 Write down two more terms in each sequence:
a $1, 4, 9, 16, \ldots$ **b** $1, -2, 4, -8, \ldots$

3 ABC is a straight line.

a Calculate the size of: (i) $\angle$ ABD (ii) $\angle$ ABF.
b Name:
  (i) the smallest acute angle
  (ii) the largest obtuse angle.

4 Solve these equations:
a $2x = 20$ **b** $y + 4 = 9$ **c** $t - 1 = 10$

5 a Draw x and y-axes on squared paper, and plot the points A$(-3, 0)$, B$(0, 5)$ and D$(0, -2)$. Join AB and AD.
b Plot C so that the y-axis is an axis of symmetry of the shape ABCD.
c (i) Write down the coordinates of C.
  (ii) What type of shape is ABCD?

6 a How far will the two canes reach when placed end to end?
b How much longer is one than the other?

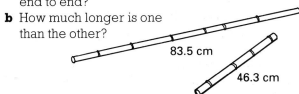

83.5 cm

46.3 cm

7

a What will the time be on Julian's digital watch in:
  (i) 35 minutes (ii) 4 hours?
b What is the am/pm time on the watch?

8 The end–view of an office block is L–shaped. The lengths are in metres. Calculate:
a its perimeter **b** its area.

 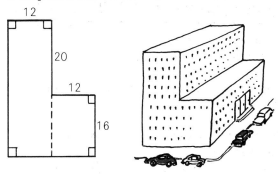

12

20

12

16

9 Make a scale drawing of the end of the office block in question **8**, using a scale of 1 cm to 4 m.

10 Do you know how to play noughts and crosses? How many straight lines of three crosses (across, up and down, or corner-to-corner) could you make in each grid?

a **b** **c**

11 There are seven cars in Crocus Grove—some old, some quite new. The bar chart tells the story. Calculate:
a the range of ages (greatest age − smallest age)
b the mean age of the cars.

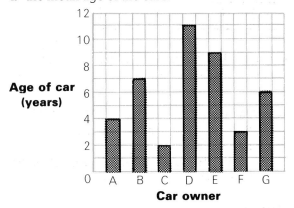

12 Ally goes to America on holiday, and Milly goes to Canada. How much foreign currency would each get in exchange for £250?

Foreign Exchange for £1 Sterling	
US dollars for £1	1.56
Canadian dollars for £1	2.02

155

GENERAL REVISION EXERCISE 2B

1 Solve each equation:
  a $x+2 = 7$ **b** $4x-1 = 7$ **c** $3x-1 = 2x+1$.

2 *Maths in Action Book 1* is 14 mm thick.
  a This bookshelf holds 12 copies. Calculate the length of the shelf.

  b Another book is 8 mm thick. How many of these could you pack into the shelf?

3 Saturday's scores were:
```
2-1  1-1  1-2  1-0  3-3  1-0  3-0  0-2
2-1  1-0  4-1  0-0  1-3  1-2  0-1  3-1
5-2  1-3  0-2  0-1  1-0  2-0  0-0  4-1
```
  a How many:
     (i) home wins   (ii) away wins
     (iii) draws, were there?
  b Draw a pie chart, with the radius 3 cm. Use a protractor to make the angles at the centre.

4

  a Just what Hilary needs, a new camera for her holidays. How much will it cost if she pays £5.50 and six payments?
  b How much cheaper is it by cash?

5 a On squared paper, draw a line from O, in colour, to show this journey: 5 km east, 4 north, 3 west, 2 south, 1 east.

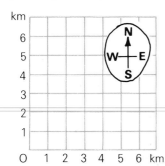

  b Write down the coordinates of each point where you had to turn.

6

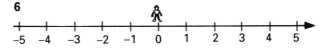

  Calculate: **a** $0+4$ **b** $3-3$ **c** $3-4$
       d $-1+2$ **e** $5-4+3-2+1$.

7 a Use 1 significant figure in each number to *estimate*:
     (i) 38×52 (ii) 9.6×24.1 (iii) $83 \div 7.9$
  b Use your calculator to work out each answer to **a** (in (iii) correct to 1 decimal place).

8 How many litres of petrol cost the same as one gallon (correct to 3 significant figures)?

9 Slim is a free-fall expert. He drops s metres in t seconds, where $s = 5t^2$.
  Calculate:
  a s when $t = 5$
  b t when $s = 80$.

10 Use Pythagoras' Theorem to calculate:
  a x **b** y.

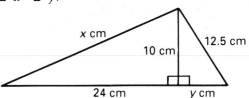

11 Simplify:
  a $t+t+2$ **b** $n+1-n$ **c** $7ab-ab$ **d** $2 \times y \times y$

12 a Calculate these earnings:
     (i) 5% commission on sales of £380
     (ii) 14 window frames made at a piece rate of £16.25 per frame.
  b Shiva's basic rate of pay is £8.50 an hour. In the week ending 4th March she worked 40 hours at basic rate and 7 hours overtime at time and a half. Calculate her week's pay.

GENERAL REVISION EXERCISE 3A

1 The local group calculate the expenses for their Friday concert to be £375. How many tickets costing £3 each would have to be sold to cover the cost?

2 Tom draws a picture on his computer by joining up these points in order. (Squared paper will do just as well.)

x	4	4	2	2	4	5	5	9	9	8	8	5	5	4
y	1	5	5	7	7	8	5	5	1	1	3	3	1	1

  a What did he draw?
  b Add a tail.

3 Solve:
  a $6x = 42$ **b** $x - 7 = 12$
  c $2y + 3 = 11$ **d** $4t - 2 = 2t + 4$

4 a Copy this table, and complete it for the cost of three canes and four canes.

GLEN GARDEN CENTRE

GARDEN CANES

	3 ft	4 ft	5 ft	6 ft
1 cane	23p	26p	28p	33p
2 canes	46p	52p	56p	66p
3 canes				

  b Use your table to find the cost of two canes at 6 ft, three canes at 5 ft and four canes at 4 ft.

5 a Calculate $\angle$ AOC and $\angle$ BOD.
  b List the acute, obtuse and right angles.

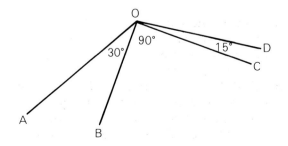

6 Face north. What is the smallest number of degrees that you can turn clockwise to face:
  a east   **b** south-east
  c south   **d** west
  e north?

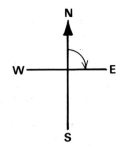

7 How much did Rhoda pay for these?

SALE
15% Discount on all clothes
12% off all footwear
JEANS £20
SHOES £23.75

8 The diameter of the cassette reel is 50 mm. Calculate, to the nearest mm and mm² respectively:
  a its circumference
  b its area.

9 Pete is on a long journey–two hours at an average speed of 50 km/h, then three hours at an average speed of 45 km/h. Calculate:
  a the total time he takes
  b the length of his journey, in kilometres
  c his average speed for the whole journey.

10 Draw a distance/time graph of Pete's journey in question **9** on squared paper, using the scales shown.

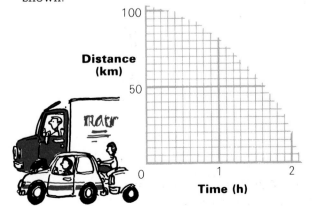

GENERAL REVISION EXERCISE 3B

1 A box contains Chocobars. There are nine layers, with 24 bars in each layer.
  a How many bars are in the box?
  b A bar costs 25p. How much is a full box worth?

2 Copy and complete the table.

x	1	2	4		
$x+5$	6		10		
$3x-2$		4			7

3 There are four flight paths from Riverside Airport.

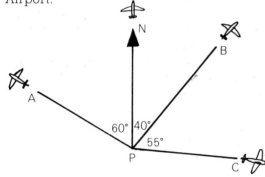

  a Name the acute angles with NP as one arm.
  b Calculate the size of the largest obtuse angle.
  c PN points north. Write down three-figure bearings from P of: (i) B (ii) C (iii) A.

4 The dining room floor in Karim's home measures 5.5 m by 3.8 m, and the lounge is 5.2 m by 4.1 m. Which room has the larger area? By how much?

5 All the lengths in this picture are in metres.

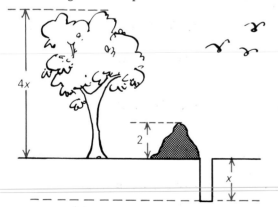

Using x, write down the vertical distances from:
  a the top of the tree to the bottom of the trench
  b the top of the pile of earth to the bottom of the trench
  c the top of the tree to the top of the pile of earth.

6 Use trigonometry to calculate x in each diagram, correct to 1 decimal place.

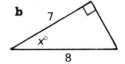

7 a Sketch each shape below, and draw its axes of symmetry. How many axes does each one have?

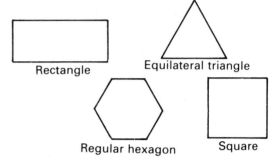

  b Write down the order of rotational symmetry of each shape about its centre.

8 At 60 words per minute, Sheila typed a letter for her boss in eight minutes. How long would it take her at:
  a 40 wpm **b** 80 wpm?

9 Triangle ABC is right-angled at B.
  a Calculate x (Pythagoras' Theorem).
  b Show that $AC^2 + CD^2 = AD^2$.

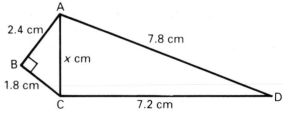

10 The HP terms are: deposit $33\frac{1}{3}\%$ of cash price, plus 12 equal monthly payments. Calculate:
  a the deposit
  b the monthly payment.

TIP TOP TV
cash price £270
HP price £324

11 The equation of a line is $y = 2x - 8$. Calculate:
  a y when (i) $x = 4$ (ii) $x = 1$
  b x when (i) $y = 0$ (ii) $y = 10$.

GENERAL REVISION EXERCISE 4A

1 List the missing entries:

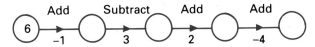

2 This pie chart shows the proportions of ages of 60 students in a school club. Measure the angles at the centre, and calculate the number of pupils in each age group.

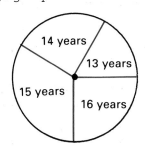

3 Calculate the value of:
 a $2x+1$, when $x=4$ **b** $y-3$, when $y=6$
 c $z-3$, when $z=2$ **d** $2t$, when $t=-5$
 e $-3k$, when $k=10$ **f** $10v$, when $v=0$.

4 a Make two copies of this square and right-angled isosceles triangle.
 b Complete one so that it has half-turn symmetry about its centre O.
 c Complete the other so that it has quarter-turn symmetry about O.

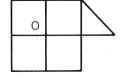

5 John Jones paid £2800 for a second-hand car in 1988. One year later its value had fallen to £2380. Calculate the depreciation as a percentage of the 1988 price.

6 a On squared paper plot the points A(-2, 3), B(3, 3) and C(3, -1).
 b (i) Plot D so that ABCD is a rectangle.
 (ii) Plot E so that ABEC is a parallelogram.
 c Calculate the areas of the rectangle and parallelogram.

7 Solve each equation for x:
 a $2x+3=1$ **b** $4x-1=x+5$ **c** $3(x-2)=6$.

8 The Sawyers insure their house for £80 000, and its contents for £15 000. The Resteasy Insurance Company's rates are 24p per £100 for the house and 60p per £100 for the contents. Calculate the:
 a total annual premium   **b** monthly premium.

9 Copy and complete:

Fraction	$\frac{1}{2}$			$\frac{1}{4}$		
Decimal		0.1			0.75	
Percentage			30%			88%

10

Place	Time
Shell Bay	10 30
Seaview	12 30
Hillcrest	13 00

 a How long does the bus take from:
 (i) Shell Bay to Seaview
 (ii) Seaview to Hillcrest?
 b The first journey is 58 miles, the second 19 miles. Calculate the average speed of the bus on each journey.

11 Simplify:
 a $2x+2+2x$ **b** $3(y+2)-4$
 c $5(n-1)+2(n+1)$

12 Ben's front garden is a 15 m by 9 m rectangle. The lawn is a similar rectangle 6 m broad.

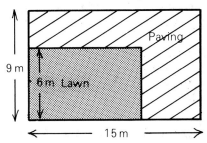

Calculate:
 a the scale factor from garden to lawn
 b the length of the lawn
 c the area of the paved part.

13 Calculate:
 a 10^3 **b** 2^6 **c** $\sqrt{169}$ **d** $15-(8-1)$
 e $7.5+2.5\times5$

14 a Measure the distance on the map from A to B in cm.
 b Calculate the actual distance in:
 (i) cm   (ii) km.

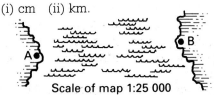

Scale of map 1:25 000

159

GENERAL REVISION EXERCISE 4B

1 Make as many true statements as you can, for example $-2 > -3$, using these cards. Be methodical!

2 a $a = 3$ and $b = 2$. Calculate the value of:
  (i) $a^2 + 2ab$ (ii) $a(a + 2b)$.
b Factorise $a^2 + 2ab$. Then check your answer to part **a**.

3 O is the centre of the circle.

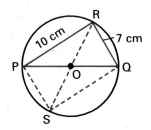

a Why is $\angle PRQ = 90°$?
b Calculate $\angle QPR$ (to the nearest degree) by trigonometry.
c Write down the lengths of PS and SQ. Give a reason.

4 Solve:
  a $3(x - 1) = 6$ **b** $5(y + 1) > 10$ **c** $4x - 1 > 2x - 3$

5 From this list of temperatures: $2°, -2°, 3°, 1°, 0°, -4°, 4°$, write down:
  a the highest and lowest temperatures
  b the difference between the highest and lowest temperatures
  c the sum of all the temperatures.

6 a Copy the diagram, and fill in the sizes of all the angles.

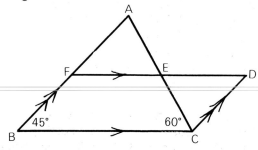

b What two special types of quadrilateral are in the diagram?

7 Make an equation for each picture, then solve it to find the number of weights in each bag.

8 The side of a footpath bridge is made of 1 m girders.

a Copy and complete this table:

Number of girders in base	1	2	3	4	5		n
Number of girders in side	3						

b Write down a formula for the number N of girders in the side which has n girders in the base.
c How many girders are needed for a side with 12 girders in the base?
d How many girders are in the base of a bridge which has 71 girders in the side?

9 A sample of students is asked how many teachers teach them during one week. The results are:

14 9 12 12 11 10 14 17 11 14
13 11 18 15 12 10 13 13 15 12
16 14 17 11 10 13 11 16 14 11

a Make a frequency table, and calculate the mean number of teachers per student (to the nearest whole number).
b Find the median and modal number of teachers.
c Draw a frequency diagram.
d Calculate the probability that a student chosen at random will have:
  (i) fewer than 11 teachers
  (ii) more than 15 teachers.

GENERAL REVISION EXERCISE 5A

1 Nick Lyle buys 1 dozen golf balls at £1.30 for each ball and 2 dozen at £1.60 each. How much does he pay altogether?

2 Solve these equations:

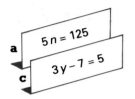
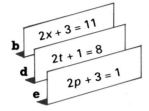

a $5n = 125$

c $3y - 7 = 5$

b $2x + 3 = 11$

d $2t + 1 = 8$

e $2p + 3 = 1$

3 a Plot the points A(2, 1), B(4, 2), C(4, 4), D(2, 3).
  b What shape is ABCD?
  c P, Q, R, S are the images of A, B, C, D under reflection in the y-axis. Write down their coordinates. What shape is PQRS?

4 An oil tank in the shape of a cuboid is 250 cm long, 180 cm broad and 120 cm high.
  a Calculate the volume of the tank in cm³.
  b How many litres can it hold?
  (1 litre = 1000 cm³.)

5 Write inequalities, using the given letters.
  a 'Don't drive faster than 30 mph.' Your speed is S mph.
  b 'Eat more than 15 g dietary fibre daily.' Weight of fibre is W g.
  c 'Take at least 3 tablets, but not more than 8 daily.' Number of tablets is N.

6 There are 20 congruent sectors on a dartboard. One of them is shaded.
  a Calculate:
   (i) ∠ABC (ii) ∠ABE.
  b How many sectors would you need to make an angle of 108° at the centre?

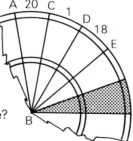

7 Calculate the probability that a dart landing at random on a board numbered 1–20 strikes a sector showing a number which is:
  a even **b** 17 or over
  c divisible by 3 **d** a multiple of 4.

8 a Share 80p in the ratio: (i) 3:5 (ii) 4:1.
  b Mrs Khan paid £43.50 for six rolls of wallpaper. How much would she have paid for eight rolls?

9 L mm of wire are needed to make the skeleton cuboid.
  a Make a formula for L.
  b Calculate L if $x = 9$.

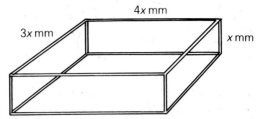

10 Garry paid cash. Gareth decided on HP. How much more will Gareth have to pay?

Cash £89.99 or 10% deposit and 12 payments of £7.45

11 An observation tower has been built for the Garden Festival. From a point 26 m from the foot Janie estimates that the angle of elevation of the top is 60°. Calculate, to the nearest metre:
  a BC (sin, cos or tan?)
  b AC.

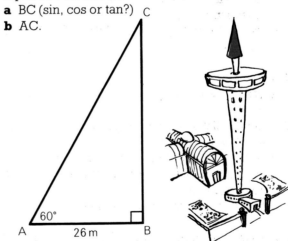

12 Cheryl Brown's annual salary as a cosmetic salesgirl is £9800. Her income tax allowances total £3600. Calculate:
  a her taxable income
  b the tax she pays at 25p in the £
  c her net income.

13 The cost (£C) of an order for calculators is directly proportional to the number (N) ordered. The cost is £6000 for 500 calculators.
  a Find a formula for C in terms of N.
  b Calculate the cost of 800 calculators.

GENERAL REVISION EXERCISE 5B

1 Stan Speedie is attempting to run the mile in under four minutes. His quarter-mile lap times are: 59.72, 61.43, 62.09 and 56.13 seconds. Does he succeed? By how many seconds does he succeed or fail?

2 Make an equation, and solve it. How many weights are in each bag?

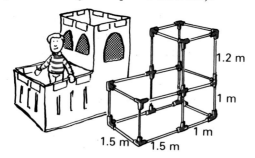

Each bag contains x weights

3 This playfort has a skeleton frame. Calculate:
a the total length of rod needed for the frame
b the area of plastic covering on all its surfaces (not including the top and the base).

1.2 m
1 m
1 m
1.5 m 1.5 m

4

Berlin	Paris	London	Moscow	Zurich	Oslo
3°C	−1°C	1°C	−4°C	0°C	−2°C

a Arrange the cities in order, coldest to warmest.
b How many degrees colder than Berlin is each place in the table?
c Madrid was 10° warmer than the second coldest place in the table. How much warmer was it in Madrid than in the second warmest place?

5 The instructions for a ladder say that the bottom should be one quarter as far from the wall as the top is up the wall. What angle will the ladder make with the ground, to the nearest degree? Show this in a diagram.

6 Solve these inequalities:
a $x+2 \geqslant 3$ **b** $4y < 10$
c $3x \leqslant x-4$ **d** $6n-2 > 4n+1$

7 The frame of a swing is held rigid by horizontal bars BE and CD, and struts BD and CE.

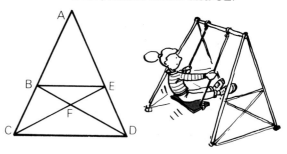

a Name two pairs of equal:
   (i) corresponding angles
   (ii) vertically opposite angles
   (iii) alternate angles.
b The frame has a vertical axis of symmetry. ∠EBD = 30° and ∠EBC = 110°. Copy the diagram, and fill in as many angles as you can.

8 a From the farm to the village is 3 km, and the tractor's top speed is 36 km/h. Can the tractor make the journey in less than five minutes?
b The tractor then travels 2 km in four minutes, followed by 5 km in 11 minutes. Calculate its average speed for the 7 km.

9 a (i) Name two similar triangles in this figure.

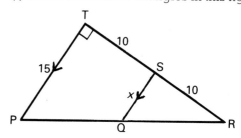

   (ii) Calculate the reduction scale factor from △PTR to △QSR.
   (iii) Calculate x. Lengths are in cm.
b Use Pythagoras' Theorem to calculate PR.

10 Members of Loch Doon Anglers' Club keep records of their catches. At the end of the season the total weights of their catches (in pounds) are:

23 18   7 24 40 16 28 37   4
36 24 20   4 16   8 42 31   9
18 39 12 30 19 23 32 36 25

a Calculate the mean weight of their catches.
b Make a frequency table with class intervals of 5, starting 1–5. Use mid-interval values 3, 8, etc., to calculate the mean weight again.
c Use the data in the table to draw a frequency diagram.

GENERAL REVISION EXERCISE 6A

1 At The Great Glass Company, 2.5 m² of glass cost £6. Calculate the cost of 4 m².

2 $x = -1$ and $y = 3$. Calculate the value of:
a $x+y$ **b** $x-y$ **c** xy
d $2x$ **e** $3y^2$ **f** $6x+2y$.

3 Which of these numbers are:
a prime numbers
b multiples of 3
c factors of 12?

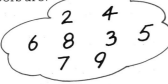

2 4
6 8 3 5
7 9

4 Calculate x in each diagram below.

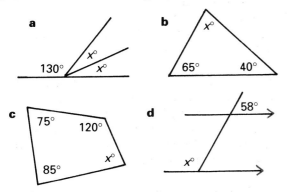

a 130° $x°$ $x°$

b $x°$ 65° 40°

c 75° 120° 85° $x°$

d 58° $x°$

5 Which is greater in each pair, and by how much?
a 1.02 or 0.92 **b** 3.14159 or 3.14160 **c** $\frac{3}{4}$ or $\frac{4}{5}$

6 All the angles are right angles.
a Calculate the perimeter and area of the field. (Make a sketch.)
b Express the area as a fraction of a hectare (1 hectare = 10 000 m²).

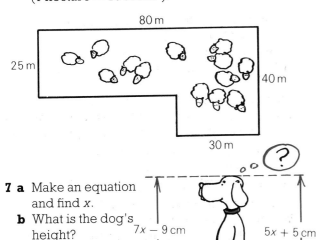

80 m
25 m
40 m
30 m

7 a Make an equation and find x.
b What is the dog's height?

$7x - 9$ cm $5x + 5$ cm

8 A recipe for onion soup (to serve five) contains: 250 g onions, 50 g butter, 20 g flour and 800 ml water. How much of each item would be needed to serve: **a** one **b** eight?

9

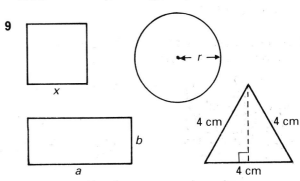

x

$\leftarrow r \rightarrow$

b

a

4 cm   4 cm
4 cm

a Write down formulae for the perimeters (P) and areas (A) of the square, circle and rectangle.
b Calculate the perimeter and area of the equilateral triangle, giving the area correct to 1 decimal place.

10 Saturn is 1430 million km from the sun, and the eccentricity of its orbit is 0.0558. Write both of these numbers in standard form, $a \times 10^n$.

11 Here is a distance/time graph for a train journey from Glasgow to Ayr and return.

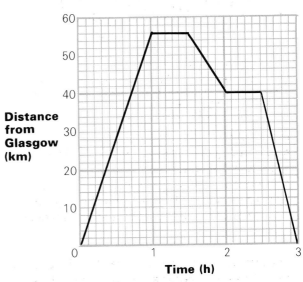

Distance from Glasgow (km)

Time (h)

a Find how long the train:
  (i) took to reach Ayr
  (ii) remained at Ayr
  (iii) was held up by a signal failure on the return journey.
b Calculate the average speeds of the journeys to and from Ayr.

163

GENERAL REVISION EXERCISE 6B

1 The Maradonna Diamond is being sold in Spain. How much would Des the diamond dealer have left from £100 000 if he purchased the diamond? (The exchange rate is 200 pesetas to the £.)

2 The Wilsons have just bought a house for £64 500. The Sandcastle Building Society gave them a 95% mortgage.
  a Calculate:
    (i) the amount of the loan
    (ii) the amount the Wilsons have to put down as a deposit.
  b They pay back £424 a month for 25 years. How much do they pay in total?

3 O is the centre of the circle, BC = BD and AB ∥ ED. ∠BCD = 65°.

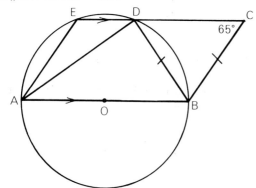

Copy the diagram and fill in as many angles as you can.

4 A traffic island is in the shape of a triangle.
  a Make a scale drawing of the island.

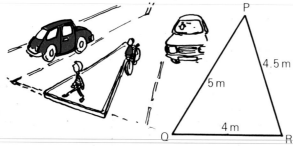

  b The angles are said to be 49°, 59° and 72°. How close to these are your angles?
  c To calculate the area of the island you'll have to draw a line through P in the triangle. Draw and measure the line, then calculate the area of the triangle, correct to 1 decimal place.

5 a Write down two expressions for the area of garden (i). If the area is 48 m², find x. (All the lengths are in metres.)

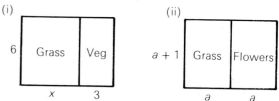

  b Tom says that the area of garden (ii) is $2a^2 + 2a$ m². Do you agree? Calculate the area when $a = 5$.

6 How many cubes with edges 3 cm long can be packed into a box 15 cm by 12 cm by 9 cm?

7 Calculate, correct to 2 significant figures:
  a sin BAC   **b** cos BAC
  c tan BAC   **d** AD
  e CD
  f the area of quadrilateral ABCD.

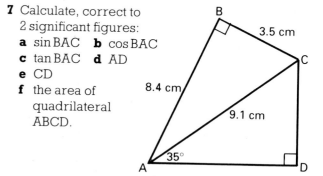

8 Calculate the volume and the surface area of a cylindrical oil storage tank with height 20 m and diameter of base 12 m. Give your answers correct to 3 significant figures.

9 Sheena is on holiday in Holland. She makes a table to change £s to florins.

Pounds (P)	1	2	3	4	5	6
Florins (F)			9			18

  a (i) Copy and complete the table.
     (ii) Make a formula connecting F and P.
  b Draw a graph of F against P.
  c Calculate the gradient of the graph. Compare with the first pair of entries in your table.
  d Use the formula to find the number of pounds for: (i) 60 florins   (ii) 36 florins.

10 A brick is 20 cm long and 8 cm wide, each to the nearest cm.
  a Write down its greatest and least possible lengths and widths.
  b Calculate the greatest and least possible areas of its base.

GENERAL REVISION EXERCISE 7A

1 A metal rod 1 metre long, weighing 1.8 kg, is cut into five equal lengths. Calculate, for each part:
 a its length in cm **b** its weight in g.

2 Factorise:
 a $2q + 2r$ **b** $3p - 6$ **c** $8 - 10y$ **d** $ab - ac$
 e $2a - 4b + 6c$.

3 On squared paper sketch the net of:
 a a cube
 b a tetrahedron (a pyramid on a triangular base)
 c a prism on a triangular base.

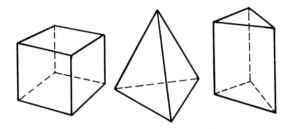

4 A balancing toy is made from a rubber cylinder with a plastic platform going through it. Copy the cross-section on the right. AB is a diameter. You should be able to fill in all the angles.

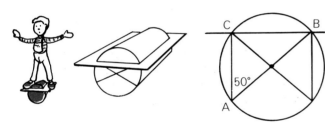

5 A cubical tank 3.5 m long is lined with copper. The tank has no top on it. Calculate the area of copper used.

6 a Copy and complete the table:

Number of horizontal cards (N)	1	2	3	4		N
Total number of cards (T)	5					

1 horizontal card   2 horizontal cards

b Write down a formula for T in terms of N.
 c Calculate T when $N = 50$.

7 *Starshine* is 23 km south of the headland H. She is on a course 051°. Calculate, correct to 0.1 km:
 a how close she passes to H
 b how far she is then from S.

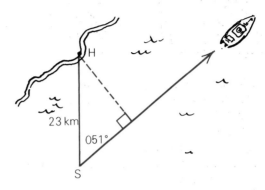

8 Tahir has £125.60 in his bank account.
 a What will his bank balance be after £37.80 is withdrawn and £92.20 is put into the account?
 b Calculate a year's interest on the new balance at 7% per annum.

9 Solve:
 a $6x - 2 = 2x - 14$ **b** $5(x - 3) > 10$

10 Make an equation, and find the lengths of the sides of the triangle.

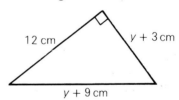

11 a Copy and complete to find points on the graph of $x + 2y = 10$.
 When $x = 0$, $y = \ldots$, so $(0, \ldots)$ is on the graph.
 When $y = 0$, $x = \ldots$, so $(\ldots, 0)$ is on the graph.
 b Using the scales shown, draw the graph of $x + 2y = 10$.
 c On the same diagram, draw the graph of $y = 2x$.
 d Use your graphs to solve the pair of equations
 $\left. \begin{array}{l} x + 2y = 10 \\ y = 2x \end{array} \right\}$.

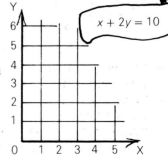

GENERAL REVISION EXERCISE 7B

1 Thomson's, the local hardware shop, sells bags of sand in two sizes. One holds $2\frac{1}{2}$ kg, and the other is two and a half times as heavy. Calculate:
a the weight of the heavier bag
b the largest number of each kind that can be filled from a 100 kg delivery of sand.

2 A sports arena consists of a rectangle with semi-circular ends. Find formulae for:
a the perimeter (P)
b the area (A), of the arena.

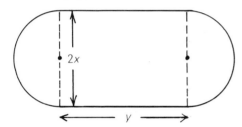

3 ABCDEFGH is a cube. The length of each edge is 4 m.

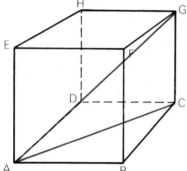

Calculate, correct to 1 decimal place and to the nearest degree:
a face diagonal AC
b space diagonal AG
c ∠CAG.

4 Claire puts £600 into her building society account at 8% p.a. rate of interest. She leaves the annual interest in her account each year. Calculate the total amount in her account after:
a one year **b** two years.

5 A clock is set in a wooden stand. Its clockface diameter is 12 cm, and its base is 36 cm long. Calculate:
a (i) AC (ii) CB
b the angle AB makes with the base (to the nearest degree).

6 Bluebell Nursery sells starter plant kits for £4, plus £1 per box of plants. Daisy Garden Centre offers starter kits at £7, plus 50p per box of plants.
a Copy and complete the table.

Boxes of plants	0	2	4	6	8
Total cost—Bluebell					
Total cost—Daisy	7	8			

b Draw graphs of both on squared paper.

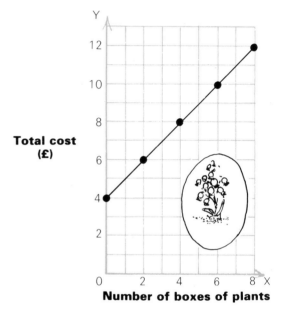

c When are the total costs equal?
d Which is cheaper for:
(i) 2 boxes (ii) 20 boxes?

7 Solve these pairs of equations, graphically or otherwise.
a $y = x$
$y = 6 - 2x$
b $x + y = 8$
$x - y = 2$
c $y = 3x$
$2x + y = 10$

8 In an exam, Julie scored five more than Grace, and Aisha scored twice as many as Julie.
a Taking Grace's score as x, write down Julie and Aisha's scores.
b All three scores totalled 75. Make an equation, and solve it. Then write down each girl's score.

9 a Make a tree diagram for two spins of the spinner.
b Calculate:
(i) for one spin, P(W) and P(L)
(ii) for two spins, P(W, W), P(L, L) and P(a Win and a Lose).

GRADIENTS AND GRAPHS OF STRAIGHT LINES

Page 1 Looking Back

1a Between A and B **b** near the beginning and end of the journey; the steeper the slope, the faster the speed **2** $\frac{3}{4}$
3a 3 **b** $\frac{1}{2}$ **c** -1 **d** $-\frac{1}{2}$ **e** 0 **4a** 4 **b** -4 **c** 8 **d** -8
e -6 **5a** (i) 5 km (ii) 4 km **b** (i) 1 km (ii) 4 km
6 D(4, 1) **7** Rows: **a** 0, 4, 8, 12, 16, 20 **b** $-2, -1, 0, 1, 2, 3$
c $-14, -7, 0, 7, 14, 21$ **8a** 0, 400, 800, 1200, 1600, 2000
b (i) 200 (ii) 1400 (iii) 4000

Page 2 Exercise 1/Class Discussion

1a (i) Black (ii) blue (iii) red **b** (ii) **2b** DE, BC, CD, AB
3a Harry's; it may slip **c** Harry, Dick, Tom
4a $\frac{1}{2}$ **b** $\frac{1}{2}$ **c** $\frac{1}{2}$; all the ratios are $\frac{1}{2}$

Page 3 Exercise 2

1 Tom $\frac{5}{2}$, Dick $\frac{5}{3}$, Harry 1 **2a** (ii) 3, 4 **b** (ii) 2, $\frac{3}{2}$
3a $\frac{3}{4}$ **b** 4 **c** 1 **d** $\frac{1}{2}$ **e** $\frac{3}{2}$ **f** 1 **g** $\frac{1}{3}$ **h** 2 **i** 1 **4a** $\frac{3}{2}$ **b** 1
5a $\frac{2}{5}$ **b** $\frac{1}{3}$ **c** 4 **6a** It is 1 **b** more than 1 **c** less than 1
7

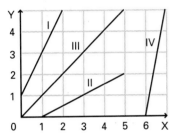

8a $\frac{3}{5}$ **b** make the horizontal and vertical parts equal

Page 5 Exercise 3A

1a $\frac{1}{4}$ **b** -1 **c** 2 **d** $-\frac{1}{2}$ **2a** -1 **b** -2 **3a** $-\frac{1}{2}$ **b** $-\frac{4}{3}$
4a 2, -2 **b** same numbers, opposite signs
5a (i) Steps (ii) slide **b** 2, $-\frac{4}{5}$ **6** AB 1, CD $\frac{1}{4}$, EF 0, GH -2
7 PQ 4, RS -1, TV -3
8

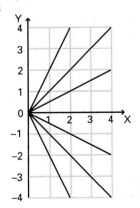

Page 6 Exercise 3B

1a PQ $\frac{1}{3}$, RS $\frac{1}{3}$, TU -1, VW -1 **b** PQ, RS and TU, VW
2a AB $\frac{1}{4}$, BC 3, DC $\frac{1}{4}$, AD 3 **b** a parallelogram
3a PQ $\frac{2}{5}$, QR -2, SR 0, PS -2 **b** a trapezium
4a AB 1, CD -1, EF 4, GH -1 **b** CD and GH
5b EF $\frac{1}{4}$, FG -2, GH $\frac{1}{4}$, EH -2 **c** a parallelogram
6

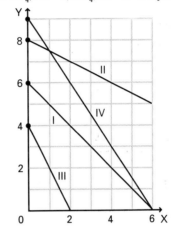

Page 7 Exercise 4

1a Row: $-4, -3, -2, -1, 0, 1, 2, 3, 4$ **c** see answer to **3**
d as far as you like **2a** $-8, -6, -4, -2, 0, 2, 4, 6, 8$
b see answer to **3** **3a** $-12, -9, -6, -3, 0, 3, 6, 9, 12$
1bc, 2b, 3b

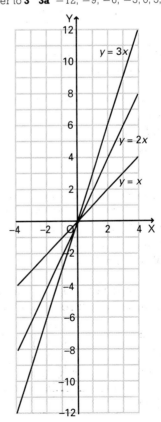

4a The origin **b** 1, 2, 3
c the number in front of x is the same as the gradient
5a 1, $y = x$ **b** 4, $y = 4x$ **c** $\frac{1}{2}$, $y = \frac{1}{2}x$ **d** $\frac{3}{4}$, $y = \frac{3}{4}x$
6a (i) $-3, -2, -1, 0, 1, 2, 3, 4, 5$ (ii) $-1, 0, 1, 2, 3, 4, 5, 6, 7$
b

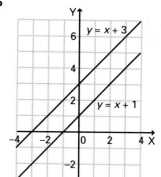

c the lines are parallel **d** 1
7a (i) $-7, -5, -3, -1, 1, 3, 5, 7, 9$
(ii) $-9, -7, -5, -3, -1, 1, 3, 5, 7$
b

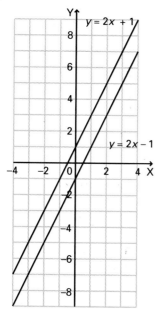

c the lines are parallel **d** 2

8a 2 **b** 4 **c** 10 **d** 1 **e** 1 **f** 3 **g** 7

Page 8 Exercise 5A

1a (i) 2 (ii) 6 **b** 2, $L = 2B$ **c** 18
2a (i) 200 km (ii) 400 km **b** 100, $D = 100T$ **c** 700 km
3a (i) 3 m (ii) 9 m **b** $\frac{3}{2}$, $W = \frac{3}{2}L$ **c** $10\frac{1}{2}$ m
4a 20 **b** $M = 20A$ **c** (i) 140 mm (ii) 160 mm (iii) 20 cm
5a 0, 3, 6, 9, 12, 15, 18, 21, 24 **c** 3, $M = 3C$ **d** 45
6a 0, 10, 20, 30, 40, 50 **c** 10, $D = 10T$ **d** (i) 25 km
(ii) 55 km **e** the gradient = the speed in km/h

Page 10 Exercise 5B

1a 10 **b** $C = 10T + 20$ **c** £140 **2a** 5
b its gradient is 5 and it cuts the C-axis 25 up from O
c £125 **3a** 2, 3, 4, 5, 6, 7, 8 **c** (i) 1 (ii) $C = D + 2$ **d** £32
4a 20, 25, 30, 35, 40, 45, 50 **c** (i) 5 (ii) $T = 5N + 20$ **d** £40
5a (i) -10 (ii) $V = -10T + 60$ **b** 10 litres
6b -6, $P = -6T + 24$ **c** 5 psi

Page 12 Check-up on Gradients and Graphs of Straight Lines

1a AB, CD, GH, MN **b** EF, KL, PQ **c** IJ
2 AB 1, CD 4, EF -1, GH 1, IJ 0, KL $-\frac{1}{3}$, MN $\frac{1}{3}$, PQ -3
3

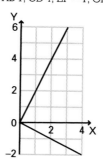

4 $\frac{5}{2}$ **5b** Gradient of LM and PN is $-\frac{1}{2}$; gradient of LP and MN is 4 **c** opposite sides are parallel
6 3, 0, 2, 0, 2 **7a** $-3, -2, -1, 0, 1, 2, 3$
b

Gradient $\frac{1}{3}$

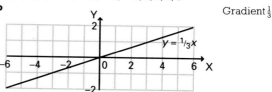

8a 10 **b** $V = 10T$ **c** 80 litres
9a 0, 10, 20, 30, 40, 50 **b** 10 **c** $C = 10T$ **d** £150
10b $C = 10T + 15$; £135

2 TRIGONOMETRY

Page 13 Looking Back

1a 9.2 **b** 35.3 **c** 0.9 **2a** 55° **b** 33° **3a** PR **b** 8.5 m
4a $\frac{1}{3}$ **b** $\frac{1}{3}$ **c** $\frac{1}{3}$ **5** OAD, OBE, OCF **6a** $\angle$BAC **b** 45°
7a 8 **b** 30 **c** 42 **8** (i) 20 (ii) 8, 30, 42
9b 10.3 km **c** 61°, 29°

Page 15 Exercise 2

1

a   **b**

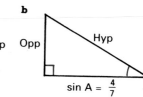

$\sin A = \frac{3}{5}$ $\sin A = \frac{4}{7}$

c   **d**

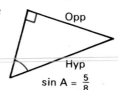   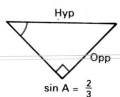

$\sin A = \frac{5}{8}$ $\sin A = \frac{2}{3}$

2a $\frac{5}{7}$ **b** $\frac{9}{11}$ **c** $\frac{1}{2}$ **d** $\frac{4}{5}$ **3a** 0.80 **b** 0.92 **c** 0.28 **d** 0.22
4a $\frac{3}{5}$, 0.60 **b** $\frac{5}{13}$, 0.38 **c** $\frac{24}{25}$, 0.96 **d** $\frac{40}{41}$, 0.98
5 0.17, 0.34, 0.50, 0.64, 0.77, 0.87, 0.94, 0.98
6a 0.37 **b** 0.91 **c** 0.16 **d** 1 **e** 0.62 **f** 0.97 **g** 0.09 **h** 0
7c 0.71 **d** approximately equal

Page 16   Exercise 3

1 $\sin 33° = \dfrac{x}{8}$, so $x = 8 \times \sin 33° = 4.4$

2a 7.7 **b** 21.7 **c** 9.4 **d** 6.1 **e** 1.9 **f** 3.6 **3a** 9.2 **b** 3.8
4a 17.2 cm **b** 15.3 cm **c** 13.2 cm **5** 0.8 m **6** 4.9 km
7a 15.5 m **b** 25.9 m **8a** 9.5 m **b** 16.3 m **c** 6.8 m

Page 17   Exercise 4

1a (i) $\frac{5}{7}$ (ii) 46° **b** (i) $\frac{5}{9}$ (ii) 34° **c** (i) $\frac{2}{3}$ (ii) 42° **d** (i) $\frac{11}{12}$
(ii) 66° **2a** 13° **b** 71° **3a** 32°, 58°
4a 60° **b** 19° **c** 65° **d** 40° **5a** (i) 63° (ii) 59° (iii) 58°
b (i), (ii), (iii) **6a** 66° **b** 17° **c** 56° **d** 40°
7c 10 cm **d** $\angle A = 37°$; $\angle C = 53°$

Page 19   Exercise 5

1

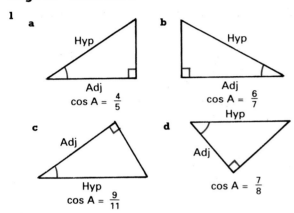

cos A = $\frac{4}{5}$ cos A = $\frac{6}{7}$

cos A = $\frac{9}{11}$ cos A = $\frac{7}{8}$

2a $\frac{5}{8}$ **b** $\frac{20}{23}$ **c** $\frac{4}{5}$ **d** $\frac{12}{13}$
3 0.98, 0.94, 0.87, 0.77, 0.64, 0.50, 0.34, 0.17

4 $\cos 32° = \dfrac{x}{1.5}$, so $x = 1.5 \times \cos 32° = 1.3$

5a 10.4 **b** 13.6 **c** 5.9 **d** 4.8 **6a** 3.4 m **b** 1.7 m
7a 4.0 m **b** 1.3 m **8a** 4.1 m **b** 20.5 m **c** 24.6 m

Page 20   Exercise 6

1a 76° **b** 85° **c** 41° **d** 60° **e** 27° **2a** (i) $\frac{6}{8}$ (ii) 48°
b (i) $\frac{18}{19}$ (ii) 19° **c** (i) $\frac{12}{13}$ (ii) 23° **d** (i) $\frac{55}{73}$ (ii) 41°
3 31° **4** 12° **5** 34° **6** 66° **7** 048°

Page 21   Exercise 7A

1

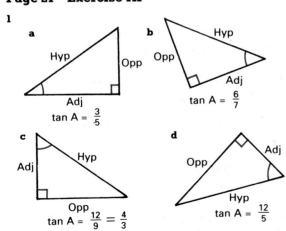

tan A = $\frac{3}{5}$ tan A = $\frac{6}{7}$

tan A = $\frac{12}{9} = \frac{4}{3}$ tan A = $\frac{12}{5}$

2a 1.43 **b** 0.83 **3a** 5.0 **b** 4.3 **c** 57.1 **d** 36.9
4a 6.4 **b** 14.4 **5a** 21.4 m **b** 83.9 m **6** 148.7 m **7** 70°
8a 24° **b** 59° **c** 60° **9a** 50° **b** 20° **10a** 14° **b** 9°

Page 22   Exercise 7B

1 20 m **2a** 300 m **b** 381 m **c** 413 m
3a 18°; alternate to given 18° angle **b** 32.5 m
4a 64° **b** 308 m

Page 23   Exercise 8A

1a $\sin x° = \dfrac{p}{q}$, $\cos x° = \dfrac{r}{q}$, $\tan x° = \dfrac{p}{r}$

b $\sin x° = \dfrac{u}{v}$, $\cos x° = \dfrac{w}{v}$, $\tan x° = \dfrac{u}{w}$

c $\sin x° = \dfrac{a}{c}$, $\cos x° = \dfrac{b}{c}$, $\tan x° = \dfrac{a}{b}$

2a 39 **b** 31 **c** 50 **d** 41 **3a** 4.2 **b** 9.3 **c** 70.7 **d** 5.6
4 29.4 m **5** 27° **6** 491 feet **7a** 31 cm **b** 41 cm **8** 71°
9a 12.6 m **b** 14.3 m

Page 24   Exercise 8B

1a 9.8 km **b** 6.9 km **2** 37°, 32°; football angle larger, so
should be easier to score **3a** 2.5 m **b** 6.9 m
4a

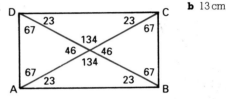

b 13 cm

5 44 m 20 cm **6a** 4.6 cm **b** 9.2 cm

Page 26   Check-up on Trigonometry

1

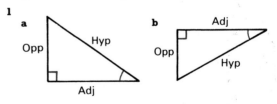

2a Sin **b** tan **c** cos **d** tan
3a $\frac{3}{5}$ **b** $\frac{7}{25}$ **c** $\frac{5}{12}$ **d** (i) $\frac{8}{15}$ (ii) $\frac{8}{17}$
4a 51° **b** 56° **c** 51° **d** 34° **5a** 3.6 cm **b** 8.1 cm
c 3.9 cm **d** 10.0 cm **6** 37° **7a** 120.4 km **b** 159.7 km
8 34° **9** 25 m, 50 m, 75 m
10a 6.9 **b** 4 **c** 10 **d** 27.6 or 27.7

REVIEW: NUMBERS

Page 27   Calculations 1

1a 1103 **b** 361 **2a** 1170 **b** 146 **3a** (i) 3.14 (ii) 3.1
b (i) 15.88 (ii) 16 **4a** 8 **b** 100 **c** 7 **d** 10
5a £6 **b** 2.5 kg **c** 8 h **6a** 5 cm **b** 5 cm
7a 70 mm **b** 200 cm **c** 1000 m **8a** 400 cm², 432 cm²
b 2500 cm², 2704 cm² **9a** $\frac{2}{5}$ **b** 0.4 **c** 40%
10a (i) 3100 (ii) 80 **b** (i) 12 (ii) 0.15 **11a** 19 **b** 6
12a 15 **b** 5° **13a** £44.40 **b** £27.90 **14** 12.8 **15** 24 km/h
16 £11 400 **17** £18 **18a** 225 cm² **b** 3375 cm³
19 1 h 50 min **20** 6.5 cm, 5.5 cm

Page 28   Calculations 2

1a £34, £408, £8160; £28, £336, £6720; £47, £564, £11 280
b £8720 **2a** 5 **b** 6 **3a** 32 **b** £4.80
4a 31, 38; add 7 **b** 44, 35; subtract 9
c 81, 243; multiply by 3 **d** 26, 37; add 3, 5, 7, . . .
5a 34 **b** 63 **c** 50 **d** 2 **e** 0 **f** 72 **6a** 84.25 **b** £16.37
7a 1.24p, 1.22p, 1.28p **b** medium, large, small
8a Dec, 480 **b** inc, 3000 **c** dec, 500 **d** inc, 900
9 £4317.85 **10a** 3.2, 3.16, 3.162 **b** 7.1, 7.07, 7.071
c 14.1, 14.14, 14.142

Page 29   Estimation and Approximation

1a   **b**

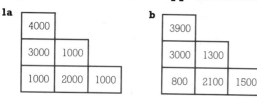

2a 910 km **b** 900 km **c** 1000 km
3a 1870 miles **b** 2454 miles
4

3950		
3010	1270	
817	2100	1480

5a 0.4, 1.1, 0.6 **b** 0.39, 1.09, 0.62 **c** 0.394, 1.094, 0.621
6a 800 **b** 320 000 **7a** 97 cm **b** (i) 240 cm, 234 cm
(ii) 2500 cm², 2340 cm² (iii) 40°–50°, 42°
8a 2000, £120, £150, £30, £180
b 1939, £114.79, £143.65, £25.14, £168.79

Page 30   Units

1a Weight **b** temperature **c** time **d** area
e volume of liquid **f** volume **g** speed **h** length
2a 1000 m **b** 10 mm **c** 1000 mg **d** 1000 ml **e** 3600 s
f 1000 kg **3a** 300 cm **b** 4.5 cm **c** 609 cm **d** 38 cm
4a $2\frac{1}{2}$ cm **b** $2\frac{1}{4}$ lb **c** $4\frac{1}{2}$ litres **d** $1\frac{1}{2}$ km
5a 26 mg **b** 0.026 g **6a** 60°F **b** 58°F
7 11.55 s and 11.65 s **8a** 8.5 m, 9.5 m; 6.5 m, 7.5 m
b 55 m², 71 m² **9a** 20 m/s **b** 504 km/h

Page 30   Some Special Numbers

1a 36 **b** 125 **c** 10 000 **d** 9 **e** 3 **2a** 8 **b** 32 **c** 128
3a 7 cm **b** 4 cm **4** 2, 3, 5, 7, 11, 13, 17, 19 **5** 23, 97
6a 25 **b** 5 **c** 35 **d** 6 **e** 6, 8, 48 **f** 48 **g** 8
7a (i) 6, 12, 18, 24, 30, 36, 42, 48, 54
(ii) 8, 16, 24, 32, 40, 48, 56 **b** 24, 48 **c** 24
8a 1, 2; 1, 3; 1, 2, 4; 1, 5; 1, 2, 3, 6; 1, 7; 1, 2, 4, 8; 1, 3, 9;
1, 2, 5, 10 **b** square numbers
9a (i) 12 min (ii) 24 min **b** (i) 36 min (ii) 72 min
10a (i) 1, 2, 3, 6, 7, 14, 21, 42 (ii) 1, 3, 7, 9, 21, 63 **b** 21
11a 2×5 **b** 2×3×3 **c** 3×3×3×3 **d** 3×5×5
e 2×2×5×5 **f** 2×2×2×2×2×5
12a 2×5 **b** 2×3² **c** 3⁴ **d** 3×5² **e** 2²×5² **f** 2⁵×5

Page 31   Ratio and Proportion

1a 1:3 **b** 2:1 **c** 3:2 **d** 5:6 **2a** 5:1 **b** 1:100 **c** 1:6
3a £3, £6 **b** 20 kg, 4 kg **c** 60 m, 40 m **d** 375 m, 625 m
4 9 litres of filler, 3 of water
5 360 g flour, 90 g marg, 45 g sugar, 225 ml milk **6a** 15 m
b 40 cm **7** 47.5 yards **8a** 50 m **b** 150 m **c** 500 m

---

9 £100 000 **10a** Row: 80, 160, 240, 320, 400, 480, 560, 640
c (i) 360 francs (ii) £75 **11a** Row: 12, 8, 6, 4.8, 4 **c** 5 hours

Page 32   Standard Form

1a 300 **b** 60 000 **c** 7500 **d** 12 300 **e** 0.7 **f** 0.09
g 0.038 **h** 0.006 5 **2a** 6×10 **b** 9×10³ **c** 4.8×10⁴
d 9.2×10⁹ **e** 8×10⁻¹ **f** 1×10⁻⁴ **g** 2.9×10⁻² **h** 7×10⁻⁷
3a 2×10⁴ = 20 000 **b** 7.3×10³ = 7300
c 4.44×10⁵ = 444 000 **d** 3×10⁻¹ = 0.3
e 2.5×10⁻³ = 0.0025 **f** 8.99×10⁻⁵ = 0.000 089 9
4a 3.84×10⁵ **b** 3×10⁸ **c** 3.5×10⁻² **d** 1×10⁻¹⁵
5 2.964×10⁸ **6** 6×10⁻³ mm **7a** 1.95×10¹⁸ **b** 3.35×10⁹
8a 9.4608×10¹² **b** 9.4608×10¹⁹

Page 32   Distance–Speed–Time

1a $D = S \times T$ **b** $S = \dfrac{D}{T}$ **c** $T = \dfrac{D}{S}$

2a 16 km/h **b** $2\frac{1}{2}$ h **c** 255 km **3** 11 am **4a** 36 km **b** 2 h
c (i) 72 km (ii) 8 h (iii) 9 km/h **5a** 65 km/h **b** 21 27
6 Rachel left at 9 am, drove for $1\frac{1}{4}$ hours at an average speed
of 64 mph, then stopped for $\frac{3}{4}$ hour. She then drove for 1 hour
at an average speed of 70 mph, reaching her destination
150 miles from home at noon. John left home at 9.30 and drove
for $2\frac{1}{2}$ hours at an average speed of 60 mph. He reached his
destination 150 miles away at noon. He passed Rachel at
10.48 am

3   FRACTIONS, DECIMALS AND PERCENTAGES

Page 33   Looking Back

1a $\frac{1}{4}$ **b** $\frac{1}{3}$ **c** $\frac{1}{2}$ **2a** $\frac{1}{4}$ **b** $\frac{1}{3}$ **c** $\frac{5}{12}$
3a £2.50 **b** £6 **c** £12 **d** £21 **4a** 30p **b** £3 **c** £25
5a 1 tenth **b** 4 hundredths **6** 8.99, 9.06, 10, 10.8, 11
7a $\frac{1}{12}$ **b** $\frac{1}{6}$ **c** $\frac{1}{4}$ **d** $\frac{1}{3}$ **e** $\frac{5}{12}$ **f** $\frac{1}{2}$ **g** $\frac{7}{12}$ **h** $\frac{2}{3}$ **i** $\frac{3}{4}$ **j** $\frac{5}{6}$ **k** $\frac{11}{12}$
8a 60% **b** 40% **9a** $\frac{9}{16}$ **b** $\frac{7}{16}$ **10a** 23.31 **b** 4.5 **c** (i) 23.4
(ii) 234 (iii) 2340 **11** Rows: $\frac{1}{4}$, $\frac{1}{5}$, $\frac{1}{2}$, $\frac{3}{4}$, $\frac{3}{25}$, $\frac{1}{20}$; 0.25, 0.2, 0.5, 0.75,
0.12, 0.05; 25%, 20%, 50%, 75%, 12%, 5% **12a** 25 ml
b 275 ml

Page 34   Exercise 1A

1a £3 **b** £7.50 **c** £1.95 **d** 3p **2a** £1.40 **b** £4.60 **c** £18
d 25p **3** 24 mm, 16 mm **4a** 1206 **b** 134 **5** £770
6a (i) 14 cm (ii) 12.25 cm² **b** (i) 18.2 cm (ii) 15.64 cm²
7a 108 g **b** 130 g **8a** (i) 11 960 (ii) 11 040 **b** 920
9 b, by £27.50 **10** 75.4 kg

Page 35   Exercise 1B

1a $\frac{3}{8}$ **b** $\frac{5}{8}$ **2a** 35% **b** 65% **3a** 2040 **b** 2000 **4** Lisa, £1
5a 64 **b** £37.70 **c** 6.9p **6** 80%, 80%, no
7a 60% **b** yes **8** 80, 87.5, 92, 70, 65

Page 36   Exercise 2A

1a £18 **b** £378 **2a** £30 **b** £170 **3a** 1750 **b** 15 750
4 1680 km/h **5a** 2040 g, 1960 g **b** 357 g, 343 g
c 61.2 g, 58.8 g **6** £28
7a (i) £1200 (ii) £21 000 **b** (i) £1272 (ii) £22 472

Page 37   Exercise 2B

1a 5p **b** 12.5% **2a** 3p **b** 8.3% **3a** £3000 **b** 20%

4a 3 kg b 6.25% 5a 102 mm, 76.5 mm
b 7500 mm², 7803 mm² c 303 mm² d 4.04% 6a C. Morris
b R. Field 7 4%, 4.8%, 8.7%, 8%, 10.7%, 6.7%
8a (i) £27.90 (ii) 4.5% b £677.06 9a 8.06, 9.85 b 18.2%

Page 38 Exercise 3A

1a 0.45 b 0.8 c 0.08 d 0.12 e 1.2
2a $\frac{3}{10}$ b $\frac{4}{5}$ c $\frac{1}{50}$ d $\frac{6}{5}$ e $\frac{9}{50}$
3a 45% b 33% c 80% d 150% e 7%
4a 30% b 13% c 7% d 80% e 12.5% 5a $\frac{7}{10}$ b $\frac{4}{5}$
c $\frac{3}{100}$ d $\frac{3}{50}$ e $\frac{7}{20}$ 6a 0.75 b 0.3 c 0.4 d 0.33 e 0.57

Page 38 Exercise 3B

1a 0.6 b $\frac{3}{5}$ c 10% d $\frac{1}{4}$ e $\frac{5}{8}$ f $\frac{7}{8}$ 2a 0.25, $\frac{1}{4}$ b 0.4, $\frac{2}{5}$
c 0.05, $\frac{1}{20}$ 3a $\frac{4}{25}$, 16% b $\frac{1}{10}$, 10% c $\frac{9}{100}$, 9% 4b (ii)
5a 30%, 0.33, $\frac{1}{3}$ b 0.62, $\frac{5}{8}$, 65% c 150%, 1$\frac{4}{5}$, 1.6
6 Hivalue, by £35 7 Rows: $\frac{4}{5}$, $\frac{9}{25}$, $\frac{17}{25}$, $\frac{3}{8}$, $\frac{13}{50}$, $\frac{1}{25}$, 1$\frac{7}{20}$, 2$\frac{9}{20}$, 3$\frac{1}{20}$;
0.8, 0.36, 0.68, 0.375, 0.26, 0.04, 1.35, 2.45, 3.05;
80%, 36%, 68%, 37.5%, 26%, 4%, 135%, 245%, 305%

Page 39 Exercise 4

1a 1$\frac{1}{2}$ b 2$\frac{1}{4}$ c 1$\frac{3}{8}$ d 3$\frac{1}{3}$ e 2$\frac{2}{5}$ 2a $\frac{7}{2}$ b $\frac{7}{4}$ c $\frac{11}{5}$ d $\frac{16}{3}$ e $\frac{11}{10}$
3a 1$\frac{3}{8}$ b 5$\frac{1}{2}$ c 2$\frac{4}{5}$ d 2$\frac{3}{10}$ e 2$\frac{2}{9}$
4a $\frac{14}{3}$ b $\frac{27}{8}$ c $\frac{17}{10}$ d $\frac{9}{8}$ e $\frac{47}{8}$
5a $\frac{15}{8}$ b $\frac{27}{4}$ c $\frac{13}{4}$ d $\frac{100}{3}$ 6 Rows: $\frac{11}{4}$, $\frac{17}{4}$, $\frac{23}{4}$, $\frac{31}{4}$, $\frac{23}{4}$;
11, 17, 23, 31, 23 7a $\frac{3}{2}$ b $\frac{4}{3}$ c $\frac{7}{2}$ d $\frac{19}{4}$
8a 1.5, 1.25 b 1.3..., 1.2 c 3.3..., 3.5 d 4.75, 4.4
9a $\frac{6}{4}$, $\frac{5}{4}$ b $\frac{20}{15}$, $\frac{18}{15}$ c $\frac{20}{6}$, $\frac{21}{6}$ d $\frac{95}{20}$, $\frac{88}{20}$

Page 40 Exercise 5A

1a $\frac{4}{5}$ b $\frac{1}{2}$ c 1 d $\frac{5}{7}$ 2a $\frac{3}{8}$ b $\frac{2}{3}$ c 0 d $\frac{1}{5}$
3a 1 b $\frac{1}{5}$ c $\frac{2}{5}$ d $\frac{1}{5}$ 4a 1$\frac{1}{5}$ b 1$\frac{3}{8}$ c 1$\frac{1}{2}$ d 1$\frac{3}{5}$
5a 1 b $\frac{3}{5}$ c 2 d 1 6a 2$\frac{1}{3}$ b 5$\frac{1}{2}$ c 3 d 3$\frac{1}{3}$
7a 2$\frac{1}{2}$ b 1$\frac{1}{4}$ c 2$\frac{1}{4}$ d 3$\frac{1}{2}$ 8a 3 b $\frac{1}{3}$ c 4 d 1$\frac{3}{8}$
9a (i) 3$\frac{1}{2}$ m (ii) 16 m b (i) 5$\frac{1}{4}$ m (ii) 16 m
10a 5$\frac{1}{2}$ miles b 7$\frac{1}{4}$ miles c 1$\frac{3}{4}$ miles
11a 5$\frac{1}{2}$ gallons b 2 gallons 12a 2$\frac{1}{4}$ h b 2 h c 1$\frac{1}{2}$ h

Page 41 Exercise 5B

1a $\frac{3}{8}$ b $\frac{5}{6}$ c $\frac{5}{6}$ d $\frac{7}{10}$ 2a $\frac{5}{8}$ b $\frac{11}{15}$ c $\frac{7}{8}$ d 1$\frac{1}{4}$
3a $\frac{1}{4}$ b $\frac{1}{8}$ c $\frac{11}{12}$ d $\frac{1}{12}$ 4a $\frac{2}{5}$ b $\frac{5}{8}$ c $\frac{1}{10}$ d $\frac{1}{10}$
5a 1$\frac{1}{3}$ b 2$\frac{1}{4}$ c 2$\frac{5}{8}$ d 3$\frac{1}{2}$ 6a 1$\frac{3}{5}$ b 2$\frac{1}{8}$ c 3$\frac{1}{6}$ d 1$\frac{3}{5}$
7 1$\frac{1}{8}$ litre 8 7$\frac{1}{4}$ tonnes 9a 6$\frac{3}{8}$ lb b 6$\frac{3}{4}$ lb c Paul, by $\frac{3}{8}$ lb
10 $\frac{4}{15}$ 11 240 12a $\frac{7}{8}$ b $\frac{1}{3}$
13a $\frac{1}{20}$ b Janice 50, Lana 25, Sean 20, Andrew 5

Page 42 Exercise 6A

1a 4 b 4 c 1$\frac{2}{3}$ d 1$\frac{3}{5}$ 2a $\frac{1}{8}$ b $\frac{1}{6}$ c $\frac{2}{5}$ d $\frac{1}{10}$
3a $\frac{1}{4}$ b $\frac{1}{12}$ c $\frac{1}{5}$ d $\frac{1}{4}$ 4a 2 b 1$\frac{1}{2}$ c 1$\frac{1}{2}$ d 3$\frac{3}{4}$
5a $\frac{1}{5}$ b $\frac{1}{8}$ c $\frac{1}{4}$ d $\frac{1}{16}$ 6a $\frac{1}{8}$ b $\frac{1}{2}$ sq unit c $\frac{1}{3}$ in each case
7a $\frac{1}{9}$ b $\frac{1}{6}$ sq unit c $\frac{4}{9}$ in each case 8 42 kg 9 12 kg 10 10
11 21 12a (i) 2 (ii) 4 (iii) 1$\frac{1}{3}$ b (i) $\frac{1}{3}$ (ii) $\frac{2}{9}$ (iii) $\frac{1}{2}$ 13 b
14 22$\frac{1}{2}$ m² 15 300 km/h 16a 25 b 40 c 100
17 Dress £38.40, each skirt £9.60

Page 43 Exercise 6B

1a 3 b 3$\frac{3}{4}$ c 12$\frac{1}{2}$ d 20 2a 2$\frac{1}{4}$ b 1$\frac{1}{2}$ c 3 d 4
3a 6 b 7$\frac{1}{2}$ c 1$\frac{1}{2}$ d 9 4a 1$\frac{9}{16}$ m² b 29$\frac{1}{4}$ cm²
5a 15$\frac{3}{4}$ b 23$\frac{1}{8}$ c 14$\frac{5}{8}$ 6a 100 b 150 7a 7$\frac{1}{2}$ km b 11$\frac{1}{4}$ km
8a 22$\frac{1}{2}$ m³ b 147 m³
9a 75, 150, 300 b each is double the previous one
10a 18 cm b 13$\frac{1}{2}$ cm² c 3$\frac{3}{8}$ cm³

Page 44 Exercise 7B

1a 8 b 15 c 8 d 12 2a 2 b 4 c 1$\frac{1}{2}$ d 2 3a 4 b 6
c 8 d 3 4a 2$\frac{2}{5}$ b 2$\frac{1}{2}$ c 1$\frac{4}{5}$ d 1$\frac{1}{2}$ 5a 4 m b 6 m 6 192
7a 4 b 2 c 5 8 6
9a 12 b 12 c 5$\frac{1}{3}$ d $\frac{3}{16}$ e 1$\frac{1}{8}$ f 2 g $\frac{1}{2}$ h 10$\frac{2}{3}$

Page 45 Check-up on Fractions, Decimals and Percentages

1a $\frac{1}{8}$ b $\frac{7}{8}$ 2a £4.60 b £147 c £1.80 d £47.25 e £3000
3a (i) 11.5 mph (ii) 28.75 mph b (i) 8.7 knots
(ii) 31.3 knots 4a £1.80 b £10.20 5 7.5%
6a £3.60 b £2.88 and £4.32 7a £5400 b £5832
8 Rows: $\frac{1}{2}$, $\frac{1}{4}$, $\frac{1}{10}$, $\frac{2}{5}$, $\frac{7}{100}$, $\frac{18}{25}$, $\frac{1}{8}$, $\frac{13}{20}$, $\frac{4}{5}$, $\frac{9}{10}$, 2$\frac{3}{4}$, 1$\frac{1}{100}$;
0.5, 0.25, 0.1, 0.4, 0.07, 0.72, 0.125, 0.65, 0.8, 0.9, 2.75, 1.01;
50%, 25%, 10%, 40%, 7%, 72%, 12.5%, 65%, 80%, 90%,
275%, 101% 9a (i) $\frac{5}{3}$ (ii) $\frac{5}{2}$ (iii) $\frac{22}{7}$ (iv) $\frac{15}{8}$ b (i) 2$\frac{1}{4}$ (ii) 3$\frac{2}{3}$
(iii) 2$\frac{7}{10}$ (iv) 3$\frac{3}{5}$
10a 1 b 3$\frac{1}{4}$ c 1$\frac{1}{4}$ d $\frac{2}{15}$ e 2 f 2$\frac{5}{8}$ g 2$\frac{1}{4}$ h $\frac{2}{3}$
11a 2 b 6 c $\frac{3}{8}$ d $\frac{8}{15}$ e $\frac{3}{10}$ f 1 g $\frac{9}{10}$ h 3
12a 30 m b 35.5 m² c 13.125 m³
13a 15 inches b 4$\frac{1}{2}$ inches c 1$\frac{1}{8}$ square inches 14 8$\frac{1}{4}$ inches

4 EQUATIONS AND INEQUALITES

Page 46 Looking Back

1a 4 b 3 c 7 2a $2x+6$ b $3t-3$ c $10+5p$
3a $2x = 16$, $x = 8$ b $3n = 21$, $n = 7$ c $5y+1 = 11$, $y = 2$
4a $x+1 = 7$, $x = 6$ b $2n = 6$, $n = 3$ 5 $3n+1 = 19$, $n = 6$
6 $4m-3 = 9$, $m = 3$ 7a $4(x+3)$ cm² b $4x+12 = 32$, $x = 5$
c 24 cm 8 $2x+2 = x+5$, $x = 3$ 9a 6 b 4 c 3
10a F b T c F d T e F
11a 1, 2, 3 b 2, 3 c $-3, -2, -1$ d $-3, -2, -1$
12a $x > 5$ b $y < 2$ c $g \geqslant 30$ d $a \geqslant 6$ e $t \leqslant 6$ f $h \leqslant 3.5$

Page 47 Exercise 1A

1a 4 b 8 c 10 2a 3 b 1 c 4 3a 3 b 2 c 1
4a 2 b 2 c 5 5a 4 b 9 c 10 6a $3x-3 = 18$, $x = 7$
b $5k-1 = 9$, $k = 2$ c $7y+4 = 25$, $y = 3$ 7a (vi) b (v)
c (iv) d (ii) e (i) f (iii) 8a $2x+3 = 15$, $x = 6$; 6
b $3x+5 = 23$, $x = 6$; 6 c $3x+4 = 13$, $x = 3$; 3
9a $5x-3 = 17$, $x = 4$ b $10y+4 = 44$, $y = 4$
c $3m-7 = 20$, $m = 9$ d $7t+9 = 30$, $t = 3$
10a $x+130 = 180$, $x = 50$ b $2y+100 = 180$, $y = 40$
c $9a = 360$, $a = 40$ d $2v+80 = 180$, $v = 50$
11a 6 b 10 c 24 d 34

Page 48 Exercise 1B

1a 4 b 5 c 6 d 3 e 1 f 2 2a 6 b 0 c 2 d 2 e 1
f 1 3a $2(x+1) = 18$, 8 b $3(2x+3) = 33$, 4
4a $8(3x+1) = 56$, 2 b $7(2x-3) = 35$, 4
c $10(5x-2) = 380$, 8 5a 2 b 2$\frac{1}{2}$ c 3$\frac{1}{2}$ d 5$\frac{1}{2}$
6a 1$\frac{1}{3}$ b 4$\frac{1}{2}$ c $\frac{1}{2}$ d 2$\frac{1}{3}$ e 1$\frac{1}{4}$ f $\frac{1}{2}$
7a -3 b -4 c -1 d -2 e -4 f -3
8a -3 b -1 c -1 d -2 9a -2 b -2 c -1
d -2 10a 1$\frac{1}{2}$ b 1$\frac{1}{3}$ c $\frac{1}{2}$ d -1 e -2 f -2

Page 49 Exercise 2A

1a 4 b 2 c 3 2a 10 b 3 c 2 3a 3 b 1 c 2
4a 7 b 5 c 6 5a 4 b 3 c 2 6a 1 b 3 c 2
7a 1 b 1 c 2 8a 4 b 2 c 2

9a $5x = 4x+7$, $x = 7$; 35   **b** $5x = 3x+4$, $x = 2$; 10
c $6x = 8-2x$, 1; 6   **d** $7x = 4x+9$, 3; 21
10a $3x = 2x+4$, 4; 12   **b** $4x = 3x+7$, 7; 28
11a $5x = x+16$, 4; 4, 8, 8   **b** $3y = 2y+4$, 4; 4, 4, 4
c $8t = 5t+15$, 5; 10, 15, 15
12 Rows: 12, 32, 18, 37; columns 23, 21, 83, 72

Page 50   Exercise 2B

1a 7 **b** 2 **c** 4 **d** 1 **e** $1\frac{1}{2}$ **f** $\frac{1}{2}$ **g** -1 **h** -1
2a $4x+4 = 3x+7$, 3 **b** $5y-2 = 3y+4$, 3 **c** $4t+1 = 6-t$, 1
3a 8 **b** 1 **c** 3 **d** 4 **e** -1 **f** 0 **g** 1 **h** $1\frac{1}{2}$
4a $7(x+5) = 5(2x+1)$, 10 **b** (i) 15, 21 (ii) 105
5a $6(y-1) = 2(y+1)$, 2 **b** (i) 1 litre, 3 litres (ii) 6 litres
6a (i) $5(n-3) = 2(n+3)$, 7 (ii) 20
b (i) $3(2x+1) = 5(2x-1)$, 2 (ii) 15
c (i) $2(7x+2) = 3(5x+1)$, 1 (ii) 18
d (i) $3(3x-2) = 5(x+2)$, 4 (ii) 30

Page 53   Exercise 3A

1a 8 **b** 5 **c** 2 **d** 0 **e** 7 **f** 1 **g** 0 **h** -2
2a F **b** T **c** T **d** F **e** T **f** F **g** F **h** F **i** T
3a $3 < 5$ **b** $2 > 0$ **c** $-1 < 1$ **d** $-2 < -1$ **e** $-3 < 3$
f $4 > -4$ **g** $0 > -1$ **h** $-1 < 0$
4a $x < y$ **b** $m > n$ **c** $u = v$ **d** $s = t$ **e** $a > b$ **f** $c < d$
5a 5 **b** 4, 5 **c** 1, 2 **d** 1, 2, 3 **e** 1, 2, 3 **f** 1, 2, 3, 4, 5
6a 1, 2 **b** -2, -1 **c** -1, 0, 1, 2 **d** -2, -1
e -2, -1, 0, 1 **f** -2, -1, 0, 1, 2 **7a** 4, 5, 6 **b** 1
c 1, 2, 3, 4, 5, 6 **8a** $x < 5$; 1, 2, 3, 4 **b** $x > 3$; 4, 5, 6, 7
c $x < 2$; 1 **d** $x > 2$; 3, 4, 5, 6, 7

Page 54   Exercise 3B

1a $x > 1$ **b** $x < 4$ **c** $y \geqslant 2$ **2a** $x > 3$ **b** $x < 2$ **c** $x < 2\frac{1}{2}$
3a $m < 3$ **b** $t \geqslant 1$ **c** $k \leqslant 1$ **4a** $p \leqslant 6$ **b** $q > -1$
c $r > -2$ **5a** $x > 6$ **b** $y < 1$ **c** $z < 5$
6a $x > 1$ **b** $y > -2$ **c** $t < 1$ **7a** $u \geqslant 2$ **b** $v < 2$
8a $t \geqslant 0$ **b** $w < 3$ **9a** $a > -3$ **b** $b < 1\frac{1}{2}$
10a $4(2x-1) > 2(x+4)$, $x > 2$ **b** (i) > 3 (ii) > 6
11a $4x+6 > 2x+12$, $x > 3$ **b** (i) > 5 (ii) > 7

Page 55   Check-up on Equations and Inequalities

1a 5 **b** 4 **c** 7 **d** 4 **e** 2 **f** 6
2a $6m-2 = 16$, 3 **b** $4n+3 = 19$, 4 **3a** $x+2 = 10$, $x = 8$; 8
b $2x+3 = 5$, $x = 1$; 1 **4a** 3 **b** 2 **c** 0 **5a** $5(x+2) = 45$, 7
b $7(2x+1) = 49$, 3 **6a** $4\frac{1}{2}$ **b** -5 **c** $1\frac{1}{2}$ **d** -5 **e** -1
f -3 **7a** 2 **b** 5 **c** -2 **8a** 2 **b** $5\frac{1}{2}$ **c** 4 **d** 5
9a $7(x+3) = 3(4x+2)$, 3 **b** 7, 6, 42; 14, 3, 42
10a T **b** T **c** T **d** F **e** T **f** F **11a** 3, 4, 5 **b** 1, 2
c 2, 3, 4, 5 **d** 1, 2, 3 **12a** $x > 3$ **b** $x < 1$ **c** $x \geqslant 2$ **d** $x \leqslant 2$
e $x > 11$ **13a** $2y+3 > 7$, $y > 2$ **b** $2x+6 > 3x+3$, $x < 3$

STATISTICS

Page 56   Looking Back

1a Food, housing **b** (i) £272.10 (ii) 6% **2a** (i) 178 cm
(ii) 162 cm **b** (i) 16 cm (ii) 170 cm **c** 172 cm
3a Frequencies: 3, 18, 7, 2 **b** 31–35 s **c** there are three fast
and two slow runners; the rest all finish within 6 seconds of
each other **4 a**, has little effect, **b** increases the yield,
c provides very mixed results. **b** is best **5** 47°

Page 57   Exercise 1

1a (i) Radio 1 (ii) Radio 3 **b** 42 million **c** Radio 5
2 The number who bought their own food increased, while
those who bought a meal decreased—perhaps due to
increased costs. The number having free meals increased,
possibly due to unemployment and the recession.
3a (i) 44%, 56% (ii) 30%, 70%
b There are more women than men alive at each stage, and
the difference increases with age
4a Fewer used cars (about $\frac{1}{4}$ fewer), same number used train,
fewer used bus ($\frac{1}{4}$ fewer), more cycled (3 times as many).
b 60, 180 **5b** Soon after age 70 only half as many smokers as
non-smokers were alive; by age 85, it was only $\frac{1}{4}$
6a (i) 45 million (ii) 45.6%, 17.8%, 5.6%, 31.1%
b angles 164°, 64°, 20°, 112°

Page 58   Exercise 2A

1a 103°F, fourth **b** ninth day **c** 100 or 101°F **d** 100.4°F
2 1 610 000 **3a** 40.2 min **b** 20 min, 31 min
c the median, as the 120 min distorts the mean, and the mode
is obviously too extreme
4a G **b** (i) 31.2, 18 (ii) 40.1, 11 **c** they all improved **5** 20

Page 59   Exercise 2B

1a 12, 72, 69, 76, 40, 12 **b** 281 **c** 100 **d** 2.81
2a Rows: 5.5, 15.5, 25.5, 35.5, 45.5, 55.5;
88, 883.5, 2448, 2911, 2002, 1276.5
b mean is 30.2 min, to 1 decimal place, so only 0.2 min out
3a Rows: 25, 75, 125, 175, 225, 275; 5, 14, 6, 7, 15, 3;
125, 1050, 750, 1225, 3375, 825
b 147 yards **c** $200 \leqslant d < 250$
d no; her mean drive is 53 yards short of this distance

Page 60   Exercise 3

1a (ii) **b** (i) **c** (iii)

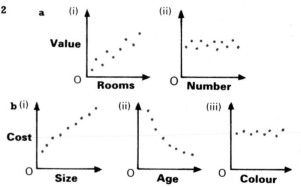

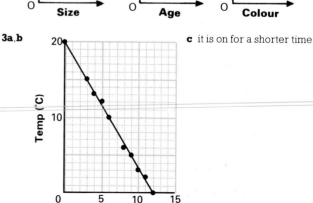

c it is on for a shorter time

4b 7.6, 166.8 cm

c

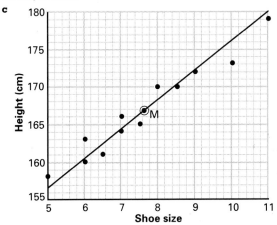

d $10\frac{1}{2}$

Page 61 Exercise 4A

1a 100 **b** 88% **2a** $30 \leqslant t < 40$ **3b** (i) 26 (ii) $40 \leqslant A < 50$
4b 76–80 **c** 81–85 **d** 81.5 **e** 65

Page 62 Exercise 4B

1a Rows: 5, 15, 45, 60, 65, 10; 45, 25, 50, 20, 20. 35, 5 **b** 200
c A 70 cm, B 57 cm **d** A is taller and more consistent
2a Rows: 8, 11, 6, 5, 0; 0, 3, 10, 11, 6 **c** in the British and
Greek resorts respectively the temperatures were: mean
18.3, 25.3 (using the frequency table); median 15–19, 25–29;
mode 15–19, 25–29; range 17, 15; highest 29, 33; lowest 12, 18.
Obviously much warmer in Greece
3b The mean distance for Tough Tyres is 29 500 km and for
Tireless Tyres 30 000 km. Tough Tyres have a smaller range
and are better up to 40 000 km

Page 64 Check-up on Statistics

1a In thousands: (i) 1000, 850, 650, 700
(ii) 300, 450, 600, 600 (iii) 1300, 1300, 1250, 1300
b Total sales stayed about the same. The trend for home sales
was downwards and for exports upwards, although these
were levelling off from 1991 **2a** (i) 10.8 h (ii) 9.7 h
b

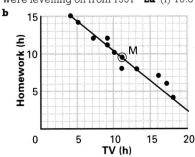

c 7 h **3a** (i) 2 years (ii) 8 years **b** (i) 3 years
(ii) 3.1 years **4b** 16% **5a** Rows: 13, 2, 2, 14; 1, 4, 7, 10;
13, 8, 14, 140 **b** 5.6 **c** the first or last week

REVIEW: SHAPE AND SPACE

(Degree symbols are not included in the diagrams.)

Page 65 Angles and Triangles

1a 4 **b** 10 **c** 2 **d** 4 **2a** (i) $\angle$ DAC (ii) $\angle$ AED or $\angle$ BEC

(iii) $\angle$ AED **b** (i) BC (ii) AB or DC **3** $x° = 120°$, $y° = 240°$
4a $a = 20$ **b** $b = 135$ **c** $c = 125$ **5a** 32 **b** 36
6 **a**   **b**

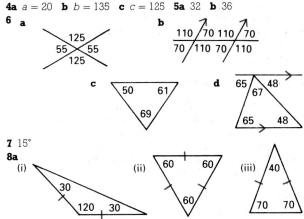

7 15°
8a
(i)   (ii)   (iii)

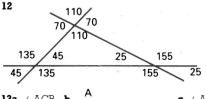

b (i) isosceles, obtuse-angled (ii) equilateral, acute-
angled (iii) isosceles, acute-angled
9 AB = QR, AC = PQ, BC = RP;
$\angle$ A = $\angle$ Q, $\angle$ B = $\angle$ R, $\angle$ C = $\angle$ P **10a** 3 m² **b** 1520 cm²
11b (i) 90° (ii) 100°
12

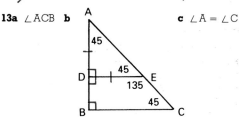

13a $\angle$ ACB **b**   **c** $\angle$ A = $\angle$ C

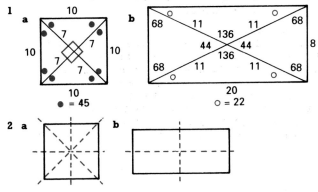

Page 66 Quadrilaterals

1
a   **b**

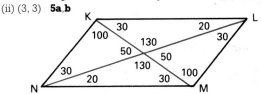

● = 45   ○ = 22

2 a   **b**

3a Parallelogram **b** kite **c** trapezium **4c** (i) (0, 4)
(ii) (3, 3) **5a,b**

c (i) KL = NM, KN = LM, NO = OL, KO = OM
(ii) △s MNO, KLO; KNO, LMO; LMN, LKN; KMN, KML
6 ABCD, by 200 m

7a 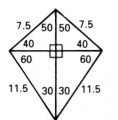 **b** 38 cm

8a,b,c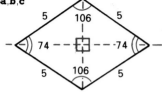

9c Kite **d** (i) (0, 0), (3, −1), (1, −3), (6, −6)
(ii) (0, 0), (−3, 1), (−1, 3), (−6, 6) **e** $y = x$

Page 67   Reflection and Rotation

1 D(−2, 2), E(−6, 0), F(−2, −2), G(0, −6), H(2, −2)
2a 6 **b** 6 **c** (i) 60° (ii) 120°

3 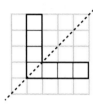 **4**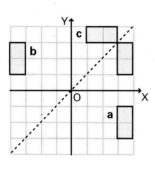

c $x = 0, y = 0$

5a,b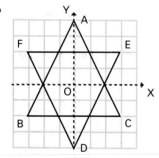

6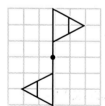

7 a 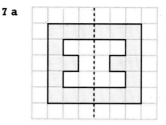 **b**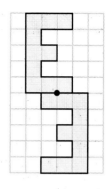

8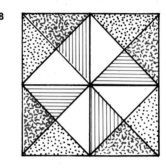

Page 68   Scale Drawing

1b (i) 6.5 cm (ii) 13 m **2a** 6 cm **b** (i) 300 000 cm
(ii) 3000 m (iii) 3 km **3b** 12.1 miles **4a** 1 cm to 10 miles
b (i) 105° (ii) 285° **5a** 55° **c** (i) 76 km (ii) 66° (iii) 024°
6b (i) 50° (ii) 100° **d** (ii) 148 miles **7a,b** (i) 60° (ii) 3.76 m

Page 69   Pythagoras' Theorem

1a 15 **b** 36 **c** 25 **d** 20 **2a** 3.46 m **b** 3.74 m
3a 27.5 cm, 21.5 cm **b** 34.9 cm
4a 26 cm, 26 cm, 40 cm, 40 cm **b** 132 cm **5** 12 cm
6a 16 cm **b** 22.6 cm **7a** 3.2 m **b** 53° **8** 14.9 km
9a 4.7 m, 6.3 m **b** 58.0°, 61.4° **10a** 12 cm **b** 13.4 cm
11 20.10 m

Page 70   Similar Shapes

1a 2 **b** 20
2a They are equiangular (pairs of angles are equal) **b** (i) $\frac{2}{3}$
(ii) 6 **3a** $\frac{5}{3}$ **b** 30 **4a** $\frac{1}{2}$ **b** 3 **5a** 60 cm², 240 cm² **b** 4
6a 12 cm², 27 cm² **b** $\frac{4}{9}$ **7a** 2; 9 cm², 36 cm²; 4; 4 = 2²
b $\frac{2}{3}$; 90 cm², 40 cm²; $\frac{4}{9}$, $\frac{4}{9}$ = $(\frac{2}{3})^2$ **8a** 2 **b** 4 **c** 9400 cm²
9 360 cm² **10** 1280 m² **11a** They are equiangular **b** (i) $\frac{5}{4}$
(ii) $\frac{25}{16}$ **c** (i) 5 (ii) 12.5 cm²

6   HOUSE AND CAR COSTS

Page 72   Looking Back

1a £2 **b** £20 000 **2a** £14.70 **b** £98.70 **3** £82.40
4a $\frac{9}{10}$ **b** 90% **5a** £6 **b** £15 **c** £9 **6a** £1140 **b** £735
7 1 book costs £$\frac{120}{16}$ = £7.50, 5 books cost £7.50 × 5 = £37.50
8 14 040 000 **9a** £15 **b** £1.25 **c** £150

Page 73   Exercise 1

1 Row: £10 000, £5000, £15 000, £4000 **2** £12 000 **3** £9000
4 Rows: £18 000, £72 000, £27 000, £90 000;
£2000, £8000, £3000, £10 000 **5a** £28 000 **b** £7000

6 £15 000 **7a** £20 000 **b** (i) 75% (ii) 25% **8** £720
9a £200 **b** £400 **c** £600 **d** £1125 **10a** £435 **b** £5220

Page 75 Exercise 2

1a £87.50 **b** £150 **c** £275
2a £157.50 **b** £252 **c** £113.75 **d** £94.50
3a £300 **b** (i) £5.77 (ii) 82p **4** £12.50
5a £2.75 **b** £343.75

Page 75 Exercise 3

1a £15 **b** £60 **c** £360 **d** £54 **2** £199.50
3a £525 **b** £420 **4** Connels £9 less **5a** £14.13 **b** £96
c (i) £110.13 (ii) £9.18 **6** £290.70+£147.60 = £438.30

Page 77 Exercise 4

1a £405 **b** £2055 **2a** 8 gallons **b** 300 gallons **3a** 200
b £460 **4a** 1250 **b** £662.50 **5** 12.5% **6a** £1710 **b** 14p

Page 78 Exercise 5

1 £895, £833, £620, £1570 **2a** £990 **b** £297 **3a** £620
b £372 **c** £248 **4a** £1136 **b** £454.40 **c** £681.60
5a (i) £615 (ii) £0 (iii) £615 **b** (i) £890 (ii) £267
(iii) £623 **c** (i) £910 (ii) £364 (iii) £546 **d** (i) £620
(ii) £310 (iii) £310 **e** (i) £780 (ii) £468 (iii) £312
f (i) £1570 (ii) £942 (iii) £628 **6** £582.40 **7** £262.60
8 £653.40

Page 80 Exercise 6B

1 £59 000 **2a** £900 **b** 5 years **3** £62 700 **4** £1800
5a £88 000 **b** £96 800 **6a** £4000 **b** 8%
7a £200, £250 **b** 17%, 25% **8a** (i) Yes (ii) yes (iii) yes
b £42 000, £42 840, £44 553.60

Page 81 Check-up on House and Car Costs

1a £59 500 **b** £10 500 **2a** £160 **b** £1920
3a £169.63 **b** £130.86 **4a** £36 **b** £81 **c** £159.30
5a £142.50 **b** £135 **c** £277.50 **6a** £920 **b** £1900 **c** 12p
7a £534 **b** £24 less **8a** £2000 **b** 3.125%
9a £1 760 000 **b** £1 548 800 **c** £1 362 944

7 PAIRS OF STRAIGHT LINES AND EQUATIONS

Page 82 Looking Back

1a (i) 40 m (ii) 55 m (iii) 65 m **b** (i) 5 s (ii) 8 s (iii) 10 s
2 Rows: 0, 2, 4, −4, −2; 4, 5, 6, 2, 3 **3a** 6 **b** 0 **c** 1 **d** −2
4b (5, 4) **c** 6.4 **5a** Row: 10, 5, 0, −5, −10 **6b** (2, 2)
7a 4 **b** 8 **8a** 2 **b** −6 **9a** 3 **b** −2 **c** $\frac{1}{2}$ **10a** 5x **b** 3y
c 3a **d** −6b **11a** x **b** −2y **c** −3u **d** 7v **12** $5\frac{1}{2}, 3\frac{1}{2}$

Page 83 Exercise 1/Class Discussion

1a 500 m **b** Kim 30 s, Ian 10 s **c** 10 s **d** (i) 250 m (ii) 5 s
2 a and c **3** (2, 2)

Page 84 Exercise 2

1a (2, 4) **b** (4, −4) **c** (−1, 2) **d** (−4, −5)
2b y = 3, (0, 3); 3, (3, 0) **d** $(1\frac{1}{2}, 1\frac{1}{2})$
3b 2, (0, 2); 2, (2, 0) **d** (−2, 4) **4** (1, 1) **5** (2, 2) **6** (2, 4)
7 (2, 0) **8** (−2, 2) **9** (0, 3) **10** (0, 0)

Page 86 Exercise 3

1a (i) Row: 20, 25, 30, 35, 40, 45
b (i) Row: 0, 10, 20, 30, 40, 50 **c** 4, £40
d (i) Speedwheels (ii) Maximiles
2a Second rows: 30, 35, 40, 45, 50, 55; 0, 15, 30, 45, 60, 75
c 3, £45 **d** (i) Fast Hire (ii) Happy Hire
3a Second rows: 40, 45, 50, 55, 60, 65, 70, 75, 80;
0, 10, 20, 30, 40, 50, 60, 70, 80 **c** for 8 months hire, £80
4a (i) £25 (ii) £50 **b** (i) £25 (ii) £5 **c** for 10 hours work
5a Rows: 1, 2, 3, . . . , 10; 4, 4, 4, 4, 4, 4, 6, 8, 10, 12
c 4 miles and 8 miles
d between 0 and 4 miles, and over 8 miles
6a Row: 10, 15, 20, 25, 30 **b** 0, 10, 20, 30, 40
d (i) £20 (ii) 100 **e** North Gas Board, £5

Page 88 Exercise 4

1 x = 3, y = 6 **2** x = 2, y = 6 **3** x = 3, y = 12
4 x = −1, y = −2 **5** x = −4, y = −20 **6** x = 1, y = 10
7 $x = 2\frac{1}{2}, y = 7\frac{1}{2}$ **8** $x = 1\frac{1}{2}, y = 6$ **9** x = 2, y = 5
10 x = −1, y = −3 **11** x = 2, y = 10 **12** x = −3, y = −15
13 $x = 2\frac{1}{2}, y = 7\frac{1}{2}$ **14** $x = 1\frac{1}{2}, y = 2\frac{1}{2}$

Page 89 Exercise 5A

1 x = 8, y = 4 **2** x = 11, y = 5 **3** x = 15, y = 5
4 x = 11, y = 4 **5** x = −1, y = −4 **6** x = −4, y = −2
7 x = 4, y = 1 **8** x = 2, y = 1 **9** x = 1, y = 1
10 x = 2, y = 2 **11** x = 4, y = 3 **12** x = 2, y = 4
13 x = 2, y = 2 **14** x = 3, y = 0 **15** x = 2, y = 2
16 x = 0, y = −3 **17** x = 1, y = −1 **18** x = −2, y = 1
19 x = −1, y = −1 **20** x = 5, y = −1

Page 90 Exercise 5B

1 x = 2, y = 3 **2** a = 2, b = 0 **3** x = 2, y = 1
4 x = 4, y = 1 **5** a = 1, b = 0 **6** u = 1, v = −1
7 x = 2, y = −1 **8** u = 1, v = −1 **9** a = 0, b = 1
10 x = 4, y = 2 **11** x = 1, y = 1 **12** x = 2, y = −2
13 u = 1, v = −1 **14** a = 1, b = −1 **15** x = −1, y = 0
16 p = 2, q = −1 **17** p = 2, q = 0

Page 91 Check-up on Pairs of Straight Lines and Equations

1 Ben jumps at 2000 m, and reaches 800 m after 30 s. Rena jumps at 2000 m, 10 s after Ben, and reaches 200 m after 20 s. She passes Ben at 1300 m after $7\frac{1}{2}$ s **2a** y = 5, x = 5
3b (2, 3) **4a** Rows: 0, 20, 40, 60, 80; 20, 30, 40, 50, 60
c (i) the first method (ii) the second method
d for 6 months **5a** Row: 40, 30, 20, 10, 0 **b** x + y = 40
c y = 3x **d** 10 of A, 30 of B **6a** x = 5, y = 10
b x = −3, y = −15 **c** x = 2, y = 3
7a x = 4, y = 2 **b** u = 1, v = 3 **c** a = 1, b = −1

REVIEW: LETTERS AND NUMBERS

Page 92 Simplification

1a 3y **b** x **c** 5k **d** 0 **e** 2m **f** 5+2x **g** v **2a** 2x+2
b 3y+4 **c** p+q+10 **3a** 2n **b** n^2 **c** 2y **d** $3p^2$
4a 3x+1 **b** 4n **c** 2y+1 **5a** 3x+3 **b** 5y−10 **c** 4−4t
d 4−2u **e** 6a+3 **f** 12b−4 **g** 24c−30
6a 2(x+3) **b** 3(y+2) **c** 4(t−2) **d** 5(u+1) **e** 2(u+v)
f 3(m+2n) **g** 5(p−q) **h** 5(2−t) **7a** 20x **b** 4u **c** 6y+1
d 6p+2 **e** 4t **8a** 3x+9 **b** 2x+6 **c** 5y−2 **d** 2n+6

9a $3(x+2) = 3x+6$ **b** $5(y-3) = 5y-15$
10a $2(a+2)$ **b** $2(a+2b)$ **c** $a(a+b)$ **d** $a(a+2)$
e $3(a+2b+3c)$ **f** $5(x^2-x-1)$ **g** $y(1-y)$

Page 93   Replacing Letters by Numbers

1a £12 **b** £4 **c** £27 **d** £7
2a 21 **b** 6 **c** 4 **d** 5 **e** 49 **f** 98 **g** 5 **h** 42
3 Rows: **a** $0, 4, 12, 20$ **b** $0, 3, 6, 9$ **c** $0, 1, 16, 81$
d $2, 5, 8, 11$ **4a** $5, 10, 15, 20$ **b** $1, \frac{1}{2}, \frac{1}{3}, \frac{1}{4}$ **c** $6, 10, 14, 18$
d $2, 6, 12, 20$ **e** $\frac{1}{2}, \frac{2}{3}, \frac{3}{4}, \frac{4}{5}$ **5a** 64 **b** 100 **c** 5 **d** 7
6a 55p **b** 130p **c** 174p

Page 94   Positive and Negative Numbers

1 Aberdeen, Newcastle, Ayr, London, Bath
2a A(2, −1), B(2, 3), C(−2, 1), D(−2, −2), E(4, 1), F(−4, 2),
G(1, 2) **b** C **3a** (i) −3°C, −5°C, 1°C, 3°C, 5°C
(ii) −7°C, −9°C, −3°C, −1°C, 1°C **b** (i) Izmar (ii) Izmar
4a 2 **b** 2 **c** −3 **d** 0 **e** 1 **f** −1 **g** −3 **h** −5 **i** 0
j −2 **k** −3 **l** −2 **5a** (i) £300 inc. (ii) £600 dec.
(iii) £400 inc. (iv) £500 dec. **b** (i) £700 (ii) £140
6a −9 **b** 1 **c** −4 **d** −5 **e** −5 **f** −2 **g** −7 **h** −6
i −30 **j** −10 **k** −16

Page 95   Equations

1a 9 **b** 11 **c** 4 **d** $1\frac{1}{2}$ **e** −1 **f** 2
2a $2x+1 = 15, x = 7, 14$ **b** $3x+2 = 11, x = 3, 9$
c $7x+3 = 31, x = 4, 28$ **d** $5x+4 = 39, x = 7, 35$
3a $2y+3 = 15, 6$ **b** $3k-4 = 17, 7$ **4** $4n+3 = 47, 11$
5 $2n+11 = 3, -4$
6a (i) $5x+2 = 12, 2$ (ii) 3, 4, 5 **b** (i) $6x+4 = 28, 4$
(ii) 7, 9, 12 **c** (i) $2x+8 = 4x, 4$ (ii) 5, 5, 6 **7a** 1 **b** 5 **c** $1\frac{1}{2}$
8a 1 **b** 3 **c** 3 **d** 1 **e** 2 **f** −3 **g** 4 **h** −2 **i** 1 **j** −6
9a (i) $3(x-2) = 2x, 6$ (ii) 4, 6 **b** (i) $6x = 4(x+1), 2$ (ii) 2, 3

Page 96   Formulae

1a (i) $A = xy$ (ii) $P = 2x+2y$ **b** $A = 96, P = 40$
2a $V = lbh$ **b** 540 **3a** $C = 5n$ **b** $C = 10-s$ **c** $N = 100b$
d $W = xy$ **e** $T = x+y+z$ **4** $S = 20, P = 93.75$ **5** 98
6 3.125 **7** 275 **8** 11.9 **9a** (i) $A = x^2+xy$ (ii) $A = y^2-x^2$
b (i) 324 (ii) 81 **10a** $P = S-C$ **b** $C = 25+8n$
11a $38\,\mathrm{cm}^3$ **b** yes **12a, d, e, f**

Page 97   Sequences

1a (i) 1, 4, 9, 16 (ii) square numbers **b** (i) 2, 4, 6, 8
(ii) even numbers **c** (i) 5, 10, 15, 20 (ii) multiples of 5
d (i) 1, 3, 5, 7 (ii) odd numbers **2a** $4n-1$ **b** $5n+1$
c $3n-1$ **d** $6n-1$ **e** $4n$ **f** $3n+7$ **g** $n+9$ **h** $100n$
3 Rows: **a** $3, 7, 11, 15, 19; 4, 4, 4, 4$ **b** $2, 3, 5, 8, 12, 17;$
$1, 2, 3, 4, 5; 1, 1, 1, 1$ **4** $3, 5, 7, 9; 25; 2n+1$
5a Patterns have 13 and 16 dots **b** (i) 19 (ii) 22 (iii) $3n+1$
6 1, 4, 9, 16; 64; n^2 **7b** $c = 2n+2$ **8** 8, 10, 12, 14; 26; $2n+6$
9 Rows: $25, 35, 45, 55, 10n+15; 7, 11, 15, 19, 4n+3;$
$18, 24, 30, 36, 6n+12$

Page 98   Inequalities

1a $2 < 6$ **b** $3 > -3$ **c** $x \leqslant y$ **d** $u+1 \geqslant v$
2a T **b** T **c** T **d** F **e** F **f** T **g** F **h** T
3a $w > 8$ **b** $c < 10$ **c** $p \leqslant 17$ **d** $p \geqslant 250$
4a 3 **b** −3, −2, −1, 0 **c** −1, 0, 1, 2, 3 **d** −1, 0, 1
5a $x > 5$ **b** $y < 1$ **c** $z \geqslant -2$ **d** $t \leqslant -1$ **e** $t > 4$ **f** $n \leqslant 3$
g $p < -1$ **h** $x < 5$ **i** $y > 5$ **j** $z \leqslant 3$ **6a** $x+4 > 6, x > 2$
b $x-7 < 9, x < 16$ **c** $3x-1 > 5, x > 2$ **d** $2x+3 < 8, x < 2\frac{1}{2}$

Page 98   Graphs

1 (i) **2** (ii) **3** (iii) **4** (ii) **5** (iii) **6** (iii)
7a (ii) **b** (i) **c** (iii) **8 a** (iii), **b** (iv), **c** (ii), **d** (i)
9a $\frac{1}{4}$ **b** (i) $1\frac{1}{4}$ hours (ii) $2\frac{1}{2}$ hours **c** $\frac{1}{2}$ hour and $\frac{3}{4}$ hour
d (i) 130 km (ii) about 66 km (iii) about 64 km

 8 PROPORTION IN PRACTICE

Page 100   Looking Back

1a $\frac{1}{2}$ **b** $\frac{1}{2}$ **c** $\frac{1}{6}$ **d** $\frac{1}{4}$ **e** $\frac{1}{4}$ **2a** 15 **b** 25 **c** 35
3a 16, 2 **b** 81, 3 **c** 625, 5 **4a** 5 **b** 4 **c** 9 **5a** £6 **b** £30
6 a, b, e **7** Rows: **a** 12, 18, 24, 30 **b** 4, 8, 16, 28
8a $2, \frac{1}{2}$ **b** $y = 2x, y = \frac{1}{2}x$ **9a** 90°, 180°, 270°, 360° **b** yes
c yes **d** 30° **10c** (i) 3 (ii) $y = 3x$

Page 101   Exercise 1

1a 50p, 100p, 150p, 200p **b** 75p, 150p, 300p, 600p
2 Rows: **a** 6, 12, 18, 24, 30 **b** 5, 10, 25, 35, 70
3a 4 km **b** 8 km **c** 20 km **4a** 20 km **b** 40 km **c** 60 km
5a 94p **b** £1.88 **c** £6.58 **6a** 100 **b** 400 **c** 600
7 $£\frac{60}{8} \times 10 = £75$ **8** £36 **9** £91 **10** £432 **11** 24 km
12 37.80 **13** 15 m **14a** 4 eggs, 16 g, 100 ml
b 6 eggs, 24 g, 150 ml **c** 1 egg, 4 g, 25 ml **15a** 250 cm
b 480 cm **16 a, c, d, e**; $H \propto N, t \propto n, D \propto S, D \propto T$

Page 103   Exercise 2

1a It is a straight line through the origin **c** $F = 10P$
2a A straight line through the origin **b** yes **c** 30
d $C = 30N$ **e** 150p **3a** Yes. The graph is a straight line
through the origin **b** $N = 20T$ **c** 240
4a Row: 10, 20, 30, 40 **c** (i) I is directly proportional to P
(ii) $I = \frac{1}{10}P$ **d** £75 **5a** Yes. Graph is a straight line through
the origin **b** $\frac{3}{2}$ **c** $P = \frac{3}{2}H$ **d** £33 **6a** (i) 5 **b** $C = 5N$
c £190 **7b** The graph is a straight line through the origin
c $I = 3V$ **d** 11.4 **8b** (i) n is directly proportional to t
(ii) $n = 25t$ **c** 225

Page 105   Exercise 3

1a $y = 5x$ **b** 25 **2a** $s = 3t$ **b** 24 **3a** $y = 4x$ **b** 4
4a $p = 8q$ **b** 200 **5a** $d = s$ **b** 9 km **6a** $n = 5t$ **b** 250
7a $c = 4s$ **b** 10 kg **8a** $C = 6A$ **b** £48 **9a** $d = \frac{3}{2}p$ **b** 18
10a $P = 7H$ **b** £140 **11a** $t = \frac{1}{25}s$ **b** 36

Page 106   Exercise 4B

1a $y = 5x^2$ **b** 45 **2a** $p = q^2$ **b** 0.01 **3a** $m = 3\sqrt{n}$ **b** 18
4a $s = 5\sqrt{t}$ **b** 50 **5a** (i) $y \propto x^2$ (ii) $y \propto x$ **b** (i) $y = 2x^2$
(ii) $y = 4x$ **6a** $w = 5d^2$ **b** 720 **7a** $c = 7\sqrt{n}$ **b** 42p
8 $s = 5t^2$; 180 m **9** 22 m/s **10** 1.4 seconds
11a $\dfrac{d}{t^2} = \dfrac{4}{1} = \dfrac{16}{4} = \dfrac{36}{9} = \dfrac{64}{16} = \dfrac{100}{25}$
c (i) 4 (ii) $d = 4t^2$ **d** 400 m

Page 108   Exercise 5

1 b **2** Rows: **a** 24, 12, 6, 3 **b** 3, 6, 12, 60
3a £10 **b** £4 **c** £2 **4a** £36 **b** (i) £18 (ii) £9 (iii) £6
5 $20 \times 6 = 120$ minutes, $\frac{120}{10} = 12$ minutes
6a More, 6 hours **b** 3 hours **7** 15 minutes **8** 48 minutes
9 £144 **10** 40 **11** 3 **12** 12 cm **13** 5 **14 a, e, f**

Page 109   Check-up on Proportion in Practice

1a Doubled   **b** halved   **2** Row: **a** 12, 24, 36, 48, 60   **3** £165
4a The graph is a straight line through the origin   **b** $\frac{1}{10}$
c $F = \frac{1}{10}a$ **d** 4 newtons   **5a** $y = 2x$ **b** 18
6a $B = \frac{1}{40}P$ **b** £625   **7a** $C = 30\sqrt{T}$ **b** £90   **8** $12\frac{1}{2}$ units
9 3 hours   **10a** Row: 90, 60, 45, 36, 30   **b** 24°
11a (i) $\frac{15}{5} = \frac{30}{10} = \frac{45}{15} = \frac{60}{20} = \frac{75}{25}$ **b** $C = 3N$ **c** (i) £105   (ii) 18

9   ANGLES IN A CIRCLE

(Degree symbols are not included in the diagrams.)

Page 110   Looking Back

1a 8   **b** (i) 90° (ii) 45° (iii) 90°   **c** 16 m   **2a** 33   **b** 55
3 $a = 80, b = 100, c = 70, d = 70$ **4** 180°
5

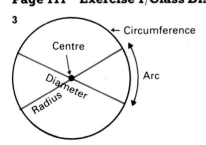

6a $x^2 = y^2 + z^2$ **b** 10   **7** 12.5 m
8a $\sin A = \frac{5}{13}, \cos A = \frac{12}{13}, \tan A = \frac{5}{12}$ **b** 22.6°   **9** 13 m
10a   **b** (i) 20 cm   (ii) 10 cm

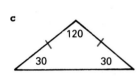

Page 111   Exercise 1/Class Discussion

3

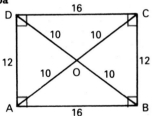

4 5 cm   **5** Yes   **6a** 3   **b** 4   **c** any number of ways   **7** b, f
8 They are all the same length   **9** They are equal
10

Page 112   Exercise 2

1a (i) OA, OB   (ii) △OAB   (iii) ∠s OAB, OBA
b (i) OC, OD   (ii) △COD   (iii) ∠s OCD, ODC
2 $a = 40, b = 110$ **3** $c = 31, d = 50$ **4** $e = 52, f = 128$
5 $g = 130, h = 230$ **6** $m = 105, n = 37\frac{1}{2}$ **7** $p = 60, q = 300$
8 54°   **9a** 45   **b** $67\frac{1}{2}$ **10a** 25   **b** 65   **c** 90°
11

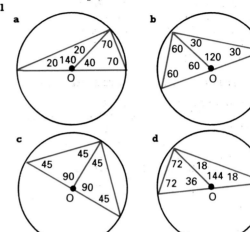

$x + y = 90$ for each circle

Page 114   Exercise 3

1d It should be 90°   **2** It is always 90°   **3a** They are equal
b they are equal   **4a** Rectangles and squares   **b** 90°
5a They are equal, and bisect each other
b a rectangle, or square   **c** 90°

Page 114   Exercise 4

1a 90   **b** 40   **c** 60   **d** 15   **2a** ∠ABC   **b** $r = 57, s = 33$
3a ∠PQR   **b** $t = 35, u = 55$
4

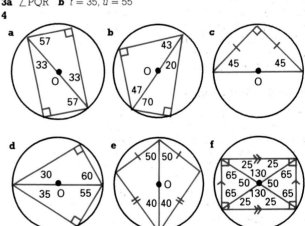

5a ∠s ADB, ACB   **b**

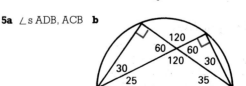

6

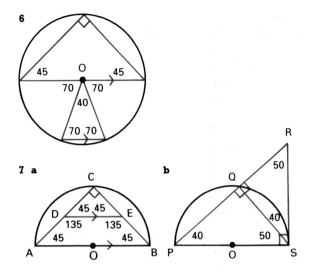

7 a

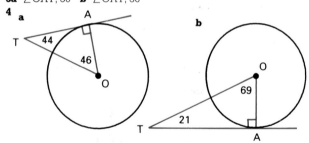

Page 116   Exercise 5

1a ∠PQR, 15   **b** ∠TSU, 13   **c** ∠VWX, 6   **d** ∠FDE, 6.5
2a ∠ACB, 10   **b** ∠HGK, 1.6   **3a** 7.2   **b** 6.6   **c** 13.6   **d** 7.8
4a 48 cm   **b** 68 cm

Page 117   Exercise 6

1a (i) ∠ABC, AC   (ii) 30   **b** (i) ∠EDF, EF   (ii) 56
2a (i) ∠GHK, GK   (ii) 13.0   **b** (i) ∠UWV, UV   (ii) 6.1
3a (i) 10.4   (ii) 60.0   **b** (i) 6.9   (ii) 40.1   **4a** 1.25 m   **b** 53°

Page 118   Exercise 7A

1d It should be 90°   **2** The angles are all right angles
3a ∠OAT, 50   **b** ∠OAT, 36
4

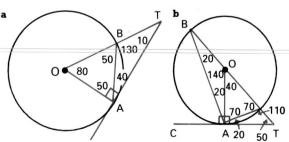

5 ∠OAT; $x = 25$, $y = 65$ **6a** 7.8   **b** 3.2   **c** 6.9   **d** 6.3
7a 50°   **b** 35°   **c** 30°   **d** 25°
8a (i) ∠OAT   (ii) 24 cm, 30 cm   **b** (i) 18 cm   (ii) 37°

Page 119   Exercise 7B

1 2 m   **2a** 65 cm   **b** 90 cm
3a Both 40°   **b** 90°; angles between tangents and radii
c 140°   **4a** 200 cm   **b** 202 cm   **5a** 21 000 km   **b** 14 600 km
6

a   **b**

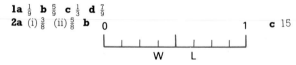

Page 121   Check-up on Angles in a Circle

1

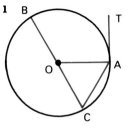

2a 35   **b** 52   **c** 25   **3a**

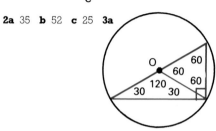

b 90°; they make up an angle in a semicircle
c 2.8 cm; side of an equilateral triangle
4a (i) ∠ACB, AB   (ii) 7.4   **b** (i) ∠PQR, PR   (ii) 47.7
c (i) ∠OAT, OT   (ii) 14.1
5

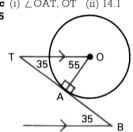

6a Angles at A and C between tangents and radii; angles at B and O between horizontal and vertical (or ∠AOC is fourth angle of a square)   **b** 42 cm   **7** 50°
8a 22 cm   **b** 31 cm   **c** 49 cm

---

10   PROBABILITY

Page 122   Looking Back

1a $\frac{1}{9}$ **b** $\frac{5}{9}$ **c** $\frac{1}{3}$ **d** $\frac{7}{9}$
2a (i) $\frac{3}{8}$ (ii) $\frac{5}{8}$ **b**

c 15

3a

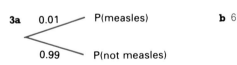

b 6

4a 0.12   **b** 780
5a

		Black			
	+	1	2	3	4
	1	2	3	4	5
	2	3	4	5	6
Red	3	4	5	6	7
	4	5	6	7	8

b (i) $\frac{1}{8}$ (ii) $\frac{3}{16}$ (iii) $\frac{5}{16}$
c P(3 or 4) = P(3) + P(4)

6a By watching the lights and keeping a record
b (i) 0.8   (ii) 1   (iii) 0
7

Page 123   Exercise 1A

1

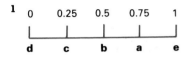

d   c   b   a   e

2 45%   **3a** 4   **b** 16   **4a** About 4 times   **b** about 18 times
5

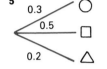

6a (i) $\frac{1}{3}$ (ii) $\frac{2}{3}$ **b** 10

Page 124   Exercise 1B

1a 0.4   **b** (i) 24   (ii) 6   **2a** About 161 or 162   **b** 28 or 29
3a

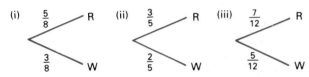

b (i)

4a (i) 0.7   (ii) 0.85   **b** (i) 7000   (ii) 8500
5a Slowed down   **b** speeded up   **c** left as it is

Page 124   Exercise 2

1a Rows: (r, R), (r, A), (r, G); (a, R), (a, A), (a, G); (g, R), (g, A), (g, G)   **b** 9   **c** (i) $\frac{1}{9}$ (ii) $\frac{5}{9}$ (iii) $\frac{2}{9}$
2a

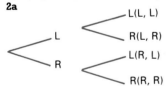

L(L, L)
R(L, R)
L(R, L)
R(R, R)

b (i) Axbury   (ii) Carport   **c** $\frac{1}{4}$
3a Rows: (H, W), (H, D), (H, L); (A, W), (A, D), (A, L)
b (i) $\frac{1}{6}$ (ii) $\frac{1}{3}$ **c** $\frac{2}{3}$
d

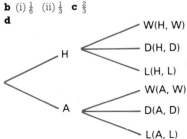

W(H, W)
D(H, D)
L(H, L)
W(A, W)
D(A, D)
L(A, L)

4a Rows: (K, K), (K, F), (K, S); (F, K), (F, F), (F, S); (S, K), (S, F), (S, S)   **b** (i) $\frac{1}{9}$ (ii) $\frac{1}{3}$ (iii) $\frac{2}{9}$
c

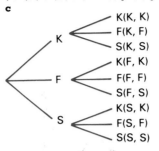

K(K, K)
F(K, F)
S(K, S)
K(F, K)
F(F, F)
S(F, S)
K(S, K)
F(S, F)
S(S, S)

5a (H, 1), (H, 2), (H, 3), (H, 4), (H, 5), (H, 6); (M, 1), (M, 2), (M, 3), (M, 4), (M, 5), (M, 6); (L, 1), (L, 2), (L, 3), (L, 4), (L, 5), (L, 6)   **b** (i) $\frac{1}{3}$ (ii) $\frac{1}{18}$ (iii) $\frac{2}{9}$
6a Rows: (1, 1) . . . (1, 6); (2, 1) . . . (2, 6); (3, 1) . . . (3, 6); (4, 1) . . . (4, 6); (5, 1) . . . (5, 6); (6, 1) . . . (6, 6);
b 36   **c** (i) $\frac{1}{36}$ (ii) $\frac{11}{36}$ (iii) $\frac{5}{12}$

Page 126   Exercise 3

1a 0.55   **b** Terry's   **2a** 0.75, 0.8
b B; more homes surveyed   **3a** Row: 0.3, 0.24, 0.2, 0.17
b 0.17   **4a** Row: 0.32, 0.28, 0.26, 0.25, 0.25
b yes. P(W) = $\frac{1}{3}$ = 0.33 . . . for a true spinner   **c** about 250
5a 0.0167, 0.008, 0.0127   **b** Vale High
c about 334, 160 and 254

Page 127   Exercise 4A

1a $\frac{5}{12}$ **b** $\frac{3}{12}$ **c** $\frac{8}{12}=\frac{2}{3}$ **d** $\frac{9}{12}=\frac{3}{4}$ **2a** $\frac{1}{4}$ **b** $\frac{1}{4}$ **c** $\frac{1}{2}$ **d** $\frac{3}{4}$ **e** 1
3a 0.9   **b** 0.8   **c** 0.3   **4a** (i) 0.6   (ii) 0.4   (iii) 0.85
b (i) 60   (ii) 40   (iii) 85   **5a** (i) $\frac{1}{9}$ (ii) $\frac{2}{9}$ (iii) $\frac{1}{3}$ **b** 17 or 18

Page 128   Exercise 4B

1 a, b, d   **2a** (i) 0.1   (ii) 0.23   (iii) 0.19   **b** 2900
3a Rows: 2,3, . . . , 7; 3,4, . . . , 8; 4,5, . . . , 9; 5,6, . . . , 10; 6,7, . . . , 11; 7,8, . . . , 12;   **b** (i) 7   (ii) 2 and 12
c $\frac{1}{36}, \frac{1}{18}, \frac{1}{12}, \frac{1}{9}, \frac{5}{36}, \frac{1}{6}, \frac{5}{36}, \frac{1}{9}, \frac{1}{12}, \frac{1}{18}, \frac{1}{36}$ **d** (i) $\frac{1}{6}$ (ii) $\frac{1}{6}$ **4a** $\frac{13}{36}$ **b** $\frac{23}{36}$

Page 129   Exercise 5

1a (H, H), (H, T), (T, H), (T, T)   **b** (i) $\frac{1}{2}$ (ii) $\frac{1}{2}$ (iii) $\frac{1}{4}$
2a (1, 1), (1, 2), (1, 3), (1, 4); (2, 1), (2, 2), (2, 3), (2, 4); (3, 1), (3, 2), (3, 3), (3, 4);   **b** (i) $\frac{1}{3}$ (ii) $\frac{1}{4}$ (iii) $\frac{1}{12}$
3a (1, 1) . . . (1, 4); (2, 1) . . . (2, 4); (3, 1) . . . (3, 4); (4, 1) . . . (4, 4)   **b** (i) $\frac{1}{4}$ (ii) $\frac{1}{4}$ (iii) $\frac{1}{16}$
4a (H, 1) . . . (H, 6); (T, 1) . . . (T, 6);   **b** (i) $\frac{1}{2}$ (ii) $\frac{1}{6}$ (iii) $\frac{1}{12}$
(iv) P(H, 6) = P(H) × P(6)   **5** 0.81   **6a** 0.04   **b** 0.64
7a 0.52   **b** (i) 0.23   (ii) 0.27   **8a** $\frac{2}{5}$ **b** $\frac{2}{5}$ **c** $\frac{4}{25}$
9a $\frac{1}{49}$ **b** $\frac{1}{2704}$ **10a** $\frac{1}{20}$ **b** $\frac{1}{10}$

Page 131   Check-up on Probability

1a $\frac{1}{5}$ **b** $\frac{4}{5}$ **2a** (i) $\frac{3}{5}$ (ii) $\frac{3}{10}$ (iii) $\frac{1}{10}$ (iv) 0
b

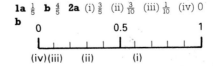

(iv)(iii)   (ii)   (i)

3a
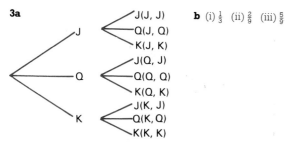
b (i) $\frac{1}{3}$ (ii) $\frac{2}{9}$ (iii) $\frac{5}{9}$

4a
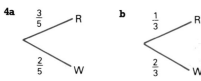
b

5a
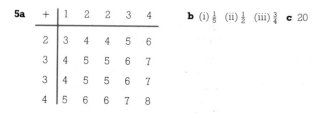
b (i) $\frac{1}{5}$ (ii) $\frac{1}{2}$ (iii) $\frac{3}{4}$ **c** 20

6a (i) 0.4 (ii) 0.35 **b** 80
7a 0.01 **b** 0.04 **c** 0.09 **d** 0.16 **e** 0.02

REVIEW: AREAS AND VOLUMES

Page 132   Exercise 1A

1a 36 cm², 24 cm **b** 40 cm², 26 cm **2a** 12 cm² **b** 6 cm²
3a 90 cm² **b** 108 cm² **4** 40 cm² **5a** 78.5 cm² **b** 31.4 cm
6a Square **b** both the same **7a** 3.8 cm **b** 2.3 cm²
8a 33 m² **b** 48 m² **c** 77 m² **d** 150 m² **e** 30 m² **f** 12 m²

Page 133   Exercise 1B

1 36 m² **2** 96 m² **3** 184 m² **4** 413.1 m² **5** 34.7 m²
6 11.4 m² **7a** 300 cm² **b** 75 cm² **c** 225 cm² **8a** 60 cm²
b 25.1 cm² **c** 34.9 cm² **9a** 1600 cm² **b** 1256.6 cm²
c 2856.6 cm² **10a** 625 cm² **b** 30 cm² **c** 505 cm²

Page 135   Exercise 2A

1a 24 000 mm³ **b** 504 cm³ **c** 1.8 m³ **d** 900 cm³
e 1728 cm³ **f** 1125 cm³ **2a** (i) 60 000 cm³ (ii) 60 litres
b 10 cm **3a** 2 cm **b** 2.5 cm **4a** 75 cm³ **b** 7.5 m³
5a 30 cm² **b** 540 cm³ **6a** 600 cm³ **b** 75.4 m³
7a 28 274.3 cm³ **b** 28.3
8a 400 cm³ **b** 4 cm **c** 2 cm **d** 25 cm²

Page 136   Exercise 2B

1a (i) 25 m² (ii) 375 m³ (iii) 1125 m³ **b** $\frac{1}{3}$ **2** 75 000 cm³
3a (i) 18 849 556 cm³ (ii) 18 850 litres **b** no
4a 226.2 cm³ **b** 6 **5a** 1.4 m² **b** 2.8 m³ **c** 16.8 m³
6a 9424.8 cm³ **b** 1885 **7a** 4320 **b** 180 000 cm³
8a 31 416 cm³ **b** 20 106 cm³ **c** 11 310 cm³

Page 138   Exercise 3

1a 4 cm² **b** 24 cm² **2a** 25 cm² **b** 125 cm²

3a

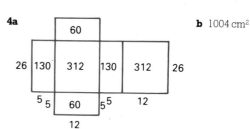
b (i) 144 cm² (ii) 576 cm²

4a
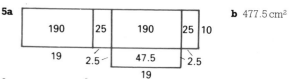
b 1004 cm²

5a
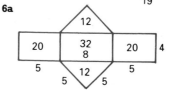
b 477.5 cm²

6a

b (i) 20, 32, 20 m² (ii) 12 m² (iii) 96 m²
7a 240 cm² **b** 72 cm² **c** 624 cm²
8a   25.1 cm

b (i) 200.8 cm² (ii) 50.3 cm² (iii) 301.4 cm²
9a One end of the cylinder is open, to put the golf clubs in the
bag **b** length of rectangle = circumference of
bag = 56.5 cm **c** 5089 + 254.5 cm² = 5343.5 cm²
10 5890.5 cm²

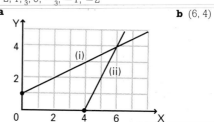

CHAPTER REVISION EXERCISES

Page 143   Revision Exercise on Chapter 1:
Gradients and Graphs of Straight
Lines

1a $\frac{2}{3}$ **b** 2 **c** −1 **d** −2 **e** 1 **f** 0 **g** $-\frac{1}{3}$
2 2, 1, $\frac{2}{3}$, 0, $-\frac{1}{3}$, −1, −2
3a   **b** (6, 4)

4a AB $\frac{1}{2}$, BC $-\frac{1}{2}$, AD $-\frac{5}{2}$, DC $\frac{5}{2}$; EF 1, FG -1, HG 1, EH -1;
KL 2, LM $\frac{1}{2}$, NM 2, KN $\frac{1}{2}$ **b** ABCD is a kite, EFGH a square,
KLMN a parallelogram **5a** $\frac{1}{2}$ **b** $-\frac{1}{3}$
6a Row: $-10, -5, 0, 5, 10$ **c** 5
7

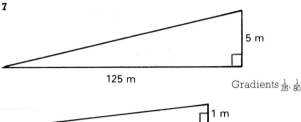

125 m — 5 m

Gradients $\frac{1}{25}$, $\frac{1}{80}$

80 m — 1 m

8a $\frac{1}{2}$, $y = \frac{1}{2}x$ **b** 1, $y = x$ **c** 2, $y = 2x$ **d** $-\frac{1}{2}$, $y = -\frac{1}{2}x$
e -1, $y = -x$ **f** -2, $y = -2x$
9a (i) £10 (ii) £17.50 **b** (i) 5 (ii) $C = 5T$

Page 144 Revision Exercise on Chapter 2: Trigonometry

1a tan; 4.2 **b** cos; 6.5 **c** sin; 49 **d** tan; 54 **2a** 54.9 m
b 31.8 m **3** 72° **4a** 21.2 km **b** 21.2 km
5 only **a** is too steep **6a** 252 m **b** 34° **7a** 10.3 m **b** 10°
8 62 cm² **9a** 4.8 cm **b** 10.3 cm **c** 44 cm²

Page 145 Revision Exercise on Chapter 3: Fractions, Decimals and Percentages

1 A = £77.47, B = £13.56, C = £91.03 **2a** £80 **b** £960
3a $\frac{3}{10}$ **b** $\frac{2}{5}$ **c** $\frac{3}{50}$ **d** $\frac{3}{4}$ **e** $\frac{6}{25}$
4a 3% **b** 37.5% **c** 90% **d** 35% **e** 34%
5a 2397 **b** 39% **6a** £130.05 **b** (i) £43.35 (ii) £86.70
7a 3p **b** 12% **8a** $5\frac{1}{2}$ **b** $1\frac{1}{2}$ **c** $1\frac{1}{3}$ **d** $10\frac{2}{3}$ **e** $3\frac{1}{2}$
9a $\frac{15}{4}$ **b** $\frac{27}{10}$ **c** $\frac{6}{5}$ **d** $\frac{19}{8}$ **e** $\frac{31}{8}$ **10a** $\frac{1}{8}$ **b** 12.5%
11 Columns: 6 lb, 2 lb, 6 lb, 5 oz, 1 lb;
4, 4 tbs, 4 tbs, 4 tbs, 3 pt, salt, pepper **12a** £1 560 000
b £1 638 000 **13a** $\frac{3}{8}$ inch **b** $\frac{5}{16}$ inch **14a** 9.75 cm
b 73 cm, 86 cm **c** 326.8 cm², 446.3 cm² **15** He saves £3240.
Food £2700, house £4500, insurance £1800, holidays £1800,
income tax £3960

Page 146 Revision Exercise on Chapter 4: Equations and Inequalities

1a 5 **b** 12 **c** -1 **2a** 5 **b** 2 **c** -1 **3a** 10 **b** 2 **c** $\frac{1}{2}$
4a 10 **b** 3 **c** 0 **5a** $6(3x+1) = 42, 2$ **b** $7(5x+6) = 427, 11$
c $8(12-x) = 24, 9$ **6a** 1 **b** 1 **c** -2 **7a** 1 **b** 2
8a 6 **b** -5 **9a** (i) $7x = 2(3x+2), 4$ (ii) 7, 4, 28; 14, 2, 28
b (i) $3(4x-2) = 5(x+3), 3$ (ii) 10, 3, 30; 6, 5, 30
10a 11 **b** 26 **c** 40 **11a** $9(x-1) = 6x, 3$; £2, £3
b $2(3x+2) = 8x, 2$; £8, £4 **12a** 0, 1, 2, 3 **b** 4, 5, 6, 7, 8
c 6, 7, 8 **d** 7, 8 **e** 0, 1, 2 **f** 8 **g** 0, 1, ..., 8 **13a** $m > 2$
b $n < 3$ **c** $n \geqslant 2\frac{1}{2}$ **d** $n \geqslant 2$ **e** $p \leqslant 4$ **f** $n < 2$ **g** $x \geqslant 2$
h $x \leqslant -8$ **14a** $3x+3 > 6, x > 1$ **b** $3x+2 < 2x+6, x < 4$

Page 147 Revision Exercise on Chapter 5: Statistics

1a Production: 10, 15, 20, 23, 25, 25; Sales: 2, 4, 8, 16, 32, 40
b production rose steadily from 10 to 25 a month, settling at
25. Sales began slowly but exceeded production after
4 months **2a** Angles: 90°, 108°, 54°, 36°, 72°
b (i) 1250 (ii) 1000 **3a** 20 ohms **b** 50 ohms
4a Frequencies: 1, 3, 7, 12, 7 **b** 16.5
5a English **b** science **c** very variable (large range)

6a Yes, very **b** (i) £1900 (ii) £27 375
c **d** £30 000

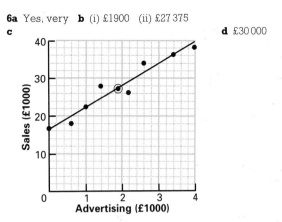

7a $3\frac{1}{2} \leqslant t < 4$ **b** $4 \leqslant t < 4\frac{1}{2}$ **c** 4.0 h

Page 148 Revision Exercise on Chapter 6: House and Car Costs

1 Row: £15 000, £6000, £9600, £6500 **2** £6000
3a £15 000 **b** 18.75% **4a** £500 **b** £150 000 **c** £100 000
5a £137.50 **b** £123 **c** £260.50 **6a** £293.25 **b** £650.75
7a (i) 320 miles (ii) 440 miles **b** (i) 3.1 gallons
(ii) 2.3 gallons **8a** £539 **b** £534
9a £94 500, £7200 **b** £99 225, £6480 **10** Car damage and
related house damage; fire, water damage, damage by falling
tree, theft of TV etc, broken window, hole in roof

Page 149 Revision Exercise on Chapter 7: Pairs of Straight Lines and Equations

1a (i) 10 (ii) 150 000 km **b** (i) the meteor
(ii) the spaceship **2a** A is $x+y = 10$, B is $2x-y = 5$
b (5, 5) **3b** (3, 6) **4c** (i) 4 hours after the start (ii) 4 cm
d C1, 12 hours; C2, 6 hours
5a Rows: 0, 1, 2, 3, 4, 5, 6, 7, 8, 9, 10, 11, 12;
5, $5\frac{1}{2}$, 6, $6\frac{1}{2}$, 7, $7\frac{1}{2}$, 8, $8\frac{1}{2}$, 9, $9\frac{1}{2}$, 10, $10\frac{1}{2}$, 11
c for a 10-day hire **d** (i) Pedal Power (ii) Soft Saddles
6a $x = 3, y = 6$ **b** $x = -1, y = -3$ **c** $x = 3, y = 2$
7a $x = 7, y = 4$ **b** $x = -1, y = 1$ **c** $x = 1, y = 0$
8 Question **2**, $x = 5, y = 5$; question **3**, $x = 3, y = 6$;
question **4**, $x = 4, y = 4$ **9** After 40 days

Page 150 Revision Exercise on Chapter 8: Proportion in Practice

1 Yes, in **a** **2** £1.44 **3 b** **4a** $s = 5t$ **b** 40 **5** 2.4 tonnes
6 50 **7c** (i) 5 (ii) $E = 5T$ **d** 17 **8a** Row: 12, 6, 4, 3, 2, $1\frac{1}{2}$, 1
b 12 **c** inversely proportional **9** 10 days (less time)
10 54 seconds (more) **11a** (i) $\frac{13}{1000} = \frac{26}{2000} = \frac{39}{3000} = \frac{52}{4000}$
b $S = 0.013R$ **c** 65 mph **12** 96 cm²

Page 151 Revision Exercise on Chapter 9: Angles in a Circle

1a Isosceles **b** (i) 36° (ii) 108° **2** 25°
3

4 $x = 25$, $y = 130$, $z = 100$

5

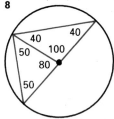

6a Angles in semicircles   **b** (i) 60°   (ii) 42°
7a 90°   **b** $a = b = c = d = 45$ **c** a square

8

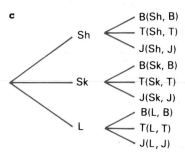

9a ∠DFE, DE   **b** 39 cm   **10** 22.6°
11a Angle between tangent and radius   **b** (i) 50°
(ii) 5.1 cm   **12** $x = 2.5$, $y = 10$ **13a** 35°   **b** 12.2 cm
14a 13 m   **b** 5 m   **c** 12 m   **d** 45°

Page 152   Revision Exercise on Chapter 10: Probability

1a (i) $\frac{4}{10} = \frac{2}{5}$ (ii) $\frac{2}{10} = \frac{1}{5}$ (iii) $\frac{7}{10}$ (iv) $\frac{1}{2}$ (v) 0   (vi) 1
b

```
0              0.5              1
├──┼──┼──┼──┼──┼──┼──┼──┼──┤
(v)      (ii)   (i)(iv)  (iii)      (vi)
```

2a Past data   **b** survey   **c** counting outcomes
d experiment   **3** B and E
4a

	B	T	J
Sh	(Sh, B)	(Sh, T)	(Sh, J)
Sk	(Sk, B)	(Sk, T)	(Sk, J)
L	(L, B)	(L, T)	(L, J)

b (i) $\frac{2}{3}$ (ii) $\frac{2}{9}$ (iii) $\frac{4}{9}$

c

```
         ┌── B(Sh, B)
   Sh ───┼── T(Sh, T)
         └── J(Sh, J)
         ┌── B(Sk, B)
   Sk ───┼── T(Sk, T)
         └── J(Sk, J)
         ┌── B(L, B)
   L ────┼── T(L, T)
         └── J(L, J)
```

5a (i) 0.3   (ii) 0.7   **b** (i) 3600   (ii) 8400
6a (i) 0.8   (ii) 0.2   **b** (i) 0.25   (ii) 0.04   **7a** $\frac{1}{16}$ **b** $\frac{1}{169}$ **c** $\frac{1}{2704}$

GENERAL REVISION EXERCISES

Page 153   General Revision Exercise 1A

1 £440   **2a** 35, 42   **b** 16, 22   **3** 3 minutes 31.6 seconds
4 J215 BSD   **5a** (i) $P = 4d$ (ii) $A = d^2$ **b** 52 cm, 169 cm²
6a 53   **b** (i) 0.2   (ii) 20%   **7a** The last digit must be 5
b 15 275   **c** (i) 3.62   (ii) 3.6   **8** 3
9a   **b** 3

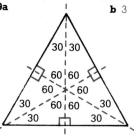

10a (i) 18°C   (ii) Friday   **b** (i) 4°C   (ii) $33\frac{1}{3}$%   (iii) 14°C
11a 2121   **b** 6879   **12b** D(-1, -2)   **13** 19 30 and 21 00
14

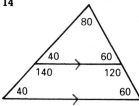

15 £183.75

Page 154   General Revision Exercise 1B

1a £14   **b** £25   **2** 4   **3a** 90°   **b** 120°   **4a** 120°   **b** 240°
5a 5.4×10^7 **b** 0.0025   **6** Row: 5, 3, 0, -1, -3
7a 13, 15, 17, 19   **b** (i) 1, 8, 27, 64   (ii) 1, 4, 9, 16
9 48 cm³, 88 cm²   **10a** $\frac{1}{8}$ **b** $12\frac{1}{2}$%
11a At the end of week 5; 15 cm   **b** (i) B   (ii) A   **c** (i) A
(ii) U   **12a** 36   **b** 12   **c** 60 cm²   **13a** £162   **b** £174.96
14a (i) Reflection in y-axis   (ii) rotation of 180° about O
(iii) reflection in x-axis   **b** 4   **15** $\frac{1}{6}$

Page 155   General Revision Exercise 2A

1a £9   **b** yes   **2a** 25, 36   **b** 16, -32 **3a** (i) 90°   (ii) 65°
b (i) ∠CBE   (ii) ∠DBF   **4a** 10   **b** 5   **c** 11
5a,b   **c** (i) C(3, 0)   (ii) a kite

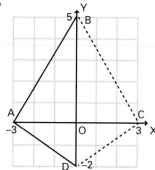

6a 129.8 cm   **b** 37.2 cm   **7a** (i) 13 37   (ii) 17 02   **b** 1.02 pm
8a 120 m   **b** 624 m²   **10a** 8   **b** 4   **c** 5
11a 9 years   **b** 6 years   **12** Ally $390, Milly Can $505

Page 156   General Revision Exercise 2B

1a 5 **b** 2 **c** 2 **2a** 168 mm **b** 21 **3a** (i) 12 (ii) 8 (iii) 4
b angles 180°, 120°, 60° **4a** £28.60 **b** £1.61
5a

b (5, 0), (5, 4), (2, 4), (2, 2)

6a 4 **b** 0 **c** −1 **d** 1 **e** 3 **7a** (i) 2000 (ii) 200 (iii) 10
b (i) 1976 (ii) 231.36 **c** 10.5 **8** 4.55 **9a** 125 **b** 4
10a 26 **b** 7.5 **11a** $2t+2$ **b** 1 **c** $6ab$ **d** $2y^2$ **12a** (i) £19
(ii) £227.50 **b** £429.25

Page 157   General Revision Exercise 3A

1 125 **2** a dog? **3a** 7 **b** 19 **c** 4 **d** 3
4a Rows: 69p, 78p, 84p, 99p; 92p, £1.04, £1.12, £1.32
b £2.54 **5a** 120°, 105°
b ∠s AOB, COD; ∠s AOC, BOD, AOD; ∠BOC
6a 90° **b** 135° **c** 180° **d** 270° **e** 0° **7a** £17 **b** £20.90
8a 157 mm **b** 1963 mm² **9a** 5 hours **b** 235 km **c** 47 km/h

Page 158   General Revision Exercise 3B

1a 216 **b** £54 **2** Rows: 1, 2, 4, 5, 3; 6, 7, 9, 10, 8;
1, 4, 10, 13, 7 **3a** ∠s NPA, NPB **b** 155°
c (i) 040° (ii) 095° (iii) 300° **4** The lounge, by 0.42 m²
5a $5x$ m **b** $(x+2)$ m **c** $(4x−2)$ m **6a** 14.7 **b** 29.0
7a

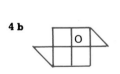

2   6   3   4

b 2, 6, 3, 4

8a 12 min **b** 6 min **9a** 3 **10a** £90 **b** £19.50
11a (i) 0 (ii) −6 **b** (i) 4 (ii) 9

Page 159   General Revision Exercise 4A

1 5, 2, 4, 0 **2** 60°, 90°, 120°, 90°;
age 13–10, 14–15, 15–20, 16–15
3a 9 **b** 3 **c** −1 **d** −10 **e** −30 **f** 0

4 b   **c**

5 15% **6b** (i) D is $(−2, −1)$ (ii) E is $(8, −1)$
c both 20 sq. units **7a** −1 **b** 2 **c** 4 **8a** £282 **b** £23.50
9 Rows: $\frac{1}{2}, \frac{1}{10}, \frac{3}{10}, \frac{1}{4}, \frac{3}{4}, \frac{22}{25}$; 0.5, 0.1, 0.3, 0.25, 0.75, 0.88;
50%, 10%, 30%, 25%, 75%, 88% **10a** (i) 2 h (ii) $\frac{1}{2}$ h
b (i) 29 mph (ii) 38 mph **11a** $4x+2$ **b** $3y+2$ **c** $7n−3$
12a $\frac{2}{3}$ **b** 10 m **c** 75 m² **13a** 1000 **b** 64 **c** 13 **d** 8 **e** 20
14a 4 cm **b** (i) 100 000 cm (ii) 1 km

Page 160   General Revision Exercise 4B

1 $−3 < −2, −3 < 1, −3 < 0; −2 > −3, 1 > −3, 0 > −3$;
$−2 < 1, −2 < 0; 1 > −2, 0 > −2; 0 < 1; 1 > 0$
2a (i) 21 (ii) 21 **b** $a(a+2b)$ **3a** Angle in a semi-circle
b 35° **c** 7 cm, 10 cm; opposite sides of a rectangle are
equal **4a** 3 **b** $y > 1$ **c** $x > −1$ **5a** 4°, −4° **b** 8° **c** 4°

6a

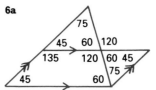

b parallelogram, trapezium

7a $4x+2 = 3x+7, x = 5$ **b** $3x = x+6, x = 3$
8a Row: 3, 7, 11, 15, 19, . . . , $4n−1$ **b** $N = 4n−1$ **c** 47
d 18 **9a** 13 **b** 13, 11 **d** (i) $\frac{2}{15}$ (ii) $\frac{1}{6}$

Page 161   General Revision Exercise 5A

1 £54 **2a** 25 **b** 4 **c** 4 **d** $3\frac{1}{2}$ **e** −1 **3b** A parallelogram
c $(−2, 1), (−4, 2), (−4, 4), (−2, 3)$; a parallelogram
4a 5 400 000 cm³ **b** 5400 **5a** $S \leqslant 30$ **b** $W > 15$
c $3 \leqslant N \leqslant 8$ **6a** (i) 18° (ii) 54° **b** 6
7a $\frac{1}{2}$ **b** $\frac{1}{5}$ **c** $\frac{3}{10}$ **d** $\frac{1}{4}$ **8a** (i) 30p, 50p (ii) 64p, 16p **b** £58
9a $L = 32x$ **b** 288 **10** £8.41 **11a** 45 m **b** 52 m
12a £6200 **b** £1550 **c** £8250 **13a** $C = 12N$ **b** £9600

Page 162   General Revision Exercise 5B

1 He succeeds by 0.63 s **2** $3x+7 = 22; x = 5; 5$ **3a** 31.8 m
b 14 m² **4a** Moscow, Oslo, Paris, Zurich, London, Berlin
b 4°, 2°, 7°, 3°, 5° **c** 7°C **5** 76° **6a** $x \geqslant 1$ **b** $y < 2\frac{1}{2}$
c $x \leqslant −2$ **d** $n > 1\frac{1}{2}$
7a (i) ∠s ABE, ACD; ∠s AEB, ADC
(ii) ∠s BFE, CFD; ∠s BFC, EFD
(iii) ∠s EBD, CDB; ∠s BEC, DCE
b

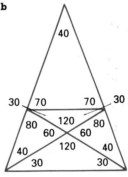

8a No **b** 28 km/h **9a** (i) △s RSQ, RTP (ii) $\frac{1}{2}$ (iii) 7.5
b 25 cm **10a** 23 **b** 23

Page 163   General Revision Exercise 6A

1 £9.60 **2a** 2 **b** −4 **c** −3 **d** −2 **e** 27 **f** 0
3a 2, 3, 5, 7 **b** 3, 6, 9 **c** 2, 3, 4, 6 **4a** 25 **b** 75 **c** 80
d 122 **5a** 1.02, by 0.1 **b** 3.141 60, by 0.000 01 **c** $\frac{4}{5}$, by $\frac{1}{20}$
6a 240 m, 2450 m² **b** 0.245 hectare **7a** $7x−9 = 5x+5$;
$x = 7$ **b** 40 cm **8a** 50 g, 10 g, 4 g, 160 ml
b 400 g, 80 g, 32 g, 1280 ml
9a $P = 4x, A = x^2; P = 2\pi r$ (or πD), $A = \pi r^2$;
$P = 2a+2b, A = ab$ **b** 12 cm, 6.9 cm²
10 $1.43 \times 10^9, 5.58 \times 10^{−2}$
11a (i) 1 hour (ii) $\frac{1}{2}$ hour (iii) $\frac{1}{2}$ hour **b** 56 km/h, $37\frac{1}{3}$ km/h

Page 164   General Revision Exercise 6B

1 £20 000 **2a** (i) £61 275 (ii) £3225 **b** £127 200
3

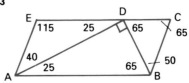

4c $4.3\,\text{m}, 8.6\,\text{m}^2$ **5a** $6(x+3), 6x+18; x=5$ **b** $60\,\text{m}^2$ **6** 60
7a 0.38 **b** 0.92 **c** 0.42 **d** $7.5\,\text{cm}$ **e** $5.2\,\text{cm}$ **f** $34.0\,\text{cm}^2$
8 $2260\,\text{m}^3, 980\,\text{m}^2$ **9a** (i) Row: 3, 6, 9, 12, 15, 18 (ii) $F=3P$
c 3 **d** (i) 20 (ii) 12
10a $20.5, 19.5\,\text{cm}; 8.5, 7.5\,\text{cm}$ **b** $174.25\,\text{cm}^2, 146.25\,\text{cm}^2$

Page 165 General Revision Exercise 7A

1a $20\,\text{cm}$ **b** $360\,\text{g}$ **2a** $2(q+r)$ **b** $3(p-2)$ **c** $2(4-5y)$
d $a(b-c)$ **e** $2(a-2b+3c)$
3
a   b   c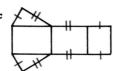

4
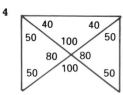

5 $61.25\,\text{m}^2$ **6a** Row: $5, 8, 11, 14, \ldots, 3N+2$ **b** $T=3N+2$
c 152 **7a** $17.9\,\text{km}$ **b** $14.5\,\text{km}$ **8a** £180 **b** £12.60
9a $x=-3$ **b** $x>5$
10 $(y+9)^2 = 12^2 + (y+3)^2$; $9\,\text{cm}, 12\,\text{cm}, 15\,\text{cm}$
11a $(0, 5), (10, 0)$ **d** $x=2, y=4$

Page 166 General Revision Exercise 7B

1a $6.25\,\text{kg}$ **b** 40, 16 **2a** $P=2y+2\pi x$ **b** $A=2xy+\pi x^2$
3a $5.7\,\text{m}$ **b** $6.9\,\text{m}$ **c** $35°$ **4a** £648 **b** £699.84 **5a** (i) $6\,\text{cm}$
(ii) $18\,\text{cm}$ **b** $18°$ **6a** Rows: 4, 6, 8, 10, 12; 7, 8, 9, 10, 11
c for 6 batches **d** (i) Bluebell (ii) Daisy **7a** $x=2, y=2$
b $x=5, y=3$ **c** $x=2, y=6$ **8a** $x+5, 2(x+5)$
b $x+x+5+2(x+5) = 75, x=15$
Grace 15, Julie 20, Aisha 40
9a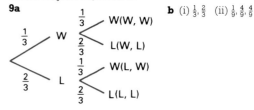

b (i) $\frac{1}{3}, \frac{2}{3}$ (ii) $\frac{1}{9}, \frac{4}{9}, \frac{4}{9}$

ICT for Teaching

this book on or before the last
date shown to:

'9

Road

Also available:

Help – There's a Computer in my Classroom / 1-84312-119-0 / Alison Ball

The Essential Guide for Competent Teaching Assistants / 1-84312-008-9 / Anne Watkinson

The Essential Guide for Experienced Teaching Assistants / 1-84312-009-7 / Anne Watkinson

Supporting Literacy and Numeracy / 1-85346-697-4 / Fox and Halliwell

Understanding Children's Learning / 1-84312-069-0 / Alfrey

Successful Study / 1-84312-106-9 / Ritchie & Thomas

Supporting Information and Communications Technology / 1-85346-626-3 / Mike & Gina Farmer